THE BEST
FORMULA
ONE Quiz Book
Ever!

THIS IS A CARLTON BOOK

Copyright © Carlton Books Limited 2000

ISBN 1 85868 919 8

Project editor: Martin Corteel
Project art director: Paul Oakley
Production: Sarah Corteel

Carlton Books Limited
20 Mortimer Street
London W1N 7RD

THE BEST FORMULA ONE Quiz Book Ever!

BRUCE JONES

CARLTON
BOOKS

Contents

Contents

Contents

Contents

Introduction

No sport produces more facts and figures than Formula One. Every race of the world championship adds a new layer of data and has done so for 50 years. In the close season, now down to four months, the fans buff up on their knowledge, while the teams keep them on their toes by swapping variables such as drivers, engines and sponsors, just to make sure that nothing stays the same for long. And that's what makes Formula One so irresistible.

Alain Prost may have won the most grands prix – it's 51, if you must ask – but there's no use lobbing in his name every time you're asked who won a race. There have been close on 700 grands prix since 1950 and 80 winners so far.

Answering Ferrari to all questions about teams may seem like a good shot. Their tally is well over the 100 wins mark, but there have been periods when the red cars have wilted and the horse on their badge has been anything but prancing. Indeed, in the past three decades, British teams – the *garagistes* as they were once known derogatively because they tended to start off from garages under railway arches – have assumed control, something that would have been unthinkable when it all began in 1950. So, more than a little grey matter is required in this quarter.

Any subject so packed with statistics will have its legion of "anoraks" for whom no fact or figure can be too trivial. To these *aficionados*, knowing when Nigel Mansell scored his first grand prix win – Brands Hatch in 1985 – is nowhere near as exciting as the fact that he continued to the end of his first grand prix in Austria in 1980 despite being soaked in petrol which was burning his skin. They will recall that it was at Copse corner at Silverstone in 1990 that he threw his gloves into the crowd and announced that he was quitting Formula One. It transpired that he didn't mean it and would race on after all, but he had produced another gem of a fact.

Knowing a lot about Formula One is something that most

people who follow the sport will reckon that they do. I thought I did, having followed motor racing since the age of 10, covered the sport as a journalist since 1983 and written numerous books on the subject. I should have been able to rattle this book out in no time at all. That was the theory, but practice proved that my memory could play tricks on me and years become transposed. Suddenly, 6,000 questions looked a very big number – some serious fact checking was required. No sooner had I discovered the possibility that I might, whisper it, be wrong on occasion, than it became clear that every fact would have to be double-checked. Providing a perfectly good question with an erroneous fact for the question master to pronounce as the answer would surely lead to much huffing and puffing.

It was also a challenge to ask 6,000 questions that didn't all follow the "who won which race in what car in which year" format. Certainly, there are some that do, but there are many more that don't. I hope you enjoy this book, treat it as a challenge, as indeed it should be. Many of you might know everything that could possibly be known about Formula One in the 1980s and 1990s, but practically nothing about what went on before then. In fact, to make it even trickier, we go back further than the first-ever round of the world championship at Silverstone in 1950, just to give you a little warm-up on the early careers of the drivers who were doing all the winning as Formula One was being created.

Split into three chapters according to the difficulty of the questions, each of these chapters is subdivided into different areas of the sport, ranging from the teams, the drivers and the circuits to the equipment and the fan culture. After all, it's as important to some to know that Vittorio Brambilla's nickname was "the Monza Gorilla" as it is to know that his March had an orange livery when it was sponsored by Beta Tools in 1975.

Easy Questions

Everyone needs a warm-up, and this chapter should serve that purpose. However, don't think that you'll be able to answer all of the questions without even breaking into a sweat. Indeed, as the chapter starts with the early years of Formula One you will probably be floundering until the period of the questions moves closer to your own childhood. Hang in there, though, and you will soon be able to answer Jim Clark with confidence or even David Coulthard. It's impossible to offer any hints, as everybody's mind works in a different way, but remembering race-turning events is often the key. A famous incident is possibly what prompted me to ask a group of questions. For example, think of the 1998 Canadian Grand Prix and you are more likely to recall Alexander Wurz's dramatic roll at the first corner on the opening lap than the identity of the driver who won the restarted race. It was Michael Schumacher, actually. But you see what I mean.

So concentrate hard, try to remember which team a driver was racing for, who his team-mate was and who his main rival drove for, and you will be in good shape to put in a good qualifying score in the medium chapter.

Competitors, please start your engines!

1   A grand prix was held in Britain in 1935. At which circuit?
2   Name the winning driver.
3   Name the Auto Union favourite of 1936.
4   Where was the Swiss Grand Prix held that year?
5   Name the British driver who, in 1936, shared victory in the grand prix held in Britain.
6   Which new French marque shone in 1937, with Louis Chiron winning first time out?
7   The German teams made their first visit to the British Grand Prix in 1937. Which team won?
8   With which driver at the wheel?
9   Which British driver upset Adolf Hitler by winning the 1938 German Grand Prix for Mercedes?
10 Which German team won the 1938 British Grand Prix?
11 Who was driving?
12 Why were there no grands prix between the end of 1939 and the start of 1947?
13 Who won the first grand prix of 1947, the Swiss?
14 What car was he driving?
15 Which future world champion won the Monaco Grand Prix in 1948?
16 What car was he driving?
17 Only one driver won two grands prix in 1949. Who was he?
18 What car was he driving?
19 Which British driver won the final grand prix of 1949?
20 What car was he driving?

1   Where was the first-ever world championship grand prix held?

2   Who won it?

3   For which team was he driving?

4   Who won the first world championship?

5   Who was the first driver to break the Alfa Romeo stranglehold?

6   Driving what car?

7   Where did this take place?

8   Who won the 1951 world championship?

9   Why were Alfa Romeo missing from the 1952 world championship?

10   Who was the Ferrari team leader?

11   Juan Manuel Fangio missed the entire season. Why?

12   Who won the 1952 world championship?

13   Who won the first round of the 1953 world championship and went on to take the title?

14   Who was the first British driver to win a grand prix?

15   Where was this?

16   What car was he driving?

17   Who won the 1954 season's opening race in Argentina?

18   Which of his compatriots led the race for Ferrari?

19   Mercedes-Benz joined in at which grand prix?

20   How did Mercedes-Benz fare in that first outing?

Answers **WORLD CHAMPIONSHIP 1960 & 1961** *(see Quiz 4)*
1 Buenos Aires. **2** Stirling Moss. **3** A Lotus. **4** Rob Walker Racing. **5** Five. **6** Graham Hill.
7 A BRM. **8** Chris Bristow and Alan Stacey. **9** Multiple injuries including two broken legs,
damaged back and broken nose. **10** Phil Hill. **11** 1.5 litre. **12** Sharknose. **13** Wolfgang von Trips.
14 Zandvoort, Holland. **15** Four. **16** Giancarlo Baghetti. **17** It was his world championship
debut. **18** Jim Clark. **19** Phil Hill. **20** Innes Ireland.

1 Who was Fangio's British team-mate with Mercedes in 1955?
2 Who flipped his car into the harbour at Monaco?
3 Where was the 1955 British Grand Prix held?
4 Who won it?
5 Juan Manuel Fangio moved to which team in 1956?
6 Who let Fangio take his car in Argentina after Fangio's failed?
7 Which British driver won two races in succession for Ferrari?
8 Three drivers went into the final round of the 1956 championship with a chance of the title. Who won?
9 Which marque filled the first four positions in the 1957 season's opening race, the Argentinian Grand Prix?
10 Who was its race-winning team leader?
11 A British marque won the British Grand Prix that year. Which one?
12 Whose car did Stirling Moss step into to secure that win?
13 Stirling Moss opened the 1958 season by giving another British marque its first win. Which one?
14 The same marque won the season's second race in Monaco. Who was driving?
15 Two British drivers had a final-round shot at the 1958 title. Who won?
16 Who slowed to allow his team-mate to take a title-clinching second place in the season's final race?
17 An Australian won the 1959 opening round in Monaco. Who was he?
18 For which team was he driving?
19 Which British marque won in Holland that year?
20 Who was driving?

Answers THE ORIGINS OF FORMULA 1 *(see Quiz 1)*

1 Donington Park. **2** Richard Shuttleworth. **3** Bernd Rosemeyer. **4** Bremgarten. **5** Dick Seaman. **6** Talbot. **7** Auto Union **8** Bernd Rosemeyer. **9** Dick Seaman. **10** Auto Union. **11** Tazio Nuvolari **12** The Second World War. **13** Jean-Pierre Wimille. **14** An Alfa Romeo. **15** Giuseppe Farina. **16** A Maserati. **17** Alberto Ascari. **18** A Ferrari. **19** Peter Whitehead. **20** A Ferrari.

1   Cooper won again in 1960's opening round. Where was this?

2   Which former Cooper driver won the second round at Monaco?

3   What car was he driving?

4   Who entered it?

5   Jack Brabham won several races in a row in 1960. How many?

6   Who crashed when leading the 1960 British Grand Prix?

7   What car was he driving?

8   Who were the two British drivers killed in the 1960 Belgian Grand Prix?

9   What injuries did Stirling Moss sustain in practice for the same event?

10 Ferrari scored a one-two-three in the 1960 Italian Grand Prix. Who was the race winner?

11 What sized engines became the standard in 1961?

12 What was the nickname of the Ferrari 156 that proved to be the car of the year in 1961?

13 Who drove the car to its first win?

14 Where was that?

15 Ferrari dominated the 1961 Belgian Grand Prix, its cars filling the first how many positions?

16 Which non-works Ferrari driver won the 1961 French Grand Prix at Reims?

17 What was remarkable about his win?

18 Wolfgang von Trips was killed in the 1961 Italian Grand Prix after colliding with whom?

19 Who went on to win the Italian Grand Prix and the title?

20 Which Scottish driver won the 1961 season's closing grand prix in the United States?

Answers *WORLD CHAMPIONSHIPS 1950–54* (see Quiz 2)

1 Silverstone, 1950. 2 Giuseppe Farina. 3 Alfa Romeo. 4 Giuseppe Farina. 5 Jose Froilan Gonzalez. 6 A Ferrari. 7 Silverstone, 1951. 8 Juan Manuel Fangio. 9 They withdrew on the grounds of cost. 10 Alberto Ascari. 11 He'd broken his neck. 12 Alberto Ascari. 13 Alberto Ascari. 14 Mike Hawthorn. 15 Reims. 16 A Ferrari. 17 Juan Manuel Fangio. 18 Jose Froilan Gonzalez. 19 The French. 20 The team won with a car driven by Juan Manuel Fangio.

1   A driver called Hill won the opening race at Zandvoort, Holland. Which one?

2   What car was he driving?

3   Cooper's new team leader won at Monaco, 1962. Who was he?

4   Which Scottish driver won a grand prix for the first time at Spa-Francorchamps in 1962?

5   An American won next time out in the French Grand Prix. Who was he?

6   What car was he driving?

7   Jim Clark won the 1962 British Grand Prix at Aintree. What car was he driving?

8   Which team gave up after showing poor form that year and missed the final two grands prix?

9   At which circuit was the 1962 season's closing South African Grand Prix held?

10   Who ended 1962 as world champion?

11   Which team finished one-two in the 1963 season's opening grand prix in Monaco?

12   Name the two drivers in finishing order.

13   Spa-Francorchamps was hated by one driver, but in 1963 he won there. Who was he?

14   In 1963, Dan Gurney was starting to shine for a team owned by which former world champion?

15   Which South African was second behind Jim Clark in the 1963 French Grand Prix?

16   What car was he driving?

17   Which former motorcycle world champion won the 1963 German Grand Prix?

18   For which team was he driving?

19   Which Central American country hosted a world championship round in 1963 for the first time?

20   When Jim Clark won the season's final race in South Africa, to how many wins did that take his 1963 tally?

Answers WORLD CHAMPIONSHIP 1966 & 1967 *(see Quiz 7)*

1 3 litres. *2* BRM. *3* John Surtees (Ferrari). *4* Jack Brabham. *5* A Repco. *6* Denny Hulme.
7 New Zealander. *8* Ferrari. *9* John Surtees joined Cooper. *10* The Mexican. *11* Pedro
Rodriguez. *12* John Love. *13* Lorenzo Bandini. *14* It marked the debut of the Ford Cosworth
DFV engine. *15* Graham Hill. *16* Jim Clark. *17* An Eagle. *18* The Le Mans Bugatti circuit.
19 Mosport Park. *20* Denny Hulme.

1 In 1964, Jim Clark was still number one at Lotus. Who was his new number two?

2 Dan Gurney lost the 1964 Belgian Grand Prix when looking sure of victory. Why?

3 Who came through to win?

4 Gurney made amends by giving the Brabham marque its first win at which circuit?

5 In 1964, the British Grand Prix moved to which circuit for the first time?

6 Who won there?

7 The 1964 Austrian Grand Prix was held for the one and only time at which circuit?

8 Who won it?

9 For which team?

10 There was a three-way shoot-out for the title in the final round. Who came out as champion?

11 The 1965 season kicked off on New Year's Day. Where?

12 A British driver won the Monaco Grand Prix for the third year in a row in 1965. Who was he?

13 What car was he driving?

14 A British driver won the 1965 Belgian Grand Prix for the fourth year in a row. Who was he?

15 What car was he driving?

16 He was followed home by a new British driver at BRM. Who was he?

17 This driver went on to win which 1965 grand prix?

18 The final race of 1965, the Mexican Grand Prix, was the only one that season won by a non-British driver. Who was he?

19 What car was he driving?

20 By winning the Mexican Grand Prix, which tyre supplier did he give its first Formula One win?

Answers *WORLD CHAMPIONSHIP 1968 & 1969 (see Quiz 8)*

1 Jim Clark. **2** He was killed in a Formula Two race. **3** Jackie Oliver. **4** McLaren. **5** Bruce McLaren. **6** Matra. **7** Jacky Ickx. **8** Belgian. **9** Rob Walker. **10** Graham Hill. **11** Jackie Stewart. **12** Montjuich Park. **13** Graham Hill. **14** Jean-Pierre Beltoise. **15** Jacky Ickx. **16** Brabham. **17** Jackie Stewart. **18** Jochen Rindt. **19** A Lotus. **20** Denny Hulme.

1　New rules meant bigger engines. What size were the new units?

2　Which marque won the first race under the new regulations?

3　Who was driving the winning car in Belgium?

4　In the French Grand Prix, a driver won in a car bearing his own name, the first time this had ever happened. Who was he?

5　What make of engine was fitted to his car?

6　The same driver won next time out at the British Grand Prix ahead of his team-mate. Name the team-mate.

7　What was the team-mate's nationality?

8　Which famous team failed to show at the British Grand Prix?

9　Ferrari's team leader quit mid-season and joined another team. Which one?

10　Which grand prix did he win for his new team?

11　Cooper won the 1967 season's opening grand prix in South Africa thanks to which driver?

12　Who led until six laps from the end in a privately entered Cooper?

13　Tragedy struck at Monaco in 1967. Who suffered fatal injuries?

14　What was notable about the 1967 Dutch Grand Prix?

15　Which Lotus driver claimed pole position for that race?

16　Which Lotus driver went on to win it?

17　Dan Gurney won the Belgian Grand Prix using what chassis?

18　At which circuit was the French Grand Prix held in 1967, for the one and only time.?

19　A Canadian Grand Prix was on the calendar for the first time in 1967. Where was it held?

20　Who claimed the world championship title in the final round?

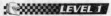
1   The 1968 season opened in South Africa. Who won this first race?

2   Why would he never win again?

3   Who replaced him at Lotus?

4   Other teams were now using Ford Cosworth DFV engines. Which was the first of these to win with one?

5   Who was driving?

6   Jackie Stewart gave another marque its first win at the next race at Zandvoort. Which one?

7   Ferrari hit winning form again in the 1968 French Grand Prix. Who was the driver?

8   What was his nationality?

9   Jo Siffert gave which long-standing privateer entrant his first win for seven years at Brands Hatch in 1968?

10   Who won the final round and with it the 1968 world championship title?

11   Matra won the opening race of the 1969 season in South Africa. Who was driving?

12   The Spanish Grand Prix moved to a new circuit that year. Which one?

13   Who scored his fifth Monaco Grand Prix victory in 1969?

14   Jackie Stewart was first again in the French Grand Prix in 1969. Name his team-mate who finished second.

15   A Belgian driver won the German Grand Prix. Who was he?

16   For which team was he driving?

17   Who scored his sixth win of the season at the Italian Grand Prix to clinch the 1969 world title?

18   At Watkins Glen, which Austrian driver scored his first grand prix win?

19   What car was he driving?

20   Which former world champion won the Mexican Grand Prix for McLaren.

Answers *WORLD CHAMPIONSHIP 1964 & 1965* (see Quiz 6)

1 Peter Arundell. *2* He ran out of fuel. *3* Jim Clark. *4* Rouen-les-Essarts. *5* Brands Hatch. *6* Jim Clark. *7* Zeltweg. *8* Lorenzo Bandini. *9* Ferrari. *10* John Surtees from Graham Hill and Jim Clark. *11* East London for the South African Grand Prix. *12* Graham Hill. *13* A BRM. *14* Jim Clark. *15* A Lotus. *16* Jackie Stewart. *17* The Italian. *18* Richie Ginther, an American. *19* A Honda. *20* Goodyear.

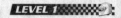
1 Which new marque arrived in force for the opening grand prix of the 1970 season in South Africa?

2 Who qualified on pole position?

3 Which Brabham driver won the race?

4 March scored its first win at the second grand prix of 1970. Where was this held?

5 Who won the 1970 Monaco Grand Prix when Jack Brabham slid off at the last corner?

6 In 1970, a former grand prix winner died testing a CanAm car. Who was he?

7 Who gave BRM its first win for four years at the 1970 Belgian Grand Prix?

8 Jochen Rindt won four races in a row before which driver won the Austrian Grand Prix?

9 What did Rindt become when he was killed in practice for the 1970 Italian Grand Prix?

10 Who replaced Rindt at Lotus and won that year's US Grand Prix?

11 Which American driver won the 1971 South African Grand Prix?

12 For which team?

13 Jackie Stewart gave which marque its first win in the 1971 Spanish Grand Prix?

14 Ferrari won again at the Dutch Grand Prix. Who was driving?

15 In 1971, the French Grand Prix was held at which new circuit for the first time?

16 Name Stewart's French Tyrrell team-mate who finished second there?

17 Stewart won the British Grand Prix that year. Which March driver finished second, as he did on three other occasions?

18 Who won the 1971 Austrian Grand Prix for BRM?

19 Who won the 1971 Italian Grand Prix for BRM?

20 Who was crowned world champion in 1971?

Answers *WORLD CHAMPIONSHIP 1974 & 1975* (see Quiz 11)

1 McLaren. 2 Mike Hailwood. 3 Clay Regazzoni. 4 Carlos Reutemann. 5 Peter Revson. 6 Niki Lauda. 7 Jody Scheckter. 8 Patrick Depailler. 9 The pit-lane exit was blocked by officials' cars. 10 Emerson Fittipaldi. 11 Jean-Pierre Jarier. 12 Carlos Pace (Emerson Fittipaldi won in Argentina). 13 Brabham. 14 Jody Scheckter. 15 Rolf Stommelen flew over the barriers. 16 Jochen Mass. 17 Niki Lauda. 18 Hesketh. 19 Vittorio Brambilla. 20 Graham Hill.

1 In 1972, who stunned the establishment in Argentina by taking pole position for his first grand prix?

2 What car was he driving?

3 At Kyalami that year, Denny Hulme put which team back on top of the podium for the first time since 1969?

4 Lotus rediscovered winning form with which driver winning the 1972 Spanish Grand Prix?

5 Which team upset the formbooks by winning at Monaco that year?

6 Who was driving the winning car?

7 The Belgian Grand Prix moved to which new circuit in 1972?

8 Which unlucky driver lost the 1972 French Grand Prix due to a puncture?

9 The 1972 title was wrapped up at Monza. What was the nationality of the new world champion?

10 Which team won that season's final two races in North America?

11 Which marque arrived at the start of the 1973 season with a pair of black cars?

12 Emerson Fittipaldi won his home race in 1973 at which circuit?

13 McLaren won the 1973 Swedish Grand Prix with which driver at the wheel?

14 Local hero Ronnie Peterson put which marque on pole there?

15 Which British driver was killed in the 1973 Dutch Grand Prix?

16 Who tried to pull him out of his blazing car?

17 Which Lotus driver won the 1973 Austrian and Italian Grands Prix?

18 The Canadian Grand Prix was confused by the deployment of a pace car, the first time one had been used. Who won?

19 Who claimed the 1973 world title at the Italian Grand Prix?

20 Why did he not contest the final round?

Answers *WORLD CHAMPIONSHIP 1976 & 1977* (see Quiz 12)
1 Copersucar Fittipaldi. **2** Long Beach. **3** Clay Regazzoni. **4** James Hunt. **5** Ferrari. **6** Nürburgring. **7** John Watson. **8** Penske. **9** March. **10** Mario Andretti in a Lotus. **11** Carlos Reutemann. **12** Wolf. **13** Jody Scheckter. **14** Gunnar Nilsson. **15** Ligier. **16** Jacques Laffite. **17** Alan Jones. **18** Shadow. **19** Watkins Glen. **20** Ronnie Peterson and Gilles Villeneuve.

1 Emerson Fittipaldi switched to which team for 1974?

2 Which former motorcycle champion was in the team's third car?

3 Fittipaldi won his home race again in 1974. Which Ferrari driver was second?

4 The 1974 South African Grand Prix yielded a first win for which Brabham driver?

5 Who died testing prior to that race at Kyalami?

6 Which Ferrari new boy won the 1974 Spanish Grand Prix?

7 Tyrrell scored a one-two in the Swedish Grand Prix that year. Who won?

8 Who finished second?

9 Why could Niki Lauda not rejoin the race from the pits at the 1974 British Grand Prix?

10 Emerson Fittipaldi and Clay Regazzoni went into the final race of 1974 equal on points. Who won the title?

11 Which Shadow driver shocked the establishment in 1975 by qualifying on pole for the season's opening two races in South America?

12 Both races were won by Brazilians. Who won in Brazil?

13 Driving for which team?

14 Who won for Tyrrell in South Africa in 1975, on his home ground?

15 The 1975 Spanish Grand Prix was stopped early for what reason?

16 Which McLaren driver was adjudged the winner?

17 Which Ferrari driver won three races in a row that year to move into the championship lead?

18 James Hunt's success in the 1975 Dutch Grand Prix gave which British marque its first win?

19 In the 1975 Austrian Grand Prix, who gave March its first win?

20 A twice world champion died in a flying accident after the end of the 1975 season. Who was he?

Answers *WORLD CHAMPIONSHIP 1970 & 1971* (see Quiz 9)

1 March. *2* Jackie Stewart. *3* Jack Brabham. *4* Jarama, Spain. *5* Jochen Rindt. *6* Bruce McLaren. *7* Pedro Rodriguez. *8* Jacky Ickx. *9* The first posthumous world champion. *10* Emerson Fittipaldi. *11* Mario Andretti. *12* Ferrari. *13* Tyrrell. *14* Jacky Ickx. *15* Paul Ricard. *16* François Cevert. *17* Ronnie Peterson. *18* Jo Siffert. *19* Peter Gethin. *20* Jackie Stewart.

1 Emerson Fittipaldi joined which team for 1976?

2 In 1976, a new grand prix was staged on America's West Coast. Where?

3 Who won it for Ferrari?

4 Which McLaren driver won the 1976 Spanish Grand Prix?

5 Which team was awarded the 1976 British Grand Prix after it was taken away from McLaren?

6 Niki Lauda nearly met his end in a bad crash at which circuit?

7 The Austrian Grand Prix again yielded a first-time winner. Who was it?

8 For which team was he driving?

9 Ronnie Peterson won the 1976 Italian Grand Prix for which team?

10 James Hunt claimed the 1976 title in the final race of the season at Fuji in Japan. Who won the race?

11 Who was Niki Lauda's team-mate at Ferrari in 1977?

12 Which new marque won the first race of 1977, in Argentina?

13 Who was driving?

14 Which Lotus driver won the 1977 Belgian Grand Prix?

15 The 1977 Swedish Grand Prix gave another team its first win. Which one?

16 Who was driving?

17 The 1977 Austrian Grand Prix yielded a first-time winner for the third consecutive year. Who was he?

18 For which team was he driving?

19 Niki Lauda wrapped up his second title at which North American circuit?

20 Which two drivers tangled at the Japanese Grand Prix as a result of which two spectators were killed?

Answers *WORLD CHAMPIONSHIP 1972 & 1973* (see Quiz 10)

1 Carlos Reutemann. 2 A Brabham. 3 McLaren. 4 Emerson Fittipaldi. 5 BRM. 6 Jean-Pierre Beltoise. 7 Nivelles. 8 Chris Amon. 9 Brazilian (Emerson Fittipaldi). 10 Tyrrell. 11 Shadow. 12 Interlagos. 13 Denny Hulme. 14 Lotus. 15 Roger Williamson. 16 David Purley. 17 Ronnie Peterson. 18 Peter Revson. 19 Jackie Stewart. 20 Team-mate François Cevert was killed in practice.

1   Ronnie Peterson rejoined which team for 1978?
2   The Shadow team's personnel splintered to form which new team?
3   Who won the 1978 Brazilian Grand Prix for Ferrari?
4   Which team surprised everybody by finishing second?
5   There was a great battle in the 1978 South African Grand Prix. Who came second?
6   For which team?
7   Patrick Depailler scored his first win at which grand prix?
8   Niki Lauda won the 1978 Swedish Grand Prix for which team?
9   The 1978 world championship was settled at the Italian Grand Prix in favour of which driver?
10 Why was it a sad race?
11 Who opened the 1979 season with two straight wins?
12 Which Canadian scored his first win for Ferrari at Kyalami in 1979?
13 Name his team-mate who won the Belgian Grand Prix that year and went on to become world champion.
14 Which French team won the1979 French Grand Prix?
15 Who was driving?
16 Which British team scored its first win in the 1979 British Grand Prix?
17 Who was driving?
18 The team's other driver won next time out in Germany. Who was he?
19 Who quit Formula One with immediate effect at the 1979 Canadian Grand Prix?
20 What was the nationality of Ferrari's 1979 world champion?

1 Who was the new Brabham team leader for 1980?

2 Which French driver scored his first win in the 1980 Brazilian Grand Prix?

3 For which team?

4 Which driver was paralysed by an accident at Long Beach?

5 A French driver scored his first win at the 1980 Belgian Grand Prix. Who was he?

6 What car was he driving?

7 Carlos Reutemann won the 1980 Monaco Grand Prix for which team?

8 At which grand prix did Nigel Mansell make his debut?

9 For which team?

10 Who won five times to clinch the 1980 world championship title?

11 Who took a surprise pole position for the 1981 season's opening race at Long Beach?

12 For which team was he driving?

13 Who ignored team orders to win the 1981 Brazilian Grand Prix?

14 Who was the team-mate he denied?

15 Name Nelson Piquet's unrated Brabham team-mate who ran second to Piquet in the 1981 Argentinian Grand Prix until his car broke down.

16 What was his nationality?

17 Which Ferrari driver led home a procession of cars in the 1981 Spanish Grand Prix?

18 John Watson won the 1981 British Grand Prix for which team?

19 The 1981 championship finale was held where?

20 Three drivers had a chance of the title. Who won?

1   Which two-times world champion made his return for McLaren in 1982?

2   Who was his team-mate?

3   In 1982, who recovered from a puncture that left him in eighth place to win at Kyalami?

4   Driving for which team?

5   Gilles Villeneuve died at Zolder after hitting the March of which driver, in practice for the Belgian Grand Prix?

6   Who replaced him at Ferrari?

7   Who spun out of the lead at Monaco but came back to win?

8   Which Lotus driver scraped home to victory in the 1982 Austrian Grand Prix?

9   Who became 1982 world champion?

10   What was notable about his title?

11   Lotus started the 1983 season without which important team member?

12   Williams started the season without what important ingredient?

13   Who was disqualified from the opening race of the 1983 season in Brazil for a push start?

14   Which team's drivers fought from the back of the grid to win at Long Beach in 1983?

15   Who won the race?

16   Which Ferrari driver won the 1983 San Marino Grand Prix?

17   Turbo power ruled, but Keke Rosberg won at Monaco in 1983 with a normally aspirated engine. For which team?

18   In Detroit, who gave the Ford Cosworth DFV its final grand prix win?

19   For which team?

20   The 1983 championship went to the final round at Kyalami. Who came away as champion?

Answers WORLD CHAMPIONSHIP 1978 & 1979 *(see Quiz 13)*

1 Lotus. *2* Arrows. *3* Carlos Reutemann. *4* Fittipaldi. *5* Patrick Depailler (Ronnie Peterson won). *6* Tyrrell. *7* Monaco. *8* Brabham. *9* Mario Andretti. *10* It claimed the life of Ronnie Peterson. *11* Jacques Laffite. *12* Gilles Villeneuve. *13* Jody Scheckter. *14* Renault. *15* Jean-Pierre Jabouille. *16* Williams. *17* Clay Regazzoni. *18* Alan Jones. *19* Niki Lauda. *20* South African (Jody Scheckter).

1   Alain Prost quit Renault to join which team for 1984?

2   He won the season's opening race at which circuit?

3   Which British driver led that race for Renault until his suspension collapsed?

4   Who won the 1984 South African Grand Prix for McLaren?

5   Michele Alboreto won the 1984 Belgian Grand Prix for which team?

6   Which British driver was leading the 1984 Monaco Grand Prix when he crashed?

7   Driving for which team?

8   Which Brazilian driver won back-to-back North American street races?

9   Which team was eliminated from the 1984 championship for a technical irregularity?

10   The 1984 championship was won by half a point. What was the nationality of the world champion?

11   Which French driver won the 1985 season's opening race, the Brazilian Grand Prix?

12   The second race, at Estoril, went to which Lotus driver?

13   What nationality was he?

14   Alain Prost was disqualified after winning at Imola in 1985. Who took maximum points?

15   Driving for which team?

16   Who won the 1985 Canadian Grand Prix in Montreal for Ferrari?

17   Which Williams driver won that year on the streets of Detroit?

18   When Nelson Piquet won the 1985 French Grand Prix, he gave which tyre company its first success since 1957?

19   Which reshaped circuit hosted the 1985 German Grand Prix?

20   Alain Prost clinched the title two races early. At which circuit?

Answers WORLD CHAMPIONSHIP 1980 & 1981 *(see Quiz 14)*

1 Nelson Piquet. 2 René Arnoux. 3 Renault. 4 Clay Regazzoni. 5 Didier Pironi. 6 A Ligier.
7 Williams. 8 The Austrian. 9 Lotus. 10 Alan Jones. 11 Riccardo Patrese. 12 Arrows. 13 Carlos
Reutemann. 14 Alan Jones. 15 Hector Rebaque. 16 Mexican. 17 Gilles Villeneuve. 18 McLaren
19 Las Vegas. 20 Nelson Piquet from Carlos Reutemann and Alan Jones.

1   Who replaced Niki Lauda at McLaren for 1986?

2   Name that driver's replacement at Williams, who won the Brazilian Grand Prix.

3   The 1986 Spanish Grand Prix was won by just 0.014 seconds. By whom?

4   Who did he pip to the finish line?

5   Alain Prost won the 1986 Monaco Grand Prix for which team?

6   Who broke his legs at the 1986 British Grand Prix at Brands Hatch?

7   Which European circuit made its first world championship appearance in 1986?

8   Mexico was back on the calendar for 1986 with victory going to which Benetton driver?

9   The final race of the 1986 season was a three-way shoot-out in Adelaide. Why did Nigel Mansell retire?

10   What was the nationality of the 1986 world champion?

11   Who set the 1987 season rolling for McLaren in Brazil?

12   Who was his new team-mate?

13   The 1987 San Marino Grand Prix was won by which Williams driver?

14   At which race did team-mates Nigel Mansell and Nelson Piquet come to blows?

15   Who scored the first of his six wins at Monaco in 1987?

16   Why did Nigel Mansell fail to finish the 1987 Hungarian Grand Prix?

17   Which grand prix required three attempts to get away without crashes?

18   The 1987 Japanese Grand Prix was back on the calendar. At which circuit?

19   Why did Nigel Mansell fail to complete the season?

20   Who won the final two races of 1987 for Ferrari?

Answers WORLD CHAMPIONSHIP 1990 (see Quiz 19)

1 Ayrton Senna. 2 Because of his disqualification from the 1989 Japanese Grand Prix. 3 Jean Alesi. 4 Tyrrell. 5 Ferrari. 6 Interlagos, Brazil, the second grand prix of the season. 7 Riccardo Patrese. 8 Gerhard Berger. 9 McLaren. 10 Ivan Capelli. 11 Mauricio Gugelmin. 12 Nigel Mansell 13 No. 14 Alessandro Nannini. 15 Thierry Boutsen. 16 Ayrton Senna. 17 Suzuka. 18 Nelson Piquet. 19 Roberto Moreno. 20 Aguri Suzuki.

1   Which team won 15 of the 16 grands prix held in 1988?
2   Which team won the remaining grand prix?
3   Name the two McLaren drivers.
4   Which McLaren driver disappeared for several hours after crashing while leading at Monaco?
5   Why did Alain Prost retire from the 1988 British Grand Prix?
6   When the dominant team's run was broken at Monza, who won?
7   Name his team-mate, who finished second?
8   Who knocked Ayrton Senna out of the lead?
9   For which team was he a stand-in driver?
10   What was the nationality of the eventual 1988 champion?
11   Who started his Ferrari career in winning style in 1989?
12   Where did he win first time out?
13   Who had a bad crash in the 1989 San Marino Grand Prix?
14   Who made amends at Monaco?
15   Which Brabham driver claimed a surprise third place at Monaco?
16   Which downtown American street circuit made its debut in 1989?
17   Who won there?
18   Who won the wet 1989 Canadian Grand Prix for Williams?
19   Why was Ayrton Senna disqualified from the 1989 Japanese Grand Prix?
20   Who was awarded the victory?

1   Who regained his racing licence just in time for the opening race of 1990?

2   Why was he in dispute with the sport's governing body?

3   He won the first race of the season, around the streets of Phoenix, but which driver pushed him hardest?

4   For which team was this driver racing?

5   Alain Prost had left McLaren and moved to which team?

6   Where was his first victory of the season?

7   Which Williams driver won the San Marino Grand Prix?

8   Who won the Canadian Grand Prix on the road but was penalized for jumping the start?

9   Driving for which team?

10   Which Leyton House driver led the French Grand Prix at Paul Ricard?

11   Name his team-mate, who ran second behind him for a while.

12   Who announced his retirement after dropping out of the British Grand Prix?

13   Did he stick to his word?

14   Who almost won the German Grand Prix by running a one-stop strategy?

15   The Hungarian Grand Prix was won by which Williams driver?

16   Who did he hold off after a fierce challenge?

17   Alain Prost and Ayrton Senna clashed for the second year in a row at which circuit?

18   Which Benetton driver won the season's last two races in Japan and Australia?

19   Who finished second behind him in Japan?

20   Which Japanese driver completed the Suzuka podium?

Answers WORLD CHAMPIONSHIP 1986 & 1987 *(see Quiz 17)*

1 Keke Rosberg. 2 Nelson Piquet. 3 Ayrton Senna. 4 Nigel Mansell. 5 McLaren. 6 Jacques Laffite. 7 Hungaroring. 8 Gerhard Berger. 9 He had a tyre blow-out. 10 French (Alain Prost). 11 Alain Prost. 12 Stefan Johansson. 13 Nigel Mansell. 14 The Belgian Grand Prix. 15 Ayrton Senna. 16 He lost a wheel nut. 17 The Austrian. 18 Suzuka. 19 He hurt his back. 20 Gerhard Berger.

1 Ayrton Senna kicked off the 1991 season by winning how many races in a row?

2 Which future world champion impressed in the United States Grand Prix in Phoenix, despite his steering wheel coming off?

3 For which team was he driving?

4 Who finally scored a win on home ground at Interlagos?

5 Ayrton Senna was led for the first time at the San Marino Grand Prix. By whom?

6 Which driver surprised everyone by finishing third at Imola?

7 For which team was he driving?

8 Which Tyrrell driver gave chase to Ayrton Senna at Monaco?

9 Which British driver failed to win the Canadian Grand Prix when his car stopped at the penultimate corner?

10 Why?

11 Who came through to win?

12 Driving for which team?

13 Who flipped in qualifying for the Mexican Grand Prix yet finished third?

14 The French Grand Prix moved to which new venue?

15 Where did Mansellmania reach its peak?

16 For which team did the object of their adulation drive?

17 Why did Ayrton Senna fail on the last lap in the British and German Grands Prix?

18 Which Jordan driver was set for second place in the Belgian Grand Prix but retired?

19 What did Nigel Mansell lose during a pit stop at Estoril?

20 Ayrton Senna clinched his second title in a row at the Japanese Grand Prix. Who did he let through to win the race?

Answers WORLD CHAMPIONSHIP 1988 & 1989 *(see Quiz 18)*

1 McLaren. **2** Ferrari (the Italian). **3** Alain Prost and Ayrton Senna. **4** Ayrton Senna. **5** In heavy rain, he thought conditions too treacherous. **6** Gerhard Berger. **7** Michele Alboreto. **8** Jean-Louis Schlesser. **9** Williams. **10** Brazilian (Ayrton Senna). **11** Nigel Mansell. **12** Jacarepagua, Brazil. **13** Gerhard Berger. **14** Ayrton Senna. **15** Stefano Modena. **16** Phoenix. **17** Alain Prost. **18** Thierry Boutsen. **19** For receiving a push-start. **20** Alessandro Nannini.

1   For its opening race, the world championship returned to where for the first time since 1985?

2   Who won?

3   Driving for which team?

4   He won the next how many grands prix?

5   Name his team-mate who finished second behind him in the first three races.

6   Who was second in the Spanish Grand Prix when Patrese spun off?

7   For which team was he driving?

8   Who broke Nigel Mansell's winning streak at Monaco?

9   Why did Nigel Mansell drop back to second?

10   Gerhard Berger won the Canadian Grand Prix for which team?

11   Why was the French Grand Prix stopped and restarted?

12   Which British driver was third in both the French and British Grands Prix?

13   Driving for which team?

14   At which grand prix did Nigel Mansell wrap up the title with five races still to run?

15   Michael Schumacher scored his first grand prix win at which circuit?

16   Who announced his retirement at the Italian Grand Prix?

17   Which manufacturer announced that it too was pulling out?

18   Who flipped on the start/finish straight at Estoril?

19   Nigel Mansell waved team-mate Riccardo Patrese through to win at which circuit?

20   Who won the Australian Grand Prix after Nigel Mansell and Ayrton Senna clashed over the lead?

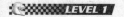
1   Who replaced Nigel Mansell at Williams for 1993?

2   Who was the Williams number two?

3   What had his previous role with the team been?

4   Why did Alain Prost go out of the Brazilian Grand Prix?

5   Who came through to win?

6   The European Grand Prix was next. Where was it held?

7   Who was heading for second place until fuel pressure problems?

8   For which team was he driving?

9   Who was Ayrton Senna's McLaren team-mate?

10 Which Ligier driver was on the podium in the South African and German Grands Prix?

11 Damon Hill challenged Alain Prost for victory in France, Britain and Germany. Where did he make his breakthrough?

12 Who survived a huge accident in qualifying at Spa-Francorchamps?

13 For which team was he driving?

14 Who somersaulted over the finish line in the Italian Grand Prix?

15 For which team was he driving?

16 Who scored his only podium finish at Monza?

17 The same driver was immediately replaced by whom?

18 Which driver scored his second win ahead of Prost in the Portuguese Grand Prix?

19 Who upset Ayrton Senna on his debut for Jordan at the Japanese Grand Prix?

20 What did Senna do about it?

1 Ayrton Senna moved to which team for 1994?

2 Michael Schumacher set the ball rolling by winning for which team at Interlagos?

3 Why did Ayrton Senna fail to score at his home circuit?

4 Who flipped his car mid-race?

5 For which team was he driving?

6 Who was blamed for the accident?

7 Which new Japanese circuit was visited for the Pacific Grand Prix?

8 Who tipped Ayrton Senna off at the first corner?

9 The San Marino Grand Prix was marred by the death of whom in qualifying?

10 For which team was he driving?

11 Who was killed in the race itself?

12 Which Austrian driver fell into a coma after crashing at Monaco?

13 For which team was he driving?

14 Who was Senna's replacement driver at Williams?

15 Michael Schumacher won at Monaco. Who was second for McLaren?

16 Which team brought Nigel Mansell back from America for the French Grand Prix?

17 Why was Michael Schumacher disqualified from the British Grand Prix?

18 What was the nationality of the driver enveloped by flames during the German Grand Prix?

19 The title race was settled when Michael Schumacher and Damon Hill clashed at which circuit?

20 Who came through to win the race?

Answers WORLD CHAMPIONSHIP 1991 (see Quiz 21)

1 South Africa. 2 Nigel Mansell. 3 Williams. 4 Four. 5 Riccardo Patrese. 6 Michael Schumacher. 7 Benetton. 8 Ayrton Senna. 9 He got a puncture. 10 McLaren. 11 Heavy rain. 12 Martin Brundle. 13 Benetton. 14 Hungarian. 15 Spa-Francorchamps. 16 Nigel Mansell. 17 Honda. 18 Riccardo Patrese. 19 Suzuka. 20 Gerhard Berger.

1   Benetton swapped their Ford engines for what make of engines in 1995?

2   Who was the team's new full-time number two driver?

3   Which South American country was back on the calendar for the first time since 1981?

4   Who won this revived grand prix?

5   For which team was he driving?

6   One-stop tactics helped who score his second Monaco win in succession?

7   In Canada, who scored his first win in more than 90 attempts?

8   For which team was he driving?

9   The drivers of which team's cars filled second and third places on that podium?

10   Damon Hill and Michael Schumacher clashed a lot in 1995. Where was their first collision?

11   Who came through to win that race?

12   David Coulthard would have won the race but for what?

13   Who led the opening lap of the German Grand Prix then crashed out?

14   Name the driver who finished third for Ligier in the Belgian Grand Prix.

15   Johnny Herbert won the Italian Grand Prix for Benetton. Who came second for McLaren?

16   David Coulthard finally scored his first grand prix win in which country?

17   Who flipped his car at the start of the race?

18   For which team was he driving?

19   The Grand Prix of Europe was run at which circuit?

20   Victory at which circuit gave Michael Schumacher the title?

Answers *WORLD CHAMPIONSHIP 1993* (see Quiz 22)

1 Alain Prost. 2 Damon Hill. 3 Test driver. 4 He hit a car that had spun. 5 Ayrton Senna.
6 Donington Park. 7 Rubens Barrichello. 8 Jordan. 9 Michael Andretti. 10 Mark Blundell.
11 Hungary. 12 Alessandro Zanardi. 13 Lotus. 14 Christian Fittipaldi. 15 Minardi. 16 Michael
Andretti. 17 Mika Hakkinen. 18 Michael Schumacher. 19 Eddie Irvine. 20 He punched him.

1   Who won the season-opening Australian Grand Prix?
2   Where was this held?
3   Name his team-mate who led until his car sprung an oil leak.
4   Where did this team-mate make his grand prix breakthrough?
5   Only four cars finished the Monaco Grand Prix. Who won?
6   For which team was he driving?
7   Who finished second?
8   Michael Schumacher scored his first 1996 win at which race?
9   For which team was he driving?
10 Name his team-mate.
11 Which Benetton driver led the German Grand Prix until three laps from the finish?
12 Who came through to win?
13 At which grand prix was it rumoured that Damon Hill would not stay with Williams for 1997?
14 Who was tipped to replace him?
15 Who came through to win at Monza after Damon Hill spun off?
16 Who overtook Michael Schumacher around the outside at Estoril's final corner to win the Portuguese Grand Prix?
17 Which team's drivers collided with each other in the Portuguese Grand Prix?
18 The world championship title race came down to the final round. Where was it held?
19 Who won this race to lift the crown?
20 What happened to his only rival?

1   Who scored McLaren's first win since 1993?

2   Where did he achieve this feat?

3   Who made amends by winning the Brazilian Grand Prix?

4   Who finished a close second in Argentina?

5   Who finished third despite knocking his team-mate off?

6   Name his team-mate.

7   For which team were they driving?

8   Which Williams driver won the San Marino Grand Prix?

9   Who won the Monaco Grand Prix?

10   Which new team celebrated winning its first points with second place at Monaco?

11   Who was this new team's scoring driver?

12   Which French driver finished second in Spain behind Jacques Villeneuve?

13   Who broke his legs in the Canadian Grand Prix?

14   For which team was he driving?

15   Whose engine blew at Silverstone, which cost him his first win?

16   Which Benetton stand-in finished third at Silverstone?

17   Who came back to win the German Grand Prix?

18   The championship protagonists clashed at the Jerez finale. Who lost out?

19   Who won the 1997 world title?

20   Mika Hakkinen won the final race, the European Grand Prix, for which team?

Answers **WORLD CHAMPIONSHIP 1999** *(see Quiz 28)*

1 Eddie Irvine. **2** Williams. **3** Rubens Barrichello. **4** Stewart. **5** Mika Hakkinen. **6** Benetton. **7** Michael Schumacher. **8** Heinz-Harald Frentzen. **9** Jordan. **10** Stowe. **11** His left rear wheel came off. **12** Out of fuel. **13** Mika Salo. **14** Damon Hill. **15** Mika Hakkinen. **16** Sauber (and Jean Alesi proved true to his word). **17** La Source. **18** Mika Hakkinen. **19** David Coulthard. **20** Michael Schumacher.

1   What did the McLaren drivers adopt in Melbourne, which angered their rivals?
2   As a result, who won that opening race?
3   What was the McLarens' margin of victory over the third-placed car?
4   Who did Michael Schumacher tip out of the lead in Argentina?
5   Who was the new Argentinian driver racing for Minardi?
6   Who was the Brazilian struggling with Tyrrell?
7   Which team won the San Marino Grand Prix?
8   Who finished second at Monaco for Benetton?
9   Who came fourth for Arrows?
10 Who benefitted from McLaren problems to win in Canada?
11 Who rolled at the first start there?
12 What thwarted David Coulthard in the French Grand Prix?
13 When did Michael Schumacher take his stop-go penalty in the British Grand Prix?
14 What was his stop-go penalty for?
15 How many pit stops did Michael Schumacher make *en route* to victory in Hungary?
16 Which team scored its first win at the Belgian Grand Prix?
17 Who was the team's winning driver?
18 Why was Michael Schumacher sent to the back of the grid at the Suzuka showdown?
19 Why did he retire from the race?
20 Who won the world championship?

Answers WORLD CHAMPIONSHIP 1996 *(see Quiz 25)*

1 Damon Hill. *2* Melbourne. *3* Jacques Villeneuve. *4* Nürburgring (the European Grand Prix). *5* Olivier Panis. *6* Ligier. *7* David Coulthard in a McLaren (Johnny Herbert and Heinz-Harald Frentzen were third and fourth in Saubers). *8* The Spanish Grand Prix. *9* Ferrari. *10* Eddie Irvine. *11* Gerhard Berger. *12* Damon Hill. *13* The German Grand Prix. *14* Heinz-Harald Frentzen. *15* Michael Schumacher. *16* Jacques Villeneuve. *17* McLaren. *18* Suzuka. *19* Damon Hill. *20* Jacques Villeneuve lost a wheel.

1   Who scored his first win at the season-opening Australian Grand Prix?

2   Ralf Schumacher finished second at Melbourne for which team?

3   Which Brazilian driver led his home race?

4   For which team was he driving?

5   Who crashed out of the lead in the San Marino Grand Prix?

6   Which team's drivers filled fifth and sixth places at Monaco?

7   Who crashed out of the lead in the Canadian Grand Prix?

8   Who lost second place in the closing laps?

9   Which team took its second win in the wet French Grand Prix?

10   At which corner did Michael Schumacher break a leg in the British Grand Prix?

11   Why did Mika Hakkinen retire from the British Grand Prix?

12   Jean Alesi and Alessandro Zanardi had the same reason for retirement in the Austrian Grand Prix. What was it?

13   Who was told to move over to let Eddie Irvine win the German Grand Prix?

14   Who quit because he couldn't get on with his brakes?

15   Which driver led the Hungarian Grand Prix from start to finish?

16   Which team had both its drivers threaten to resign at the Hungarian Grand Prix?

17   At which corner did the McLarens touch at the Belgian Grand Prix?

18   Who spun out of the lead of the Italian Grand Prix?

19   Which McLaren driver spun out of the lead of the European Grand Prix?

20   Who starred on his comeback in the Malaysian Grand Prix?

1 Which team won the inaugural Constructors' Cup in 1958?

2 Which team was second?

3 A British team won the title in 1959. Which one?

4 Where did Vanwall finish in 1959?

5 More British teams were starting to shine in 1960. Which one was second?

6 New regulations helped which team to the 1961 Constructors' Cup?

7 Which British marque scored its only Constructors' Cup victory in 1962?

8 Which engines powered Lotus to second place in 1962?

9 Which British marque won its first Constructors' Cup in 1963?

10 Who scored the bulk of the points?

11 BRM scored the most points in 1964, but which marque won the title after dropped scores?

12 Despite missing the Monaco Grand Prix, which marque still finished top in 1965?

13 Which Japanese marque scored its first points that year?

14 Which British-based Australian's marque took its first title in 1966?

15 What engines did champions Brabham use in 1967?

16 What engines did runners-up Lotus use at the start of the 1967 season?

17 Lotus won the 1968 title with what engines?

18 Which marque finished in second place in 1968?

19 Which French team won in 1969?

20 Which marque was second in 1969?

Answers *THE CONSTRUCTORS' CUP 3 (see Quiz 31)*

1 Williams. 2 Ligier. 3 Brabham. 4 Renault. 5 Ferrari. 6 Ford then BMW. 7 Ferrari. 8 Renault. 9 McLaren. 10 Niki Lauda and Alain Prost. 11 TAG Porsche. 12 Lotus. 13 Williams. 14 Nigel Mansell and Nelson Piquet. 15 Williams. 16 Honda. 17 McLaren. 18 15. 19 Williams. 20 Thierry Boutsen and Riccardo Patrese.

1   Ferrari was back on form in 1970. Where did they finish?

2   Which engine dominated the Constructors' Cup in 1970?

3   Another British marque scored its first Constructors' Cup win in 1971. Which one?

4   Who was its main points scorer?

5   Which marque was crowned for the fifth time in 1972?

6   Which team founded by a motorcycle champion came fifth?

7   Lotus finished on top in 1973. Who was the lead driver?

8   Who was Lotus's number two driver in 1973?

9   Name the British team that took over the title in 1974.

10   Which British marque scored its first points that year?

11   In which position did Brabham finish in 1975?

12   Name Brabham's two drivers for 1975.

13   Which Italian marque made it two titles in a row in 1976?

14   Which marque pushed it hardest?

15   Which new marque was placed fourth overall in 1977?

16   Who was the driver?

17   Ground-effects helped which marque to the 1978 title?

18   Which marque grabbed second in 1978 with a late charge?

19   Which improving marque finished second behind Ferrari in 1979?

20   Which French marque was the first to finish in the top three since Matra won it in 1969?

Answers *THE CONSTRUCTORS' CUP 4* (see Quiz 32)

1 Honda. *2* Ferrari. *3* McLaren. *4* Renault. *5* Williams. *6* Nigel Mansell and Riccardo Patrese. *7* True. *8* Williams. *9* Williams. *10* Benetton. *11* Benetton. *12* Williams. *13* Williams. *14* Damon Hill and Jacques Villeneuve. *15* Jacques Villeneuve. *16* Heinz-Harald Frentzen. *17* McLaren. *18* Mika Hakkinen. *19* Eddie Irvine. *20* Ford.

Quiz 31 *THE CONSTRUCTORS' CUP 3*

Answers – see page 40

1 Which British marque clinched its first title in 1980?
2 Which marque ranked second overall?
3 Which marque fielded the champion driver yet had to settle for second in 1981?
4 Which French marque ranked third?
5 Which troubled marque recovered from a dreadful season to finish first in 1982?
6 What two makes of engine did Brabham use in the early eighties?
7 Which marque won its eighth Constructors' Cup in 1983?
8 Which marque held on to second place that year?
9 Which marque set a then record of 143.5 points in 1984?
10 Who were that team's drivers?
11 McLaren used what engine to become champions in 1985?
12 Name the most successful team using Renault engines that year.
13 Another British team took charge in 1986. Which one?
14 Name the two drivers.
15 Which Honda-powered team triumphed in 1987?
16 What engines did Lotus use to be ranked third in 1987?
17 Which team scored a record points tally in 1988?
18 How many of the 16 grands prix did it win?
19 Which team pushed McLaren hardest in 1989?
20 Who were the drivers?

Answers *THE CONSTRUCTORS' CUP 1* *(see Quiz 29)*

1 Vanwall. 2 Ferrari. 3 Cooper. 4 Nowhere; Vanwall had quit the sport. 5 Lotus. 6 Ferrari. 7 BRM. 8 Climax. 9 Lotus. 10 Jim Clark. 11 Ferrari. 12 Lotus. 13 Honda. 14 Brabham. 15 Repco. 16 BRM. 17 Ford Cosworth DFV. 18 McLaren. 19 Matra. 20 Brabham.

1 What engine did McLaren use to become champions again in 1990?

2 Which team finished a clear second?

3 Williams led until two races from the end of 1991. Who stole through?

4 What engine did Williams use?

5 Which team won by 65 points in 1992?

6 Name the drivers.

7 Every 1993 round was won by a British team. True or false?

8 Which team scored the most points?

9 Which team made it three in a row in 1994?

10 Which team pushed it hard and finished second?

11 Which team landed its first, and so far only, Constructors' Cup title in 1995?

12 Which team was second that year?

13 Which team finished runaway Constructors' Cup winners in 1996?

14 Name the two drivers.

15 Williams claimed a ninth Constructors' Cup in 1997. Who was the champion?

16 Who was Williams' number two driver?

17 Which team claimed its first title since 1991 after a successful 1998 campaign?

18 Who was the world champion?

19 Who gave Ferrari a winning start in the opening race of 1999?

20 Which engine supplier bought the Stewart team?

Answers THE CONSTRUCTORS' CUP 2 *(see Quiz 30)*

1 Second. 2 Ford Cosworth DFV. 3 Tyrrell. 4 Jackie Stewart. 5 Lotus. 6 Surtees. 7 Emerson Fittipaldi. 8 Ronnie Peterson. 9 McLaren. 10 Hesketh. 11 Second. 12 Carlos Pace and Carlos Reutemann. 13 Ferrari. 14 McLaren. 15 Wolf. 16 Jody Scheckter. 17 Lotus. 18 Ferrari. 19 Williams. 20 Ligier (third in 1979).

1 Which country does the AGS team come from?

2 Which driver was paralysed in 1989 after crashing his AGS in testing in Brazil?

3 Alfa Romeo drivers stormed the first two drivers' championships. Name the two champions.

4 At the end of which year did Alfa Romeo quit Formula One?

5 When did it return?

6 Who was the lead driver on the team's return to Formula One?

7 From which team did most of the Arrows personnel break away?

8 In what year was the Arrows team formed?

9 Name its first driver pairing.

10 Aston Martin made its Formula One debut in which year?

11 Roy Salvadori was one of its drivers. Who was the other?

12 Formula One was not Aston Martin's main racing interest. What was?

13 Who founded the German ATS team in 1978?

14 How had he made his money?

15 Traditionally, what colour were ATS cars?

16 BAR is the acronym for what?

17 What is British American?

18 When did the team first enter the world championship?

19 With which driver as its number one?

20 In which year did the Toleman team become Benetton?

Answers *THE TEAMS 3 (see Quiz 35)*

1 Stirling Moss (the Argentinian Grand Prix). *2* 1959 *3* Giampaolo. *4* BMS Scuderia Italia. *5* Alex Caffi. *6* Andrea de Cesaris or JJ Lehto. *7* Giampaolo Dallara. *8* Piers Courage. *9* Dan Gurney. *10* 1967. *11* Spa-Francorchamps. *12* Mo Nunn. *13* 1973. *14* Clay Regazzoni. *15* English Racing Automobiles. *16* Raymond Mays. *17* Enzo. *18* Red. *19* Niki Lauda. *20* Michael Schumacher.

1 Who scored Benetton's first grand prix win?

2 In which year was that?

3 Who is Benetton's only world champion so far?

4 Jack Brabham was one of the founders of Brabham. Who was the other?

5 In which year did Brabham make its Formula One debut?

6 When did Brabham win the first of its two Constructors' Cup titles?

7 Who bought the team in 1972?

8 Who founded BRM?

9 Who was BRM's only world champion?

10 In what year did he win the world championship?

11 BRP is the acronym for what?

12 Which driver's father was one of the two founders?

13 In what colour did its cars traditionally run?

14 Bugatti contested just one world championship grand prix. Which one?

15 What is the first name of the founder of the Coloni team?

16 With which driver did Coloni graduate to Formula One in 1987?

17 A scion of which wealthy construction family helped finance the formation of Connaught?

18 Who bought the team at the end of 1957?

19 Name the father and son who formed the Cooper team?

20 In what formula did they make their name?

1 Who in 1958 gave Cooper its first Formula One win?

2 In what year did Cooper claim its first Constructors' Cup title?

3 What is the first name of Italian designer Dallara?

4 Which team ran his cars in Formula One from 1988 to 1992?

5 Who was the team's first driver?

6 Name one of the two Dallara drivers to stand on a podium?

7 Who designed the 1970 De Tomaso 505 chassis?

8 Who drove it until he was killed?

9 Who founded the Eagle marque?

10 An Eagle won just once. In which year?

11 At which circuit was the only Eagle victory achieved?

12 Name the founder of the Ensign team.

13 In what year did Ensign make its Formula One debut?

14 Who crashed an Ensign in 1980 and was paralysed?

15 ERA is the acronym for what?

16 Who founded the team?

17 What was the first name of the founder of Ferrari?

18 What is the team's traditional colour?

19 Which Austrian driver helped the team rediscover its winning touch in the mid 1970s?

20 Which German driver has echoed this feat in the late 1990s?

Answers THE TEAMS 1 *(see Quiz 33)*

1 France. 2 Philippe Streiff. 3 Giuseppe Farina and Juan Manuel Fangio. 4 1951. 5 1979.
6 Bruno Giacomelli. 7 Shadow. 8 1978. 9 Riccardo Patrese and Rolf Stommelen. 10 1959.
11 Carroll Shelby. 12 Sportscars. 13 Hans Gunther Schmid. 14 Making alloy wheels. 15 Yellow.
16 British American Racing. 17 A tobacco company. 18 1999. 19 Jacques Villeneuve.
20 1986.

1 Which Fittipaldi brother formed the family team?

2 Which company was the team's principal sponsor?

3 What was the team's traditional colour?

4 What team was taken over and renamed Fondmetal in 1991?

5 What product is made by Fondmetal?

6 The Japanese Footwork corporation took over which team in 1991?

7 Name the team's two drivers for 1991.

8 Which British driver drove for Footwork in 1993?

9 What was the first name of the founder of the Forti team?

10 Which Brazilian driver financed its graduation to Formula One?

11 In which year was this?

12 Which British sportscar builders fielded a Formula One car in 1952?

13 Who was their driver?

14 What nationality was the Gordini team?

15 HWM is the acronym for what?

16 Who founded the HWM team?

17 Who founded the Hesketh team?

18 Who was the team's first driver?

19 At which circuit did the team score its only win?

20 In which year did Honda arrive in Formula One?

Answers **THE TEAMS 2** *(see Quiz 34)*

1 Gerhard Berger. **2** 1986. **3** Michael Schumacher. **4** Ron Tauranac. **5** 1962. **6** 1966.
7 Bernie Ecclestone. **8** Raymond Mays. **9** Graham Hill. **10** 1962. **11** British Racing Partnership.
12 Stirling Moss. **13** Pale green. **14** The 1956 French Grand Prix. **15** Enzo. **16** Nicola Larini.
17 McAlpine. **18** Bernie Ecclestone. **19** Charles and John. **20** Formula Three.

1   Who was Honda's driver for its first year in Formula One?

2   Who gave Honda its first win?

3   In which grand prix?

4   Name the founder of the Jordan team.

5   In which year did Jordan graduate to Formula One?

6   Who gave the team its first pole position?

7   Who gave Jordan its first win?

8   What was the only season in which Lamborghini raced in Formula One as a constructor?

9   Which Lamborghini driver was heading for points at Imola until his fuel pump failed?

10 Lancia made its Formula One debut in which season?

11 Which motor manufacturer took over the company and its racing team in 1955?

12 For what branch of motor sport did Lancia become famous in the 1970s and 1980s?

13 What is the first name of the Larrousse team founder?

14 In what branch of the sport did he shine before turning to Formula One?

15 In what year did he enter the first Larrousse chassis?

16 In what business did the Leyton House company earn the money to go into Formula One?

17 With which established team did Leyton House become involved?

18 What was the team's traditional colour?

19 Who were its two drivers from 1988 to 1991?

20 In what sport was Guy Ligier a famed participant before going into racing?

Answers THE TEAMS 7 *(see Quiz 39)*

1 Teddy Mayer. *2* 1973. *3* Emerson Fittipaldi (1974). *4* James Hunt (1976). *5* 1954. *6* Juan Manuel Fangio. *7* Over 80 spectators were killed at Le Mans when a Mercedes crashed into the crowd. *8* Italian. *9* Pierluigi Martini. *10* Luca Badoer. *11* Mike Earle. *12* 1989 *13* Stefan Johansson. *14* Enzo. *15* Eddie Cheever. *16* Piercarlo Ghinzani. *17* Keith Wiggins. *18* JJ Lehto *19* Bertrand Gachot. *20* John Watson.

1 In what year did Ligier make its Formula One debut?

2 Who was the lead driver for Ligier that year?

3 In which country did Ligier score its first grand prix win?

4 Who founded Lola?

5 What former world champion used a Lola chassis for his own team?

6 When did Lola enter Formula One for the one and only time in its own right?

7 Who founded Lotus?

8 Who was the Lotus team's first world champion?

9 Who was the Lotus team's second world champion?

10 Which American driver led Lotus back to glory in the late 1970s?

11 Of which Formula One team was FIA president Max Mosley one of the founders?

12 In which year did this team makes its Formula One debut?

13 Who gave the marque its first win?

14 Who won the Austrian Grand Prix for March in 1975 and then crashed?

15 Which driver gave Maserati its first Formula One win?

16 The marque's most famous chassis was introduced in 1954. What was it?

17 Juan Manuel Fangio became world champion for Maserati in which year?

18 In what branch of engineering was Matra's background?

19 Which British team entrant ran Matra cars in Formula One?

20 In which year did a Matra driver become world champion?

Answers *THE TEAMS 8* (see Quiz 40)

1 The Austrian. **2** 1976. **3** 1961. **4** Dan Gurney. **5** The 1962 French Grand Prix. **6** Ligier.
7 Olivier Panis. **8** Jarno Trulli. **9** John Macdonald and Mick Ralph. **10** 1983. **11** Skoal Bandit.
12 Renault. **13** 1977. **14** Jean-Pierre Jabouille. **15** Dijon-Prenois. **16** Swiss. **17** 1993. **18** Karl
Wendlinger. **19** CanAm sportscars. **20** Tom Pryce.

1 Who ran McLaren after Bruce McLaren's death?

2 In which year did McLaren introduce its M23 chassis?

3 Who was McLaren's first world champion?

4 Who was McLaren's second world champion?

5 Mercedes-Benz entered the world championship in which season?

6 Who was its number one driver?

7 Why did Mercedes-Benz quit all racing at the end of the 1955 season?

8 What nationality is the Minardi team?

9 Who raced for Minardi for eight seasons?

10 Which Italian driver had his second spell with the team in 1999?

11 Who formed the Onyx team?

12 In what season did it make its Formula One debut?

13 Name the Swedish driver who scored six points for Onyx that year?

14 What is the first name of the founder of Osella?

15 Which American driver graduated from Formula Two with the team in 1980?

16 Which Italian driver's sponsorship-hunting skills kept him in the team in the mid 1980s?

17 Who founded the Pacific team?

18 Which Formula One driver did he guide to the 1988 British Formula Three title?

19 Who raced for Pacific in both of its seasons in Formula One?

20 Who gave Penske its only Formula One win?

1 Penske had only one Formula One win. At which grand prix?

2 In which year was that?

3 Porsche entered its first true Formula One car in which year?

4 Which American driver gave Porsche its only Formula One win?

5 In which grand prix was this?

6 Which team did Alain Prost take over in 1997?

7 Who broke his legs when he crashed his Prost at that year's Canadian Grand Prix?

8 Which Prost driver led that year's Austrian Grand Prix?

9 Name the partners in RAM.

10 In which year did they field the first true RAM chassis?

11 Which company sponsored the team's cars in 1984 and 1985?

12 Which French marque entered the first turbocharged car in Formula One?

13 In what season was this?

14 Who was the team's driver?

15 At which circuit did Renault's first win come in 1979?

16 What nationality is the Sauber team?

17 In which year did it make its Formula One debut?

18 Which Sauber driver fell into a coma after crashing at Monaco in 1994?

19 Shadow came to Formula One in 1973 from which racing category?

20 Which driver won the 1975 Race of Champions for Shadow?

Answers *THE TEAMS 6 (see Quiz 38)*

1 1976. *2* Jacques Laffite. *3* Sweden. *4* Eric Broadley. *5* Graham Hill. *6* 1997. *7* Colin Chapman. *8* Jim Clark (1963). *9* Graham Hill (1968). *10* Mario Andretti. *11* March. *12* 1970. *13* Jackie Stewart. *14* Vittorio Brambilla. *15* Juan Manuel Fangio. *16* The Maserati 250F. *17* 1957. *18* Aerospace. *19* Ken Tyrrell. *20* 1969 (Jackie Stewart).

1 Who gave Shadow its only Formula One grand prix win?

2 Name the founder of the Simtek team.

3 In which year did Simtek arrive in Formula One?

4 Which Australian driver was Simtek's team leader that season?

5 Which Formula Two team graduated to Formula One with Honda engines in 1983?

6 Who was the team's driver?

7 Three-time world champion Jackie Stewart formed which team in 1997?

8 What is the first name of his son, one of the co-founders?

9 Who were their drivers in that first season?

10 In which grand prix did the team score its first points?

11 Which world champion on two wheels and four drove a Formula One car bearing his name?

12 Who was the fellow motorcycle racing ace who joined the team in 1972?

13 What company was the team's publicity-generating sponsor in 1976?

14 What nationality was the Talbot team?

15 What was the traditional colour of its cars?

16 Who financed the Theodore team?

17 Who was the first driver to race for the Theodore team in Formula One?

18 With which team did Theodore amalgamate in 1983?

19 How did Ted Toleman make the money to form his own Formula One team?

20 In which year did Toleman enter Formula One?

Answers THE DRIVERS 1 *(see Quiz 43)*

1 Tyrrell. **2** Caesar's Palace, Las Vegas. **3** Ferrari. **4** 1985. **5** Minardi. **6** French. **7** Italian. **8** Tyrrell. **9** The 1995 Canadian Grand Prix. **10** Ferrari. **11** Sauber. **12** Larrousse. **13** RAM. **14** Jacques Laffite. **15** McLaren. **16** England. **17** Ferrari. **18** He'd broken an arm. **19** New Zealander. **20** A puncture.

1 Which Brazilian driver was Toleman's star in 1984?

2 In which year did Tyrrell first enter a car of its own design?

3 Who won two world championships with Tyrrell?

4 Who was the last driver to win a grand prix for Tyrrell?

5 Which was Tyrrell's final season?

6 What was the name of the industrialist who formed Vanwall?

7 In what year did Vanwall enter Formula One?

8 Stirling Moss and Tony Brooks gave Vanwall its first grand prix win at which circuit?

9 In which year did Vanwall win the Constructors' Cup?

10 Frank Williams formed Williams Grand Prix Engineering with whom in 1977?

11 They entered their first Formula One car for whom in 1978?

12 In what year did this driver guide the team to its first Constructors' Cup?

13 Who was Williams's first British world champion?

14 What nationality was Walter Wolf, founder of the Wolf team?

15 In what country had he made his fortune in oil?

16 Who gave the team victory on its maiden Formula One outing?

17 What nationality was the Zakspeed team?

18 Who was Zakspeed's first driver when it entered Formula One in 1985?

19 What make of engine did Zakspeed use in its first four seasons?

20 Which British team did Zakspeed attempt to take over for 1999?

Answers **THE DRIVERS 2** *(see Quiz 44)*

1 Matra. *2* Ensign. *3* The Austrian. *4* Zeltweg. *5* Silverstone. *6* Lotus. *7* Watkins Glen, USA. *8* Ferrari. *9* Kyalami, South Africa. *10* Parnelli. *11* Lotus. *12* His son. *13* McLaren. *14* 1993. *15* Formula Two. *16* Martini. *17* Renault. *18* Dijon-Prenois. *19* Ferrari. *20* Lotus.

1   Michele Alboreto broke into Formula One with which team?

2   Where did he score his first grand prix win in 1982?

3   For which Italian team did he drive between 1984 and 1988?

4   In which season did he finish second in the world championship?

5   What was the final team Michele Alboreto drove for before quitting Formula One?

6   What nationality is Jean Alesi?

7   What nationality are Jean Alesi's parents?

8   What was his first Formula One team?

9   Which was his one and only grand prix win?

10 For which team did he score this win?

11 Which team did he quit in 1999?

12 With which team did Philippe Alliot spend the majority of his Formula One career?

13 With which team did he arrive in Formula One?

14 He joined Ligier midway through 1986 as a substitute for which injured driver?

15 For which British team did he have a one-off outing in 1994?

16 From which country does Cliff Allison originate?

17 For which team did he finish second in the 1960 Argentinian Grand Prix?

18 Why did he not start the following race at Monaco?

19 What nationality is Chris Amon?

20 What deprived him of victory in the 1972 French Grand Prix?

1. For which team did Chris Amon drive in 1971 and 1972?
2. With which team did he end his Formula One career?
3. Bob Anderson finished third in which 1964 grand prix?
4. On which circuit was the race held that year?
5. At which circuit did Bob Anderson die in testing?
6. Mario Andretti started his Formula One career in 1968 with which team?
7. He qualified in pole position at his second attempt. At which circuit?
8. With which team did Mario Andretti score his first grand prix win?
9. And at which circuit was this?
10. For which American team did Mario Andretti drive between 1974 and 1976?
11. With which team did he become world champion in 1978?
12. What relation of Mario Andretti's is Michael Andretti?
13. With which team did Michael Andretti spend his brief spell in Formula One?
14. When was that?
15. What title did René Arnoux win in 1977 before graduating to Formula One?
16. With which team did he arrive in Formula One?
17. For which team did he win his first grand prix?
18. At which circuit did he have his famous duel with Gilles Villeneuve in 1979?
19. To which team did he move in 1983?
20. Peter Arundell scored two consecutive third places for which team in 1964?

Answers **THE TEAMS 10** *(see Quiz 42)*
1 Ayrton Senna. 2 1970. 3 Jackie Stewart. 4 Michele Alboreto. 5 1998. 6 Tony Vandervell.
7 1954. 8 Aintree (1957). 9 1958. 10 Patrick Head. 11 Alan Jones. 12 1980. 13 Nigel Mansell.
14 Austrian. 15 Canada. 16 Jody Scheckter (1977 Argentine Grand Prix). 17 German.
18 Jonathan Palmer. 19 A Zakspeed. 20 Arrows.

1   Who was Peter Arundell's team-mate in 1964?

2   Alberto Ascari was twice world champion for which team?

3   In which year did he clinch the first of his world titles?

4   To which team did he transfer at the end of 1954?

5   At which circuit was he killed in 1955?

6   What sort of car was he testing at the time?

7   Richard Attwood finished second in the 1968 Monaco Grand Prix for which team?

8   Which French race yielded Richard Attwood's most famous victory?

9   Luca Badoer arrived in Formula One having just won which title?

10   With which team did he make his Formula One debut in 1993?

11   For which team did Badoer drive in 1999?

12   For which team was he test driver?

13   What record does Giancarlo Baghetti hold?

14   On what occasion did he achieve it?

15   At which circuit?

16   What make of car was he driving?

17   What nationality is Mauro Baldi?

18   With which team did he make his Formula One debut in 1982?

19   For which team did he achieve his best result of fifth place?

20   With which team did Lorenzo Bandini spend the majority of his career?

Answers THE DRIVERS 5 *(see Quiz 47)*

1 Monaco. 2 BRM. 3 Monegasque. 4 Nelson Piquet. 5 Larrousse. 6 ATS. 7 Arrows.
8 Benetton. 9 Imola. 10 His father died. 11 BMW. 12 Larrousse. 13 Jean Alesi.
14 Hockenheim, 1994. 15 Ligier. 16 Belgian. 17 Cooper. 18 Monaco, 1968. 19 Thai. 20 ERA.

1 Lorenzo Bandini scored his only win in 1964 in which grand prix?

2 At which circuit was it held?

3 At which circuit was he killed in 1967?

4 Rubens Barrichello started his Formula One career with which team in 1993?

5 He ran second to Ayrton Senna in only his second grand prix, before retiring with fuel pressure problems. Where was that?

6 For which team did he finish second at Monaco in 1997?

7 For which team is he driving in 2000?

8 What nationality was Jean Behra?

9 With which French team did he spend the first three years of his Formula One career?

10 To which team did he move in 1955?

11 At which circuit did he crash to his death?

12 Derek Bell made his Formula One debut with which team?

13 When was this?

14 Derek Bell is famous for winning which race?

15 Stefan Bellof raced for only one team in his Formula One career. Which one?

16 Who was his team-mate in 1984 and 1985?

17 Bellof's best result (before disqualification for a technical infringement) was third place. Where was this?

18 He died in 1985 in a sportscar race at which circuit?

19 Jean-Pierre Beltoise raced what at the start of his competition career?

20 With which team did he graduate to Formula One?

1   At which circuit did Jean-Pierre Beltoise achieve his only Formula One win?

2   For which team did he win that race?

3   What nationality is Olivier Beretta?

4   Which world champion helped Beretta into Formula 3000?

5   With which team did Beretta spend 1994, his only season in Formula One?

6   For which team did Gerhard Berger make his Formula One debut in 1984?

7   With which team did he spend his first full grand prix season?

8   With which team did he win his first grand prix?

9   At which circuit did he burn his hands in 1989?

10   What distracted him in 1997?

11   After he retired from racing, which manufacturer appointed him head of its motorsport programme?

12   Eric Bernard made his Formula One debut for which team in 1989, while still racing in Formula 3000?

13   Which compatriot beat him to the Formula 3000 title that year?

14   Where did Eric Bernard appear on a Formula One podium for the only time?

15   For which team was he driving that day?

16   Lucien Bianchi was born in Italy but adopted which nationality?

17   His best season was 1968, when he raced for which team?

18   At which circuit did he achieve his only podium position?

19   What nationality was "B Bira"?

20   He made his name driving what make of car in the late 1930s?

1 What car was "B Bira" driving when he finished fourth in the 1954 French Grand Prix?

2 Mark Blundell drove for four teams in his Formula One career. Which was the first?

3 Who was his team-mate that year?

4 Mark Blundell appeared on the podium twice for which team in 1993?

5 And once for which team in 1994?

6 In what category has he been racing since 1996?

7 Felice Bonetto raced for which works team in 1951?

8 For which team did Bonetto drive in 1953, his best season?

9 In which road race was he killed that year?

10 What nationality was Joakim Bonnier?

11 Which marque did he drive to its first Formula One win?

12 In which grand prix was that?

13 For which British entrant did he race through much of the 1960s?

14 Slim Borgudd had just two seasons in Formula One. With which team did he spend 1981, his first one?

15 With which team did Borgudd spend 1982, his second one?

16 What was Jean-Christophe Boullion's nickname when he arrived in Formula One?

17 For which team did he make his debut?

18 For which other team was he test driver at the time?

19 In which international touring car championship did he race in 1999?

20 Thierry Boutsen graduated to Formula One with which team in 1983?

Answers THE DRIVERS 4 *(see Quiz 46)*

1 Austrian. 2 Zeltweg. 3 Monaco. 4 Jordan. 5 Donington Park. 6 Stewart. 7 Ferrari. 8 French. 9 Gordini. 10 Maserati. 11 Avus, Berlin, during a sportscar race in 1959. 12 Ferrari. 13 1968. 14 The Le Mans 24 Hours. 15 Tyrrell. 16 Martin Brundle. 17 Monaco, 1984. 18 Spa-Francorchamps. 19 Motorcycles. 20 Matra.

1   Thierry Boutsen spent two seasons with which team between 1987 and '88?
2   In 1989, Boutsen scored his first win. Where?
3   Where did Boutsen score his second win?
4   David Brabham is what relation to Jack Brabham?
5   With which team did David Brabham break into Formula One?
6   With which team did he end his Formula One career?
7   What nationality is Jack Brabham?
8   With which team did Jack Brabham win the 1959 and 1960 world championships?
9   In which year did he first race his own cars?
10 In which year did he become world champion with one of his own cars?
11 Why did he fail to win the 1970 Monaco Grand Prix?
12 What is Vittorio Brambilla's nickname?
13 Where did he score his only grand prix win in 1975?
14 For which team was he driving?
15 In which 1978 grand prix did he receive head injuries?
16 Who was Tony Brise's mentor in Formula One?
17 With what chassis did Tony Brise score his only point?
18 How did he die?
19 Tony Brooks won a non-championship Formula One race at which circuit in 1955?
20 For what was he studying at the time?

Answers *THE DRIVERS 9* *(see Quiz 51)*
1 Lancia. 2 Monaco. 3 Ferrari. 4 Motorcycle racing. 5 Theodore. 6 Toleman. 7 Broken legs.
8 Tyrrell. 9 Jackie Stewart. 10 Watkins Glen, USA. 11 Watkins Glen. 12 Italy. 13 Hesketh.
14 Ligier. 15 Arrows. 16 Maserati. 17 A Lago-Talbot. 18 Lotus. 19 1960. 20 Spa-Francorchamps.

1 Tony Brooks scored his first grand prix win driving for what team at Aintree in 1957?

2 With whom did he share this winning car?

3 Brooks moved to which team two seasons later?

4 Martin Brundle fought a long duel with which driver for 1983 British Formula Three honours?

5 For which team did Brundle make his Formula One debut?

6 A move to which German team in 1987 nearly finished his Formula One career?

7 Which world championship title did he win in 1988?

8 Who was his team-mate at Benetton in 1992?

9 What nationality was Ronnie Bucknum?

10 Bucknum was the first driver for which team when it arrived in Formula One in 1964?

11 With which team did Alex Caffi make his Formula One debut in 1986?

12 Caffi moved to which Italian team in 1988?

13 At which 1989 grand prix did team-mate Andrea de Cesaris knock off Caffi?

14 Caffi's 1991 season with Arrows was ruined by which make of engine?

15 What nationality is Adrian Campos?

16 Campos spent one and a half seasons in Formula One with which team?

17 Ivan Capelli shot to prominence in Formula One with which team in 1987?

18 Which grand prix did Capelli lead in 1990?

19 His dream ride with which team turned sour in 1992?

20 With which team did he spend his swansong in 1993?

1 With which team did Eugenio Castellotti graduate to Formula One in 1955?

2 Castellotti was second on his second outing. Where was that?

3 He moved mid-season to which team?

4 Johnny Cecotto was a world champion at what before he raced in Formula Two?

5 With which team did Cecotto arrive in Formula One in 1983?

6 Which team ran him in 1984?

7 What brought Cecotto's Formula One career to an end at Brands Hatch in 1984?

8 François Cevert spent all of his Formula One career bar his first race with which team?

9 Who was his mentor?

10 At which circuit did he score his first grand prix win, in 1971?

11 At which circuit was he killed in 1973?

12 In what country was American Eddie Cheever brought up?

13 For which team did Cheever first qualify for a grand prix?

14 Cheever first made it to the podium for which team in 1982?

15 With which team did Cheever spend his last three years in Formula One?

16 Louis Chiron was a works driver for which team in 1950?

17 For 1951 he raced what make of car?

18 Jim Clark spent his entire 72 grand prix Formula One career with which team?

19 In which year did Jim Clark make his Formula One debut?

20 At which circuit did Jim Clark score his first win in 1962?

---

1 Jim Clark competed in just one grand prix in 1968. Which one?

2 Where did he die in April 1968?

3 Peter Collins hit the Formula One big time when he joined which team in 1956?

4 Who did Collins help to that year's title by handing over his car at Monza?

5 Who referred to Collins as "Mon Ami Mate"?

6 At which circuit did Collins suffer a fatal accident in 1958?

7 Erik Comas arrived in Formula One in 1991 after winning which title?

8 With which team did Comas make his debut?

9 At which circuit did Comas have a massive accident in practice in 1992?

10 For which team did Comas drive in 1993 and 1994?

11 David Coulthard broke into Formula One as a result of the death of which driver?

12 What had been his role before that?

13 Coulthard's first grand prix win came in 1995 at which circuit?

14 Coulthard moved to which team in 1996?

15 Who has been his team-mate since then?

16 In what industry had Piers Courage's family made its fortune?

17 Who ran the Brabham Courage took to second place at Monaco and Watkins Glen in 1969?

18 What make of car was he driving when he was killed in 1970?

19 In which grand prix was this?

20 What nationality is Derek Daly?

Answers *THE DRIVERS 8 (see Quiz 50)*
1 Vanwall. *2* Stirling Moss. *3* Ferrari. *4* Ayrton Senna. *5* Tyrrell. *6* Zakspeed. *7* World Sportscar Championship. *8* Michael Schumacher. *9* American. *10* Honda. *11* Osella. *12* Scuderia Italia. *13* US Grand Prix at Phoenix. *14* Porsche. *15* Spanish. *16* Minardi. *17* Leyton House March. *18* The French. *19* Ferrari. *20* Jordan.

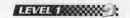
1 In an accident in Monaco in 1980, Derek Daly landed on his team-mate. Who was that?

2 For which team were they driving?

3 Daly could have won at Monaco in 1982 for which team?

4 Which flag was depicted around the base of Christian Danner's helmet?

5 With which team did Danner start his Formula One career?

6 For which team did he take a fourth place in 1989?

7 At which circuit was this?

8 What nationality is Andrea de Adamich?

9 For which team did de Adamich race in 1970?

10 How was his car different from those of his team-mates?

11 To which team did he take this engine in 1971?

12 Elio de Angelis arrived in Formula One with which team in 1979?

13 With which other team did de Angelis score his first grand prix victory?

14 In which 1982 grand prix was this?

15 Who did he pip to the chequered flag?

16 What nationality was Carel Godin de Beaufort?

17 What make of car did he drive in all but two of his grand prix outings?

18 Andrea de Cesaris raced with the support of which tobacco company in his early career?

19 For which team did he compete in his first full season in Formula One?

20 At which circuit, in 1982, did de Cesaris achieve his only pole position?

Answers THE DRIVERS 13 *(see Quiz 55)*

1 Paul Ricard. **2** Arrows. **3** Lotus. **4** Jerez. **5** Roger Penske. **6** McLaren. **7** Osterreichring. **8** Lotus. **9** Ayrton Senna. **10** Derek Warwick. **11** Hungarian. **12** Monte Carlo Rally. **13** Cooper. **14** Targa Florio. **15** Phi Phi. **16** A cap worn back to front. **17** A Lago-Talbot. **18** Toleman. **19** Indycars. **20** Benetton.

1   Andrea de Cesaris drove for nine different Formula One teams. Was Ferrari one of them?

2   With which team did he have his Formula One swansong?

3   What aristocratic rank does Emmanuel de Graffenried hold?

4   What is his nickname?

5   De Graffenried's best result was a fourth place in 1953 at which circuit?

6   Pedro de la Rosa broke into Formula One with which team in 1999?

7   Previously, he had been test driver for which team?

8   Which championship title did he win in 1997?

9   Patrick Depailler made his Formula One debut in 1972 with which team?

10   Often second in races, his first win finally came in 1978. Where?

11   Depailler's second win came for which team in 1979?

12   At which circuit did Depailler meet his death?

13   For which team was he driving?

14   What was Alfonso de Portago's nickname?

15   For which team was he driving when he finished second in the 1956 British Grand Prix?

16   In which road race was he killed in 1957?

17   Pedro Diniz started his Formula One career with which team?

18   In what business does his father earn the money with which Pedro bought his way into Formula One?

19   In what country is the team for which he raced in 1996 based?

20   For whom did he race in 1999?

Answers THE DRIVERS 14 *(see Quiz 56)*

1 Corrado Fabi. 2 Third. 3 Alfa Romeo. 4 It was for sportscars. 5 Connaught. 6 Sportscars. 7 Argentinian. 8 Alfa Romeo. 9 He broke his neck. 10 Mercedes. 11 Stirling Moss. 12 Alfa Romeo. 13 Silverstone. 14 Forties. 15 Nino. 16 Ferrari. 17 Swiss. 18 Ferrari. 19 The Monaco Formula Three race. 20 Jordan.

1   Martin Donnelly broke into Formula One at which circuit in 1989?

2   With which team?

3   Donnelly's only season in Formula One, 1990, was spent with which team?

4   At which circuit did he suffer near-fatal injuries?

5   Which American entrant ran Mark Donohue throughout his Formula One career?

6   What make of car did Donohue drive on his Formula One debut?

7   Where was Donohue driving when he was killed in 1975?

8   Johnny Dumfries spent only one season in Formula One, 1986, for which team?

9   Who was Dumfries's team-mate?

10 Who did this driver block from taking the drive before it went to Dumfries?

11 Dumfries's best finish was fifth place in which grand prix?

12 Vic Elford won which major motoring event in the year he came to Formula One?

13 With which team did Elford make his Formula One debut?

14 What was the major road race Elford won in Italy?

15 What was Philippe Etancelin's nickname?

16 What was Etancelin's trademark piece of racing apparel?

17 Etancelin finished fifth twice in 1950 driving what make of car?

18 Teo Fabi graduated to Formula One with what team in 1982?

19 Fabi's second season was in 1984 after a year away driving in what category?

20 Fabi spent his final two seasons in Formula One with which team?

Answers THE DRIVERS 11 *(see Quiz 53)*

1 Jean-Pierre Jarier. 2 Tyrrell. 3 Williams. 4 The Bavarian. 5 Zakspeed. 6 Rial. 7 Phoenix.
8 Italian. 9 McLaren. 10 It had an Alfa Romeo engine. 11 March. 12 Shadow. 13 Lotus. 14 The
Austrian. 15 Keke Rosberg. 16 Dutch. 17 Porsche. 18 Marlboro. 19 McLaren. 20 Long Beach,
USA.

1 What is the name of Teo Fabi's brother who also raced in Formula One?

2 Luigi Fagioli finished in what position in the 1950 world championship?

3 For which works team was Fagioli driving?

4 What was notable about the 1952 Monaco Grand Prix in which Fagioli was fatally injured?

5 Jack Fairman finished fourth in the 1956 British Grand Prix for which team?

6 In what branch of motor racing did Fairman spend most of his career?

7 What nationality was Juan Manuel Fangio?

8 For which team did Fangio take his first world championship title in 1951?

9 Why did Fangio miss the 1952 season?

10 With which team did Fangio win his second and third titles in 1954 and 1955?

11 Who was Fangio's British team-mate in 1955?

12 Giuseppe Farina was the first world champion, winning the title for which team in 1950?

13 Farina won the first Formula One grand prix. At which circuit?

14 Was Farina aged in his thirties or forties that year?

15 What was Farina's nickname?

16 For which team did he race between 1952 and 1955?

17 What nationality was Rudi Fischer?

18 What car was Fischer driving when he finished second in the 1952 Swiss Grand Prix?

19 What prestigious race did Giancarlo Fisichella win on his way to Formula One?

20 Fisichella led the 1997 German Grand Prix for which team?

Answers THE DRIVERS 12 *(see Quiz 54)*

1 No. 2 Sauber. 3 Baron. 4 Toulo. 5 Spa-Francorchamps. 6 Arrows. 7 Jordan. 8 Formula Nippon. 9 Tyrrell. 10 Monaco. 11 Ligier. 12 Hockenheim. 13 Alfa Romeo. 14 Fon. 15 Ferrari. 16 Mille Miglia. 17 Forti. 18 Supermarkets. 19 France (Ligier). 20 Sauber.

1   With which team did Fisichella secure pole position in the 1998 Austrian Grand Prix?

2   At which 1999 Grand Prix did Giancarlo spin out of the lead?

3   Christian Fittipaldi arrived in Formula One in 1992 after winning which title?

4   For which team did he score his first point?

5   Two fourth places came Christian Fittipaldi's way in 1994 for which team?

6   To which category of racing did he move in 1995?

7   Emerson Fittipaldi broke into Formula One in what year?

8   With which team?

9   How old was Emerson Fittipaldi when he became the youngest ever world champion?

10   With which team did Emerson Fittipaldi secure his second world championship title in 1974?

11   In what year did Emerson Fittipaldi move on to the family Fittipaldi team?

12   What relation is Wilson Fittipaldi to Christian?

13   What relation is Wilson to Emerson?

14   For what team did Wilson Fittipaldi race in 1972 and 1973?

15   Ron Flockhart's best result was third in the 1956 Italian Grand Prix for which team?

16   Flockhart won which major race that year?

17   In what make of car?

18   What nationality is George Follmer?

19   Follmer spent his only season in Formula One with which team?

20   Heinz-Harald Frentzen made his Formula One debut with which team in 1994?

1 Which German manufacturer backed Heinz-Harald Frentzen's graduation to Formula One?

2 In which category had Frentzen previously raced for this manufacturer?

3 To which team did Frentzen move in 1997?

4 Frentzen spent 1999 rebuilding his reputation with which team?

5 What job did Paul Frere hold down alongside his racing exploits?

6 What was Frere's best Formula One result?

7 At which grand prix?

8 For which team was he driving?

9 Bertrand Gachot arrived in Formula One with which team in 1989?

10 Why did Gachot lose his drive with Jordan in 1991?

11 Which team gave Gachot a drive on his return?

12 Gachot led which new team into Formula One in 1994?

13 What nationality is Howden Ganley?

14 Success in what formula landed Ganley a works drive with BRM in 1971?

15 What make of car did Ganley race in 1973?

16 Failure to qualify which Japanese make of car ended Ganley's Formula One career?

17 Olivier Gendebien was best known for what category of racing?

18 Which major race did Gendebien win four times?

19 With which marque was Gendebien associated in the 1950s?

20 Marc Gene broke in to Formula One in 1999 with which team?

Answers **THE DRIVERS 18** *(see Quiz 60)*

1 Scuderia Centro Sud. **2** Third. **3** Cooper. **4** Jack Brabham. **5** Ligier. **6** Phoenix. **7** Tyrrell. **8** Colombian. **9** Ensign. **10** Theodore. **11** The Indianapolis 500. **12** British Formula Three. **13** Ayrton Senna. **14** Leyton House March. **15** Jordan. **16** Ferrari. **17** Porsche. **18** Brabham. **19** Rouen. **20** Eagle.

1   Name the Spanish sponsor who helped Marc Gene to break into Formula One.

2   Name Gene's elder brother who was a race-winner in Formula 3000.

3   Peter Gethin scored the closest ever Formula One win in 1971 at which circuit?

4   What make of car was he driving that day?

5   Who did he pip to the finish line?

6   At which circuit does Peter Gethin now run a racing school?

7   Piercarlo Ghinzani won which title before graduating to Formula One?

8   Ghinzani cut his teeth with which Formula One team?

9   For which French team did Ghinzani drive in 1987?

10   Bruno Giacomelli stormed which European championship title in 1978?

11   Giacomelli made his Formula One debut for which team the previous year?

12   With which team did Giacomelli spend the bulk of his Formula One career?

13   To which British team did Giacomelli move in 1983?

14   For which team did Richie Ginther collect a second place in 1960 and 1961?

15   Ginther drove for which British team from 1962 to 1964?

16   After six more second places, Ginther's first win came where in 1965?

17   For which team was he driving?

18   What nationality is Jose Froilan Gonzalez?

19   What was his nickname?

20   Which marque did Gonzalez give its first Formula One grand prix win?

---

1   Wealthy American Masten Gregory raced a Maserati for which team in 1957?

2   In which position did Masten finish on his debut?

3   He landed the third seat in which works team for 1959?

4   Name Gregory's team leader who took that year's world championship?

5   Olivier Grouillard arrived in Formula One with which team in 1989?

6   At which circuit did Grouillard achieve the unheard of and qualify his Osella eighth in 1990?

7   For which British team did Grouillard race in 1992?

8   What nationality is Roberto Guerrero?

9   With which team did Guerrero graduate to Formula One in 1982?

10   He kept his ride for 1983 when the team merged with which other team?

11   Guerrero took pole position for which big race in 1992?

12   Mauricio Gugelmin won which championship *en route* to Formula One?

13   Gugelmin shared a house in Esher with which compatriot racing driver?

14   Gugelmin's best result was third place in the 1989 Brazilian Grand Prix for which team?

15   Gugelmin's final season,1992, was a poor one for which team?

16   Dan Gurney was given his Formula One break by which works team in 1959?

17   In 1962, Gurney gave which German marque its only Formula One win?

18   Gurney gave which marque its first Formula One win in 1964?

19   Both of these wins were in the French Grand Prix. At which circuit?

20   What was the name of the car that Gurney raced for his own team from 1965 to 1967?

Answers *THE DRIVERS 16* (see Quiz 58)

1 Mercedes. *2* Sportscars. *3* Williams. *4* Jordan. *5* Journalist. *6* Second place. *7* The 1956 Belgian Grand Prix. *8* Ferrari. *9* Onyx. *10* He was jailed for assault. *11* Larrousse. *12* Pacific. *13* New Zealander. *14* Formula 5000. *15* Iso Williams. *16* Maki. *17* Sportscars. *18* The Le Mans 24 Hours. *19* Ferrari. *20* Minardi.

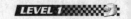
1 Who entered Mike Hailwood in Formula One in the 1960s?

2 Hailwood excelled in what form of competition in those days?

3 Hailwood's second spell in Formula One was with which team?

4 Why did Hailwood's career come to an end in 1974?

5 Which championship did Mika Hakkinen win *en route* to Formula One?

6 Which team gave him his Formula One break?

7 Which team did he join in 1993?

8 At which circuit did Hakkinen score his first Formula One win?

9 At which circuit did he wrap up the 1998 world title?

10 In which country did Mika spin out of the lead of two Grands Prix in 1999?

11 In which year did Jim Hall make his Formula One debut?

12 In 1963, Hall had one full season of Formula One with which team?

13 What did Hall do through the 1990s?

14 What make of car did Masahiro Hasemi drive in the 1976 Japanese Grand Prix?

15 What was Hasemi's notable achievement in that race?

16 Mike Hawthorn scored his first grand prix win for which team in 1953?

17 At which circuit did he achieve this?

18 In which year did Hawthorn become the first British world champion?

19 In which country did he clinch that title?

20 In which country did he die in a road accident in 1959?

Answers *THE DRIVERS 21* *(see Quiz 63)*

1 1962. 2 1968. 3 1961. 4 Ferrari. 5 ATS. 6 "Grand Prix". 7 New Zealander. 8 Brabham.
9 1967. 10 McLaren. 11 Bathurst, Australia. 12 Hunt the Shunt. 13 Lord Hesketh.
14 Zandvoort, Holland. 15 1976. 16 McLaren. 17 Belgian. 18 Ferrari. 19 Brabham. 20 Six.

Answers – see page 75

1 Brian Henton made his Formula One debut with which team in 1975?

2 What championship did Henton win in 1980 before his third spell in Formula One?

3 For which team was Henton team leader in 1981?

4 For which team did Henton set the fastest lap at Brands Hatch in 1982?

5 What did Johnny Herbert do the day he signed his first Formula One contract?

6 With which team did Herbert make his Formula One debut in 1989?

7 In which year did Herbert score his first grand prix win?

8 Who was his team-mate that year?

9 Herbert moved to Stewart in 1999. Who was his team-mate?

10 Hans Herrmann's best results in Formula One came with which team?

11 Why was Herrmann's drive with this team cut short in 1955?

12 Where did this take place?

13 Damon Hill started his competition career in what category?

14 With which team did he make his Formula One debut?

15 When did Damon Hill join Williams?

16 In which year did he become world champion?

17 What is the main colour on his helmet?

18 Graham Hill was what relation to Damon?

19 With which team did Graham Hill arrive in Formula One?

20 His first win came with which team?

Answers **THE DRIVERS 22** *(see Quiz 64)*

1 Scottish. **2** Lotus. **3** The 1961 US Grand Prix. **4** Jordan. **5** Ayrton Senna. **6** Melbourne.
7 Ferrari. **8** Jaguar Racing. **9** Renault. **10** 1979 French Grand Prix. **11** Broken legs.
12 Montreal. **13** Ligier. **14** March. **15** He qualified on pole position. **16** The Canadian.
17 Ronnie Peterson. **18** British Formula Three. **19** Spirit. **20** René Arnoux.

1 In which year did Graham Hill become world champion for the first time?

2 Returning to Lotus yielded his second world title in which year?

3 No relation to Damon and Graham, Phil Hill was world champion when?

4 For which team was he driving?

5 Phil Hill left this team to drive for whom in 1963?

6 He drove a camera car at two grands prix in 1966 for what film?

7 What nationality was Denny Hulme?

8 When Hulme arrived in Formula One in 1965, for which team did he drive?

9 In which year did he become world champion?

10 Hulme moved to which team run by a compatriot?

11 At which circuit was Hulme racing when he suffered a fatal heart attack in 1992?

12 James Hunt was known as what in his early racing years?

13 Which English aristocrat guided him into Formula One in 1973?

14 At which circuit did Hunt score his first grand prix win in 1975?

15 In which year did Hunt become world champion?

16 For which team was he driving?

17 What nationality is Jacky Ickx?

18 Ickx won the 1968 French Grand Prix at Rouen for which team?

19 Ickx finished second in the world championship for which team in 1969?

20 Ickx is most famous for the Le Mans 24 Hour race. How many times has he won it?

Answers THE DRIVERS 19 (see Quiz 61)

1 Reg Parnell. 2 Motorcycle racing. 3 Surtees. 4 He broke his leg. 5 British Formula Three. 6 Lotus. 7 McLaren. 8 Jerez. 9 Suzuka. 10 Italy. 11 1960. 12 British Racing Partnership. 13 Ran an Indycar team. 14 Kojima. 15 He set fastest lap. 16 Ferrari. 17 Reims. 18 1958. 19 Morocco. 20 England.

1   What nationality was Innes Ireland?

2   For whom did Ireland score his only grand prix win?

3   In which grand prix was this?

4   Eddie Irvine made his Formula One debut in the 1993 Japanese Grand Prix for which team?

5   Who assaulted him after the race?

6   Irvine's first win came six seasons later. Where?

7   For which team was he driving?

8   To which team did he move for 2000?

9   Jean-Pierre Jabouille is inextricably linked with which Formula One team?

10   At which grand prix did Jabouille give the team its first win?

11   What injury curtailed Jabouille's 1980 season?

12   At which circuit did this happen?

13   For which team did Jabouille make a brief comeback in 1981?

14   Jean-Pierre Jarier was given his first full season in Formula One in 1973 by whom?

15   What did Jarier do in the 1975 Argentinian and Brazilian Grands Prix for Shadow?

16   Which grand prix did Jarier lead for Lotus in 1978?

17   For which deceased driver was he a replacement?

18   Stefan Johansson won what championship on his way to Formula One?

19   With which team did Johansson first qualify for a grand prix in 1983?

20   Who lost his drive and opened the door for Johansson to join Ferrari in 1985?

Answers *THE DRIVERS 20* (see Quiz 62)

1 Lotus. 2 Formula Two. 3 Toleman. 4 Tyrrell. 5 He broke his legs. 6 Benetton. 7 1995 (British Grand Prix). 8 Michael Schumacher. 9 Rubens Barrichello. 10 Mercedes-Benz. 11 He broke his back and his ribs. 12 Monaco. 13 Motorcycle racing. 14 Brabham. 15 1993. 16 1996. 17 Very dark blue (it is not black). 18 His father. 19 Lotus. 20 BRM.

1 For which team was Stefan Johansson driving when he hit a deer at the Osterreichring in 1987?

2 Which former world champion entered Alan Jones in Formula One in 1975?

3 Another former world champion was Alan Jones's boss in 1976. Who was that?

4 Jones scored his first grand prix win for which team in the 1977 Austrian Grand Prix?

5 Jones won his world title with Williams in what year?

6 Who was Jones's team-mate that year?

7 Ukyo Katayama arrived in Formula One in 1992 with which team?

8 Which British team gave him his best results in 1994?

9 What sport has Katayama chosen to concentrate on now he's left Formula One?

10 What nationality is Karl Kling?

11 With which team did Kling spend his two-year Formula One career?

12 Which current team owner gave Jacques Laffite his Formula One break?

13 Laffite scored his first win in 1977 after moving to Ligier. At which circuit?

14 Why did Laffite quit Formula One midway through 1986?

15 Jan Lammers was Elio de Angelis's team-mate at which team in his first year of Formula One?

16 To which team did Lammers move for the start of the 1980 season?

17 For which team did Lammers win the Le Mans 24 Hours in 1988 and 1990?

18 With which team did Lammers make his comeback in 1992 after a 10-year break?

19 Pedro Lamy arrived in Formula One late in 1993 with which team?

20 For which injured driver was he a stand-in?

Answers THE DRIVERS 25 *(see Quiz 67)*

1 Brabham. 2 Lella Lombardi. 3 The 1975 Spanish Grand Prix. 4 A March. 5 South African. 6 A Cooper. 7 He had to make a pit stop for fuel. 8 A US Marine. 9 Surtees. 10 McLaren. 11 Tony Maggs. 12 Bruce McLaren. 13 French. 14 Ferrari. 15 Sportscars. 16 Porsche. 17 Danish. 18 McLaren. 19 Mika Hakkinen. 20 Stewart.

1   At which circuit did Pedro Lamy flip into a spectator tunnel when testing in 1994?

2   With which team did Nicola Larini spend his first two full seasons of Formula One?

3   Larini scored all his points in one go for which team in 1994?

4   At which grand prix?

5   Larini returned to Formula One with which team in 1997?

6   Gerard Larrousse raced just twice in 1974. What chassis did he drive?

7   What role did he turn to after this?

8   Niki Lauda started his Formula One career in 1971 with which team?

9   Which team did he move to in 1973?

10   When did Lauda start winning with Ferrari?

11   When did Lauda take his first world championship title?

12   At which circuit did Lauda quit Formula One for the first time, in 1979?

13   JJ Lehto graduated to Formula One with which team?

14   Lehto made the podium for the only time in the 1991 San Marino Grand Prix with which team?

15   At which circuit did Lehto break his neck in pre-season testing in 1994?

16   For which team was he driving at the time?

17   Stuart Lewis-Evans was the third driver for which team in 1958?

18   In which 1958 grand prix did Lewis-Evans suffer fatal burns?

19   Guy Ligier started his Formula One career with what car in 1966?

20   What make of car did Guy Ligier race to his only point at the Nürburgring in 1967?

Answers *THE DRIVERS 26 (see Quiz 68)*

1 Ferrari. *2* The Le Mans 24 Hours. *3* He committed suicide. *4* Lotus. *5* Brands Hatch. *6* Williams. *7* 1989. *8* 1992. *9* Williams. *10* Gordini. *11* Ferrari. *12* Reims. *13* Juan Manuel Fangio. *14* Maserati. *15* Nürburgring. *16* Formula 3000. *17* Minardi. *18* Phoenix. *19* The Le Mans 24 Hours. *20* Surtees.

1. Guy Ligier scored his only point in the 1967 German Grand Prix after swapping to what make of car?

2. Name the only woman to have scored a Formula One world championship point.

3. At which grand prix did this happen?

4. What car was she driving?

5. John Love caused a huge stir by finishing second in which 1967 grand prix?

6. What car was he driving?

7. Why did he fall back behind race winner Pedro Rodriguez?

8. What was Brett Lunger before he went racing?

9. Lunger's first full season in Formula One was in 1976 with which team?

10. Lunger changed team for 1977. What chassis did he drive for most of that season?

11. Which South African was a works Cooper driver in 1962?

12. He was signed as number two to whom?

13. At which grand prix did he finish second in both 1962 and 1963?

14. Which Italian team ran Umberto Maglioli sporadically in Formula One between 1953 and 1955?

15. In what other form of racing did this team run Maglioli with great success?

16. Driving which German marque did Maglioli win the Targa Florio with Wolfgang von Trips?

17. What nationality is Jan Magnussen?

18. With which team did Magnussen make his Formula One debut at the TI Circuit in 1995?

19. Magnussen was a stand-in that day for whom?

20. Which team fired Magnussen midway through the 1998 season?

Answers THE DRIVERS 23 *(see Quiz 65)*

1 McLaren. 2 Graham Hill. 3 John Surtees. 4 Shadow. 5 1980. 6 Carlos Reutemann.
7 Larrousse. 8 Tyrrell. 9 Mountaineering. 10 German. 11 Mercedes-Benz (1954 and 1955).
12 Frank Williams. 13 Anderstorp, Sweden. 14 He broke his legs. 15 Shadow. 16 ATS.
17 Jaguar. 18 March. 19 Lotus. 20 Alessandro Zanardi.

1 Willy Mairesse finished third in the Italian Grand Prix in 1960 for which team?
2 Mairesse suffered head injuries when he crashed in which classic race in 1968?
3 How did Mairesse die?
4 Nigel Mansell broke into Formula One in 1980 with which team?
5 At which circuit did he score his first win in 1985?
6 For which team was he driving?
7 In which year did Mansell move to Ferrari?
8 In which year did Mansell become world champion?
9 For which team was he driving?
10 Robert Manzon raced for which team in the 1950 world championship?
11 Manzon drove which Italian chassis in 1954?
12 At which circuit did Manzon finish third in that year's French Grand Prix?
13 Onofre Marimon was a protégé of which fellow Argentinian?
14 For which Italian works team did Marimon race in 1953 and 1954?
15 At which circuit did he crash to his death in qualifying?
16 Pierluigi Martini turned to what formula in 1986 after a weak maiden Formula One season?
17 For which team did Martini race almost throughout his Formula One career?
18 At which American circuit did Martini qualify on the front row in 1990?
19 Which classic race did Martini win in 1999?
20 Jochen Mass cut his teeth in Formula One with which team?

Answers *THE DRIVERS 24* *(see Quiz 66)*

1 Silverstone. 2 Osella. 3 Ferrari. 4 San Marino. 5 Sauber. 6 Brabham. 7 Team management.
8 March. 9 BRM. 10 1974. 11 1975. 12 Montreal. 13 Onyx. 14 Scuderia Italia. 15 Silverstone.
16 Benetton. 17 Vanwall. 18 Moroccan. 19 Cooper. 20 Brabham.

1   A move to McLaren in 1975 brought Jochen Mass's first win at which circuit?

2   What was notable about that race?

3   What colour was Mass's car painted when he raced for Arrows in 1979 and 1980?

4   At which circuit did Bruce McLaren score his first win at the end of 1959?

5   Who was his team leader that year?

6   In which year did he introduce the McLaren chassis to Formula One?

7   At which circuit did he guide McLaren to its first victory in 1968?

8   Where was he testing when he died in 1970?

9   What car was he testing at the time?

10 Carlos Menditeguy raced predominantly in his native country. Where was that?

11 For which team did Menditeguy drive when he came to Europe in the mid 1950s?

12 Arturo Merzario is famous for wearing what sort of hat?

13 Merzario scored a point on his Formula One debut in 1972 for which team?

14 In his first full season in Formula One, 1974, he was run by which current team owner?

15 Merzario built his own car for 1977. What was it called?

16 Roberto Mieres raced what chassis in his maiden Formula One season in 1953?

17 He changed to which Italian chassis for 1954 and 1955?

18 François Migault turned out for two grands prix in 1972 with which team?

19 Migault had only one full season in Formula One. In which year?

20 For which team did he drive?

Answers THE DRIVERS 29 *(see Quiz 71)*

1 Rob Walker. 2 Goodwood. 3 Maserati. 4 Juan Manuel Fangio. 5 Reims. 6 Honda. 7 Ayrton Senna. 8 Adelaide. 9 Tyrrell. 10 Prost. 11 Minardi. 12 Jordan. 13 Minardi. 14 Benetton. 15 A helicopter accident in which his arm was severed. It was reattached using micro-surgery. 16 Touring cars. 17 The 1977 Belgian Grand Prix. 18 Lotus. 19 Zolder, Belgium. 20 Cancer.

1 John Miles spent his entire one-and-a-half year Formula One career with which team?

2 What was unusual about the car he campaigned in 1969?

3 Who was Miles's team-mate in 1970?

4 Gerhard Mitter scored his only points with fourth place in which 1963 grand prix?

5 Whose old Porsche was he driving?

6 Stefano Modena arrived in Formula One at the end of 1987 having just won what title?

7 With which team did Modena finish third at Monaco in 1989?

8 With which team did Modena spend 1992, his final season in Formula One?

9 Who was his team-mate that year?

10 What business earned Gianni Morbidelli's family its wealth?

11 Which team gave Morbidelli his Formula One break in 1990?

12 For which team did he score half a point in the 1991 Australian Grand Prix?

13 For whom was Morbidelli standing-in?

14 Which three-time world champion was a childhood friend of Roberto Moreno's?

15 Moreno made an abortive Formula One debut for which team at Zandvoort in 1982?

16 For which team did Moreno finish second in the 1990 Japanese Grand Prix?

17 Who won that race?

18 Stirling Moss scored his first grand prix win for which team?

19 At which British circuit did Moss achieve this in 1955?

20 Who shadowed him to the finish?

Answers THE DRIVERS 30 (see Quiz 72)

1 Lotus. 2 BRM. 3 Mosport Park, Canada. 4 Arrows. 5 Frank Williams. 6 Brabham. 7 Brazilian. 8 In a light aircraft accident. 9 Formula Two. 10 Zakspeed. 11 Tyrrell. 12 1987. 13 Formula 3000. 14 He finished every race bar one (the French). 15 Monaco. 16 Montreal. 17 Ferrari. 18 John Surtees. 19 He broke his legs. 20 Third.

1 Which British team entrant ran Stirling Moss from 1959 to 1961?

2 Moss's career ended in 1962 when he crashed at which British circuit?

3 Luigi Musso started his Formula One career with which Italian team?

4 Musso scored his only grand prix win, the 1956 Argentinian Grand Prix, sharing with whom?

5 Musso suffered a fatal accident in the 1958 French Grand Prix at which circuit?

6 Which manufacturer helped Satoru Nakajima into Formula One?

7 Who was Nakajima's team-mate at Lotus in 1987?

8 At which circuit did Nakajima set fastest lap in the wet in 1989?

9 Which British team ran Nakajima in 1990 and 1991?

10 Shinji Nakano made his Formula One debut with which team in 1997?

11 To which team did Nakano move the following year?

12 After losing his drive for 1999, for which team did Nakano become test driver?

13 Alessandro Nannini made his Formula One debut with which team?

14 With which team did he spend the bulk of his career?

15 What ended his career in 1990?

16 In which form of racing did Nannini shine in the early 1990s?

17 Gunnar Nilsson won only one grand prix. Which one?

18 For which team was he driving?

19 At which circuit?

20 What illness claimed Nilsson's life in 1978?

1   Jackie Oliver joined which team as a replacement for Jim Clark in 1968?

2   With which British team did Oliver spend 1969 and 1970?

3   Oliver's second third-place finish came at which circuit for Shadow in 1973?

4   Of which team was Oliver a co-founder in 1978?

5   Which team owner ran Carlos Pace in a March in 1972?

6   For which team did Pace drive from mid 1974 until his death early in 1977?

7   Which grand prix in 1975 provided Pace's only win?

8   How did he die?

9   Jonathan Palmer arrived in Formula One as champion in what category?

10 With which German team did Palmer have a fruitless spell in 1985 and 1986?

11 Palmer spent three seasons with which British team?

12 In which year did he win the Jim Clark Cup for normally aspirated runners?

13 What championship did Olivier Panis win in 1993 to earn his Formula One break?

14 What was notable about Panis's first season with Ligier in 1994?

15 Panis's only win to date came for Ligier in 1996 at which circuit?

16 At which circuit did Panis break his legs in 1997?

17 Mike Parkes raced sportscars for which team before he moved into Formula One?

18 Parkes landed his ride there after the departure of which compatriot?

19 What ended Parkes's Formula One career at Spa-Francorchamps in 1967?

20 In what position did Reg Parnell finish in the 1950 British Grand Prix?

Answers THE DRIVERS 28 (see Quiz 70)

1 Lotus. 2 It was four-wheel drive. 3 Jochen Rindt. 4 German. 5 Carel Godin de Beaufort.
6 Formula 3000. 7 Brabham. 8 Jordan. 9 Mauricio Gugelmin. 10 Building racing motorcycles.
11 Scuderia Italia. 12 Ferrari. 13 Alain Prost. 14 Nelson Piquet. 15 Lotus. 16 Benetton.
17 Nelson Piquet. 18 Mercedes-Benz. 19 Aintree. 20 Juan Manuel Fangio.

1   For which team did Reg Parnell drive in 1950?

2   Parnell was in the points again at Silverstone in 1951 for which team?

3   Riccardo Patrese made his Formula debut in 1977 with which team?

4   Patrese was the driver for which new team in 1978?

5   In which grand prix did he score his first win?

6   What car was he driving?

7   Patrese later spent five years with which other British team?

8   Roger Penske appeared only twice in Formula One as a driver. In which grand prix?

9   What did Penske go on to become?

10 In what branch of racing is he now involved?

11 In what position did Cesare Perdisa finish on his Formula One debut at Monaco in 1955?

12 For which team was Perdisa driving?

13 Henri Pescarolo is most famous for winning which classic race?

14 Pescarolo finished third in which 1970 grand prix?

15 For which team was he driving?

16 What colour helmet did Pescarolo wear?

17 Ronnie Peterson started his Formula One career in 1970 driving what car?

18 What colours were on his helmet?

19 In which year did Peterson finish runner-up to Jackie Stewart in the world championship?

20 What was unusual about the Tyrrell Peterson raced in 1977?

Answers THE DRIVERS 33 *(see Quiz 75)*

1 Welsh. *2* The non-championship 1975 Race of Champions. *3* Shadow. *4* Kyalami, South Africa. *5* LEC. *6* Silverstone. *7* In an aircraft aerobatics accident. *8* Mexican. *9* Lotus. *10* Brabham. *11* Ferrari. *12* Italian. *13* BRM. *14* Williams. *15* Long Beach, USA. *16* Brabham. *17* Ferrari. *18* Niki Lauda. *19* 1981. *20* Politician.

1 To which team did Ronnie Peterson return for 1978?

2 At which circuit did Peterson suffer fatal injuries?

3 Nelson Piquet broke into Formula One with which team midway through 1978?

4 Piquet's seven years with Brabham yielded how many world titles?

5 For which team was he driving when he won the 1987 world title?

6 Piquet moved to which team in 1988?

7 With which team did Piquet end his Formula One career in 1991?

8 Didier Pironi broke into Formula One with which team in 1978?

9 A move to which team produced Pironi's first win in 1980?

10 At which circuit did he score this victory?

11 Why did Pironi's Formula One career come to an end at Hockenheim in 1982?

12 How was Pironi killed in 1987?

13 Whose seat did Emanuele Pirro fill at Benetton midway through 1989?

14 To which team did Pirro move for 1990?

15 In what category of racing did Pirro excel after quitting Formula One?

16 Alain Prost arrived in Formula One in 1980 with which team?

17 Prost scored his first win the following year for another team. Which one?

18 In which year did Prost take the first of his four world titles?

19 Name his McLaren team-mate from that season.

20 Prost's fourth world title came with which team in 1993?

Answers *THE DRIVERS 34 (see Quiz 76)*

1 American. 2 Lotus. 3 McLaren. 4 Silverstone. 5 March (1977). 6 "Jesus Saves". 7 Fittipaldi.
8 Cooper. 9 Jack Brabham. 10 Watkins Glen, USA. 11 The Lotus 72. 12 Monza. 13 Cooper.
14 South African. 15 BRM. 16 Younger. 17 Ferrari. 18 Mexican. 19 International Trophy.
20 Theodore.

1 What was Tom Pryce's mother tongue?

2 What was his only Formula One win?

3 For which team did Pryce drive for all but one of his grands prix?

4 Where was Pryce killed in an accident caused by a marshal running across the track?

5 Name David Purley's family refrigeration company after which he named his car in 1977.

6 At which circuit did Purley suffer a life-threatening, body-shortening accident in 1977?

7 How did Purley die?

8 What nationality is Hector Rebaque?

9 What car was he driving when he scored his first point in 1978?

10 Rebaque's most successful season came in 1981 when he was racing for which team?

11 Clay Regazzoni drove for which team in 1970, his first season in Formula One?

12 In which grand prix did he achieve his first win that season?

13 Regazzoni took a year away from his first team with which team in 1973?

14 Which team did Regazzoni give its first win at Silverstone in 1979?

15 At which circuit did Regazzoni crash in 1980, ending his career?

16 Carlos Reutemann spent the first five years of his Formula One career racing for which team?

17 To which team did he move at the end of 1976?

18 Whose injury gave him this opportunity?

19 In which year did Reutemann freeze at Las Vegas and lose out on winning the world title for Williams?

20 What is Reutemann's current profession?

Answers THE DRIVERS 31 (see Quiz 73)

1 Alfa Romeo. 2 BRM. 3 Shadow. 4 Arrows. 5 The 1982 Monaco Grand Prix. 6 A Brabham.
7 Williams. 8 The US Grand Prix. 9 A team owner. 10 Champ Cars. 11 Third. 12 Maserati.
13 The Le Mans 24 Hours. 14 Monaco. 15 Matra. 16 Bright green. 17 A March. 18 Blue and
yellow. 19 1971. 20 It was a six-wheeler.

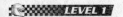
1   What nationality was Peter Revson?

2   With what chassis did Revson have his first crack at Formula One in 1964?

3   Revson returned to Formula One full-time in 1972 when he joined which works team?

4   At which circuit did he score the first of his two wins in 1973?

5   Alex Ribeiro spent one full season in Formula One with which team?

6   What was the religious message that Ribeiro used to carry on his car and helmet?

7   With which team did Ribeiro fail to qualify twice in two outings in 1979?

8   With which works team did Jochen Rindt enjoy his first full season of Formula One?

9   For 1968, Rindt joined the team founded by which former world champion?

10   A move to Lotus in 1969 brought Rindt his first win. Where was that?

11   The arrival of what classic chassis boosted Rindt's 1970 season?

12   Rindt became the first posthumous world champion that year. Where was he killed?

13   With which team did Pedro Rodriguez achieve his first Formula One win in 1967?

14   In which grand prix did he do this?

15   Rodriguez's second win came in 1970 with which other British team?

16   Was Ricardo Rodriguez the older or younger of the Rodriguez brothers?

17   For which team did Ricardo Rodriguez drive throughout his brief Formula One career?

18   In qualifying for which non-championship grand prix was Ricardo Rodriguez killed in 1962?

19   Which non-championship Formula One race did Keke Rosberg win in 1978?

20   For which team was he driving?

Answers THE DRIVERS 32 *(see Quiz 74)*

1 Lotus. *2* Monza. *3* Ensign. *4* Two. *5* Williams. *6* Lotus. *7* Benetton. *8* Tyrrell. *9* Ligier.
10 Zolder, Belgium. *11* He broke his legs. *12* Competing in a powerboat race. *13* Johnny
Herbert's. *14* Scuderia Italia. *15* Touring cars. *16* McLaren. *17* Renault. *18* 1985. *19* Niki
Lauda. *20* Williams.

1 Which world champion retired to give Keke Rosberg a seat with Wolf in 1979?

2 Rosberg got his big break with Williams and became world champion in what year?

3 In which grand prix did Rosberg score his one win that year?

4 What make of car did Louis Rosier race in 1950 and 1951?

5 Rosier returned to form with what make of car in 1956?

6 Rosier died when he crashed in a sportscar race at which French circuit?

7 With which team did Ricardo Rosset arrive in Formula One in 1996?

8 The following season was over for Rosset after one non-qualification for which team?

9 Where did Rosset clash with Jacques Villeneuve in qualifying in 1998?

10 Huub Rothengatter began his Formula One career with which team?

11 With which team did Rothengatter spend his second season?

12 Which driver does Rothengatter manage?

13 Luis Perez Sala drove in Formula One for just two seasons. With which team?

14 Who was Sala's Spanish team-mate in 1988, his first season?

15 With which Italian driver's arrival was Sala reduced to the role of number two?

16 What nationality is Eliseo Salazar?

17 Which world champion took a swing at him after a crash at Hockenheim in 1982?

18 For which team was Salazar racing at the time?

19 Mika Salo fought with which driver for 1990 British Formula Three honours?

20 In which country did Salo spend the next four years?

Answers THE DRIVERS 37 *(see Quiz 79)*

1 A Trojan. 2 Honda. 3 He crashed and was burned to death. 4 None. 5 Zakspeed.
6 Mercedes. 7 Jordan (Belgian Grand Prix). 8 Benetton (Italian Grand Prix.) 9 Spa-
Francorchamps (1992). 10 1994. 11 1996. 12 Brother. 13 Jordan. 14 Giancarlo Fisichella.
15 Williams. 16 Alessandro Zanardi. 17 Ensign. 18 Embassy Racing or Surtees. 19 He had a
partly formed arm. 20 Connaught.

1 Mika Salo's Formula One debut came with Lotus, but he drove for which team for three years?

2 Which Formula One teams used Salo as a stand-in in 1999?

3 To which team did he move for 2000?

4 What nationality is Roy Salvadori?

5 The 1957 British Grand Prix yielded Salvadori's first points. For which team was he driving?

6 Salvadori's best result was second place at which circuit in 1958?

7 Ludovico Scarfiotti was related to which Italian automotive family?

8 This helped him land a ride in 1963 with which team?

9 In which grand prix did Scarfiotti achieve his only Formula One win?

10 At which 1973 grand prix did Jody Scheckter make his presence felt by triggering a pile-up?

11 At which circuit was it being held that year?

12 For which team was Scheckter driving at the time?

13 Scheckter's first win was for Tyrrell in 1974. At which circuit?

14 For which team did Scheckter become world champion in 1979?

15 Who was his team-mate that year?

16 American driver Harry Schell was born in which European capital?

17 Schell's best result, second in the 1958 Dutch Grand Prix, was for which team?

18 At which circuit was Schell killed in testing in 1960?

19 The death of which driver gave Tim Schenken his place in the Frank Williams-run De Tomaso in 1970?

20 With which team did Schenken achieve his best result of third place in the 1971 Austrian Grand Prix?

Answers *THE DRIVERS 38* (see Quiz 80)

1 Spa-Francorchamps. 2 Toleman. 3 Portuguese. 4 1988. 5 1990. 6 Imola. 7 A Ferrari. 8 The 1950 Italian Grand Prix. 9 Nelson Piquet. 10 Fittipaldi (1981 and 1982). 11 Arrows. 12 The 1968 Monaco Grand Prix. 13 A works Matra. 14 Tyrrell. 15 Switzerland. 16 1968. 17 Rob Walker. 18 Brands Hatch. 19 Alfa Romeo. 20 Ferrari.

1 What unusual make of car did Tim Schenken campaign in 1974?

2 For which team did Jo Schlesser contest the 1968 French Grand Prix?

3 What happened to Schlesser?

4 How many points did Bernd Schneider score in his Formula One career?

5 Schneider spent two seasons with which German Formula One team?

6 Which manufacturer has since guided him to international touring car and GT sportscar titles?

7 Michael Schumacher made his Formula One debut in 1991 with which team?

8 A race later, Schumacher had switched to which other team?

9 At which circuit did Schumacher score his first grand prix win?

10 In which year did he win his first world championship title?

11 In which year did he move to Ferrari?

12 What relation is Ralf Schumacher to Michael?

13 Ralf Schumacher made his Formula One debut in 1997 with which team?

14 In the 1997 Argentinian Grand Prix, Ralf Schumacher knocked off his team-mate. Who was he?

15 For which team did Ralf Schumacher race with impressive results in 1999?

16 Name his team-mate, whom he dominated in 1999?

17 Vern Schuppan raced half a season for which team in 1974?

18 Name one of the two other teams Schuppan drove for before concentrating on sportscars.

19 What was unusual about Archie Scott-Brown?

20 Scott-Brown made just one world championship appearance, in 1956, for which team?

Answers THE DRIVERS 35 *(see Quiz 77)*

1 James Hunt. 2 1982. 3 Swiss. 4 A Lago-Talbot. 5 A Maserati. 6 Montlhery. 7 Footwork. 8 Lola. 9 Monaco. 10 Spirit. 11 Osella. 12 Jos Verstappen. 13 Minardi. 14 Adrian Campos. 15 Pierluigi Martini. 16 Chilean. 17 Nelson Piquet. 18 ATS. 19 Mika Hakkinen. 20 Japan.

1   At which circuit did Scott-Brown suffer fatal injuries in a sportscar race in 1958?

2   Ayrton Senna broke into Formula One with which team in 1984?

3   A move to Lotus in 1985 yielded Senna's first win in which grand prix?

4   A further move to McLaren produced his first world title in which year?

5   When did Senna take his second world title?

6   At which circuit did Senna die in 1994?

7   Dorino Serafini finished second in his only grand prix. What car was he driving?

8   In which grand prix was this?

9   Which compatriot of Chico Serra's was his bitter rival on their way to Formula One?

10   Serra spent his two full seasons in Formula One with which team?

11   With which team did he have four outings in 1983?

12   Johnny Servoz-Gavin stunned the Formula One world by leading in only his second grand prix. Which was this?

13   What car was he driving?

14   For which team did Servoz-Gavin turn out three times in 1970 before quitting?

15   In what country was Jo Siffert born?

16   Siffert started in Formula One in 1962, but when did he score his first win?

17   This was at Brands Hatch in a Lotus run by which privateer entrant?

18   At which circuit was Siffert killed at the end of 1971?

19   Pre-war race ace Raymond Sommer won Le Mans in 1932 and 1933 for which team?

20   For which team did he finish fourth at Monaco in 1950?

Answers *THE DRIVERS 36* (see Quiz 78)

1 Tyrrell. *2* BAR and Ferrari. *3* Sauber. *4* British. *5* Cooper. *6* Nürburgring. *7* The Agnellis. *8* Ferrari. *9* Italian. *10* British. *11* Silverstone. *12* McLaren. *13* Anderstorp, Sweden. *14* Ferrari. *15* Gilles Villeneuve. *16* Paris. *17* BRM. *18* Silverstone. *19* Piers Courage. *20* Brabham.

1 Mike Spence began his Formula One career in 1963 with which works team?

2 Which privateer entrant ran a Lotus for him in 1966?

3 It was while practising for which race that Spence was killed in 1968?

4 What was unusual about Alan Stacey?

5 For which team did he race in Formula One from 1958?

6 What caused Stacey to crash to his death in the 1960 Belgian Grand Prix?

7 Jackie Stewart began his Formula One career in 1965 with which British team?

8 He won a grand prix before the year was out at which circuit?

9 What car was Stewart driving when he took his first world title in 1969?

10 And his second?

11 In which year did Stewart retire after winning his third world title?

12 Rolf Stommelen impressed driving what chassis in 1970?

13 Stommelen scored his final point with a one-off outing in Germany in 1976 for which team?

14 Which team gave Stommelen a full-time ride for 1978?

15 At which circuit was Stommelen racing when he crashed to his death in 1978?

16 Philippe Streiff made his Formula One debut at the end of 1984 for which team?

17 Streiff's best season, 1987, was with which British team?

18 At which circuit was Streiff paralysed in 1989 after an accident during testing?

19 Hans-Joachim Stuck burst into Formula One in 1974 with which works team?

20 Stuck achieved two consecutive podium finishes in 1977 with which team?

Answers THE DRIVERS 41 *(see Quiz 83)*

1 Haas Lola. 2 Osella. 3 AGS. 4 Touring cars. 5 Ferrari. 6 Bremgarten, Switzerland (1952). 7 Lotus. 8 Dutch. 9 British Racing Partnership. 10 He was the youngest starter ever at 19 years, 5 months and 29 days. 11 Tyrrell. 12 Montreal. 13 Gordini. 14 Ferrari. 15 Rob Walker Racing. 16 Flavio Briatore (Benetton). 17 Minardi. 18 Olivier Panis. 19 Austrian. 20 Jordan.

1   Hans-Joachim Stuck's final season in Formula One was in 1979 when he scored just once for which German team?

2   Hans Stuck, a top racer in the 1930s, was what relation of Hans-Joachim's?

3   Danny Sullivan had just one season of Formula One, 1983. With which team?

4   Sullivan's best result was second in the Race of Champions. Where was this race held?

5   What major American race did Sullivan win in 1985?

6   What nationality is Marc Surer?

7   What did he break when he crashed his ATS at Kyalami in 1980?

8   Surer crashed at Kyalami again in 1982, breaking his legs. For what team was he driving?

9   A crash in what motorsport event ended Surer's career in 1986?

10   In what discipline of racing was John Surtees world champion before he tried Formula One?

11   With which team did Surtees make his Formula One debut in 1960?

12   Surtees became world champion in 1964 with which team?

13   At which grand prix did Surtees clinch the 1964 title?

14   In which year did Surtees start competing with his own cars?

15   Aguri Suzuki is the only Japanese driver to have finished in the first three. In which grand prix did he achieve this?

16   For which team was he driving?

17   Suzuki shared a ride at Ligier in 1995 with which other driver?

18   Which Far Eastern mogul guided Patrick Tambay into Formula One in 1977?

19   Tambay raced for McLaren in 1978. Who was his team-mate?

20   Tambay got his break with Ferrari in 1982 as replacement for whom?

Answers *THE DRIVERS 42* (see Quiz 84)

1 Modena. 2 San Marino. 3 His fuel pump had failed. 4 German. 5 JJ Lehto. 6 Hockenheim (1994). 7 Simtek. 8 McLaren. 9 Ferrari. 10 Montreal. 11 Didier Pironi. 12 Zolder, Belgium. 13 His son. 14 Indycar. 15 Damon Hill. 16 1997. 17 Craig Pollock. 18 Gigi. 19 Ferrari. 20 Lancia.

1 With which team did Patrick Tambay spend his final year in Formula One in 1986?

2 Gabriele Tarquini made his Formula One debut for which team in 1988?

3 A move to which team yielded Tarquini's only point in 1989?

4 Tarquini has since been a champion in what category of racing?

5 For which Italian team did Piero Taruffi race in 1951 and 1952?

6 At which circuit did he score his only win?

7 Trevor Taylor made his first Formula One start with which team in 1960?

8 He started 1961 well by finishing second in which grand prix?

9 Taylor's final season in Formula One was in 1964 with which team?

10 What was notable about Mike Thackwell's Formula One debut in 1980?

11 With which team was this?

12 At which circuit?

13 Maurice Trintignant raced predominantly for which team from 1950 to 1953?

14 For which team did he win at Monaco in 1955?

15 For which team did he win at Monaco in a Cooper in 1958?

16 Jarno Trulli's rise to Formula One was financed by which team owner?

17 For which team did he drive on his debut in 1997?

18 Who broke his legs to give Trulli a shot with Prost?

19 Which grand prix did Trulli lead for the French team?

20 Which team did Trulli join for 2000?

Answers THE DRIVERS 39 *(see Quiz 81)*

1 Lotus. **2** Reg Parnell. **3** The Indianapolis 500. **4** He had an artificial lower right leg. **5** Lotus. **6** He was hit in the face by a bird. **7** BRM. **8** Monza. **9** A Matra. **10** A Tyrrell. **11** 1973. **12** A Brabham. **13** Brabham. **14** Arrows. **15** Riverside, USA. **16** Renault. **17** Tyrrell. **18** Jacarepagua, Brazil. **19** March. **20** Brabham (third in the German and Austrian Grands Prix).

94

1   Eric van de Poele broke into Formula One in 1991 driving a Lamborghini with which team?

2   At which grand prix was he heading for fifth place until he stopped on the final lap?

3   Why did he stop?

4   Which Formula Three title did Jos Verstappen win on his meteoric rise to Formula One?

5   Verstappen made his Formula One debut with Benetton in 1994 after who broke his neck?

6   At which circuit was Verstappen engulfed in a pit fire?

7   For which team did Verstappen race in 1995?

8   Which team gave Gilles Villeneuve his Formula One break in 1977?

9   Which team immediately snapped him up?

10 Gilles Villeneuve scored his first grand prix win at which circuit at the end of 1978?

11 With which driver did he fall out after the 1982 San Marino Grand Prix?

12 At which circuit did Gilles Villeneuve crash to his death?

13 Jacques Villeneuve is what relation to Gilles?

14 What championship did Jacques Villeneuve win in 1995 before arriving in Formula One?

15 Who was his team-mate at Williams in 1996?

16 In which year did Jacques Villeneuve win the world championship?

17 Name his former manager who formed a team around him for 1999.

18 What was Luigi Villoresi's nickname?

19 Villoresi was a member of which Italian team in 1950?

20 Which team kept him waiting until the last race of 1954 before its car was ready?

Answers *THE DRIVERS 40* (see Quiz 82)

1 ATS (fifth in the US Grand Prix East). 2 His father. 3 Tyrrell. 4 Brands Hatch. 5 The Indianapolis 500. 6 Swiss. 7 His ankles. 8 Arrows. 9 A rally. 10 Motorcycles. 11 Lotus. 12 Ferrari. 13 Mexican. 14 1970. 15 Japanese (he was third). 16 Larrousse. 17 Martin Brundle. 18 Teddy Yip. 19 James Hunt. 20 Gilles Villeneuve.

1 Which marque guided Wolfgang von Trips into Formula One in 1956?

2 Von Trips won the 1961 British Grand Prix at which circuit?

3 Who collided with von Trips in a fatal accident at Monza in 1961?

4 Which little-rated car did Derek Warwick propel into a temporary second place at Brands Hatch in 1982?

5 Derek Warwick moved to Renault in 1984 and was leading which grand prix before his suspension collapsed?

6 At which circuit did Warwick flip in 1990 and then run to the pits to get the spare car for the restart?

7 What sort of car was he driving at the time?

8 What chassis did John Watson drive in Formula One in 1973 and 1974?

9 Watson gave which team its first win at the 1976 Austrian Grand Prix?

10 His next win came five years later with McLaren in which grand prix?

11 At which American circuit did Watson come through from the back to win in 1983?

12 Which future Formula One rivals did Karl Wendlinger beat to the 1989 German Formula Three title?

13 With which team did Wendlinger make his Formula One debut in 1991?

14 A serious accident at which circuit put Wendlinger into a coma for 19 days?

15 For which team was he driving at the time?

16 Ken Wharton won which famous Dutch rally three times?

17 In which car did he make his Formula One debut in 1952?

18 Which car did he race for BRM in 1954?

19 Gentleman racer Peter Whitehead came third in the 1950 French Grand Prix in what make of car?

20 What colour was his painted?

Answers *THE GREAT RACES 1* (see Quiz 87)

1 Roland Ratzenberger. 2 Ayrton Senna. 3 JJ Lehto. 4 Pedro Lamy. 5 Tamburello. 6 Michael Schumacher. 7 Nicola Larini. 8 Michele Alboreto. 9 Nicola Larini. 10 Ferrari. 11 Nigel Mansell. 12 The engine stalled. 13 The Pits Hairpin. 14 Nelson Piquet. 15 Benetton. 16 Riccardo Patrese. 17 He got a puncture and finished third. 18 Stefano Modena. 19 Jordan. 20 Andrea de Cesaris

1 Peter Whitehead was killed in an accident in what motoring event in 1958?

2 Who was Roger Williamson's mentor?

3 With what make of car did Williamson make his Formula One debut in 1973?

4 At which circuit did he suffer fatal burns?

5 Which British driver fought through the flames to try to release him?

6 Which team gave Manfred Winkelhock his Formula One break in 1982?

7 Winkelhock swapped over to drive which car in 1985?

8 What nationality is Reine Wisell?

9 Wisell finished third on his Formula One debut for which team in 1970?

10 Alexander Wurz got his Formula One break with Benetton as a stand-in for whom?

11 Wurz finished third in which grand prix that year?

12 Who was his team-mate in that race?

13 At which circuit did Wurz barrel-roll in 1998?

14 Alessandro Zanardi started his first spell in Formula One with which team in 1991?

15 Zanardi suffered a major accident in qualifying at which circuit in 1993?

16 Zanardi spent three years in the USA winning two titles in what category?

17 A return to Formula One came in 1999 with which team?

18 Ricardo Zonta was Formula 3000 champion in which year?

19 Zonta arrived in Formula One with which team in 1999?

20 At which grand prix did Zonta crash and put himself out for the next three races?

Answers **THE GREAT RACES 2** *(see Quiz 88)*

1 Damon Hill. *2* Jacques Villeneuve. *3* Williams and Williams. *4* Jacques Villeneuve. *5* Hill.
6 When Villeneuve retired. *7* He lost a wheel and crashed. *8* Michael Schumacher. *9* Ferrari.
10 Mika Hakkinen. *11* La Source. *12* David Coulthard. *13* Rubens Barrichello. *14* He had hit a
drainage grate. *15* Ricardo Rosset. *16* Michael Schumacher. *17* Ralf Schumacher. *18* Jean
Alesi. *19* Damon Hill. *20* Giancarlo Fisichella.

1. Who was killed in qualifying for the 1994 San Marino Grand Prix?
2. Who went on to take pole position?
3. Who stalled on the grid?
4. Who piled into the back of his car?
5. At which corner did Ayrton Senna crash to his death after the safety car pulled in?
6. Who went on to win the race?
7. Who finished second for Ferrari?
8. Who had a wheel fly off in the pit lane?
9. Which Italian driver completed the podium
10. For which team was he driving?
11. Which Williams driver lost victory in the 1991 Canadian Grand Prix when he waved to the crowd on the final lap?
12. Why did his car stop?
13. At which corner was he when this happened?
14. Who came through to snatch victory?
15. For which team was he driving?
16. Name the other Williams driver in that race.
17. Why didn't he win?
18. Who claimed second place for Tyrrell?
19. Which team had its drivers finish fourth and fifth for its first points
20. Which of its drivers finished fourth?

Answers *THE DRIVERS 43* (see Quiz 85)

1 Ferrari. 2 Aintree. 3 Jim Clark. 4 A Toleman. 5 Brazilian. 6 Monza. 7 A Lotus. 8 Brabham. 9 Penske. 10 British. 11 Long Beach. 12 Heinz-Harald Frentzen and Michael Schumacher. 13 Leyton House. 14 Monaco. 15 Sauber. 16 The Tulip Rally. 17 A Frazer Nash. 18 A Maserati. 19 A Ferrari. 20 Green.

1 Which British driver went to the 1996 Japanese Grand Prix with a chance of the title?

2 Who was his rival?

3 Name their respective teams.

4 Which of them qualified on pole position?

5 Who led away at the start?

6 When did the eventual champion know he had become champion?

7 What misfortune befell the losing contender?

8 Who chased the new 1996 champion to the finish?

9 For which team was he driving

10 And which McLaren driver finished third?

11 There was a pile-up at the start of the 1998 Belgian Grand Prix. It started out of which corner?

12 Who triggered the pile-up?

13 Which driver was slightly injured in the pile-up and did not make the re-start?

14 Why was his car unsettled as he accelerated?

15 Which Tyrrell driver piled into the spinning pack at unabated speed?

16 Who smashed into the back of David Coulthard's McLaren late in the restarted race?

17 Who was told to back off and support his team-mate in the closing laps?

18 Who was sitting right on his tail?

19 Who went on to win the race for Jordan?

20 Which Benetton driver exited the race in a big way at the Bus Stop?

Answers **THE DRIVERS 44** *(see Quiz 86)*

1 The Tour de France. **2** Tom Wheatcroft. **3** A March. **4** Zandvoort, Holland. **5** David Purley.
6 ATS. **7** A RAM. **8** Swedish. **9** Lotus (US Grand Prix). **10** Gerhard Berger. **11** British (1997).
12 Jean Alesi. **13** Montreal. **14** Jordan. **15** Spa-Francorchamps. **16** Indycars. **17** Williams.
18 1997. **19** British American Racing. **20** Brazilian.

1   Who started the 1999 Austrian Grand Prix from pole position?

2   For which team was he driving?

3   Name his team-mate who tipped him into a spin at the second corner.

4   Who took the lead for Ferrari at mid-distance?

5   Mika Hakkinen fought his way through the field to what finishing position?

6   Which Stewart driver ran second for the first half of the race, but retired?

7   Why did Alessandro Zanardi retire?

8   Why did Jean Alesi retire?

9   Who won the race?

10   Who scored points on home ground?

11   Which two drivers were sharing the lead of the World Championship when they arrived for the European Grand Prix?

12   At which circuit was it held?

13   Which team qualified on pole?

14   Who led until his first pitstop?

15   Whose chances were thwarted by a puncture?

16   And who came through to win?

17   Who finished second for Prost?

18   Who scored the final point, for sixth?

19   Which driver rolled at the first start and ripped the rollhoop off his car?

20   Which Benetton driver led but spun out?

Answers *THE CIRCUITS 2 (see Quiz 91)*

1 Fuji. **2** James Hunt. **3** Jim Clark. **4** Ostkurve. **5** Mika Hakkinen. **6** Hungary. **7** An underground spring had been plugged. **8** No. **9** Villeneuve. **10** Enzo Ferrari's son Dino. **11** The Brickyard. **12** Turn 4. **13** Sao Paulo. **14** Emerson Fittipaldi (1973). **15** Ayrton Senna. **16** Madrid. **17** Jacky Ickx and Jackie Oliver. **18** Sherry. **19** Curva Dry Sac. **20** The Ayrton Senna Chicane.

1   The A1-Ring was built over what Austrian circuit?

2   In which year did the A1-Ring first host a grand prix?

3   Name the South Australian city that was awarded the Australian Grand Prix in 1985.

4   Which was the last year the Formula One circus visited that city?

5   The Avus circuit can be found in which German city?

6   If one of the circuit's corner names can be translated as the South Curve, how would you translate the name of the other one?

7   Name the famous Brands Hatch corner located at the start of each lap.

8   In which year did Brands Hatch last host a grand prix?

9   Who won the race that year?

10 Which Argentinian president oversaw the construction of the Buenos Aires circuit?

11 Who won there on Formula One's last visit in 1998?

12 Outside which Spanish city is the Circuit de Catalunya located?

13 In which year was a temporary tyre chicane built after the Campsa corner?

14 Name the driver who won the grands prix there in 1998 and 1999?

15 Which British circuit hosted the European Grand Prix in 1993?

16 Who was victorious in the rain that day?

17 Which Portuguese circuit hosted a grand prix between 1984 and 1997?

18 Who won the first grand prix held there for McLaren?

19 Who overtook Michael Schumacher around the outside at the final corner in 1996?

20 Which was the final year that Estoril hosted a grand prix?

Answers THE CIRCUITS 3 (see Quiz 92)

1 Johannesburg. 2 Tom Pryce. 3 1976. 4 Chris Pook. 5 Nevers. 6 Adelaide. 7 Albert Park. 8 Damon Hill. 9 The Peralta. 10 Pedro and Ricardo Rodriguez. 11 Monte Carlo. 12 Ste. Devote. 13 Prince Rainier. 14 Gilles Villeneuve. 15 Nigel Mansell. 16 Alexander Wurz. 17 Monza (the race was held at Imola in 1980). 18 Parabolica. 19 Toronto. 20 Jody Scheckter.

1   The Japanese Grand Prix was held for the first time in 1976 at which circuit?

2   Who clinched the world championship there that year?

3   Hockenheim will always be remembered for the death of which world champion?

4   Name the corner at the far end of the circuit?

5   Who had a major blow-out and spun into the barriers coming into the stadium in 1999?

6   In which country would you find the Hungaroring?

7   Why was it possible to straighten the circuit after Turn 3 in 1989?

8   Imola hosts the San Marino Grand Prix, but is it in the principality of San Marino?

9   Name the corner at which Roland Ratzenberger was killed in 1994?

10   Whose son is honoured when the circuit uses its full name?

11   What is the nickname of the Indianapolis Motor Speedway?

12   Name the circuit's final corner.

13   In which Brazilian city would you find Interlagos?

14   Who won the first world championship grand prix held there?

15   After which driver are the esses at the first corner named?

16   If you were going to Jarama, which Spanish city would you head for?

17   Which two drivers were involved with a flame-enveloped wreck there in 1970?

18   For what is the region of Spain in which Jerez is located famous?

19   At which corner did Michael Schumacher clash with Jacques Villeneuve in the 1997 title decider?

20   At which corner did Mika Hakkinen take the lead on the final lap in 1997?

Answers THE GREAT RACES 3 *(see Quiz 89)*

1 Mika Hakkinen. 2 McLaren. 3 David Coulthard. 4 Eddie Irvine. 5 Third. 6 Rubens Barrichello.
7 He ran out of fuel. 8 He ran out fuel. 9 Eddie Irvine. 10 Alexander Wurz. 11 Mika Hakkinen
and Eddie Irvine. 12 Nürburgring. 13 Jordan. 14 Heinz-Harald Frentzen. 15 Ralf Schumacher's.
16 Johnny Herbert. 17 Jarno Trulli. 18 Marc Gene. 19 Pedro Diniz. 20 Giancarlo Fisichella.

1   In which South African city is the Kyalami circuit located?

2   Which British driver was killed at Kyalami when a marshal crossed the straight in front of him?

3   In which year did Long Beach first host a Formula One grand prix?

4   Name Long Beach's British promoter.

5   What is the closest town to rural Magny-Cours?

6   Name the circuit's uphill hairpin.

7   In what park would you find Melbourne's race circuit?

8   Who won on Formula One's first visit there in 1996?

9   Name the Mexico City circuit's slightly banked final corner.

10   After which two racing brothers is the circuit named?

11   In which principality is the Monaco circuit located?

12   Name the first corner.

13   Who is always on the winner's rostrum there?

14   Who won the first time Montreal hosted a Grand Prix?

15   Who blew victory there in 1991 by waving to the crowd?

16   Who barrel-rolled at the first corner in 1998?

17   Which circuit has been the home of the Italian Grand Prix every year bar one since 1950?

18   Name the final corner.

19   What is the closest Canadian city to Mosport Park?

20   Mosport Park last hosted a grand prix in 1977. Who won it?

Answers *THE CIRCUITS 1* *(see Quiz 90)*
1 The Osterreichring. *2* 1997. *3* Adelaide. *4* 1995. *5* Berlin. *6* North Curve. *7* Paddock Hill Bend. *8* 1986. *9* Nigel Mansell. *10* Peron. *11* Michael Schumacher. *12* Barcelona. *13* 1994. *14* Mika Hakkinen. *15* Donington Park. *16* Ayrton Senna. *17* Estoril. *18* Alain Prost. *19* Jacques Villeneuve. *20* 1996.

1   What is the name of the original Nürburgring circuit?
2   Who won the first race at the revised Nürburgring in 1984?
3   Who cartwheeled over the pack at the first corner of the French Grand Prix at Paul Ricard in 1989?
4   In which years did Phoenix host the US Grand Prix?
5   Which French circuit was famed for slipstreaming battles in the 1950s?
6   Name the sharp right-hand corner on to the start/finish straight at this circuit.
7   Which circuit has hosted the British Grand Prix more times than any other?
8   Name the corner at the end of the Hangar Straight?
9   Name the corner on to the start/finish straight?
10 In what region of Belgium is Spa-Francorchamps located?
11 Name its most famous and most feared corner.
12 Name the hairpin that precedes this.
13 Which Japanese motor manufacturer owns Suzuka?
14 Who won the Japanese Grand Prix at Suzuka in 1996 to clinch the world title?
15 Watkins Glen is in which US state?
16 Who was killed when he crashed there in 1973?
17 Name the hairpin that is Zandvoort's first corner.
18 The final Dutch Grand Prix was held at Zandvoort in which year?
19 Zolder last hosted a Belgian Grand Prix in 1984. Who won it?
20 At which corner was Gilles Villeneuve killed in 1982?

Answers THE BUSINESS OF FORMULA ONE 2 *(see Quiz 95)*

1 HSBC. *2* Ford. *3* Sylvester Stallone. *4* Stewart. *5* Bernie Ecclestone. *6* Michael Schumacher. *7* British American Racing. *8* Lucky Strike and 555. *9* Cigarettes. *10* Ferrari (Tic Tac). *11* Mobil. *12* Petronas. *13* Prost. *14* t-minus. *15* Petrochemical products. *16* Saucepans. *17* A bond issue. *18* Telefonica. *19* Nicola Foulston. *20* Jaguar Racing.

1 Team Lotus was taken over by a brother of which world champion?

2 Which president supported the return of Formula One to Argentina for 1995?

3 Which tobacco company became Ferrari's main sponsor in 1995?

4 What is made by Red Bull, the chief sponsor of Sauber since 1995?

5 Which French team failed in its plans to show up late in 1995?

6 Which tobacco sponsor started backing Jordan in 1996?

7 Who was the former Ferrari boss who joined Prost as sporting director in 1996?

8 Which London jeweller started backing Ferrari in 1996?

9 Which three teams held out before signing the 1997 Concorde Agreement?

10 Who joined Ferrari as technical director for 1997?

11 McLaren swapped tobacco brands from Marlboro to what in 1997?

12 With which team had this tobacco brand previously been involved?

13 Which credit-card company arrived in Formula One in 1997 with Lola and stayed on longer than the team?

14 Which Middle Eastern country announced midway through 1997 that it wanted to host a grand prix?

15 To whom did Ken Tyrrell sell his team at the end of 1997?

16 Williams changed sponsors in 1998 to which tobacco brand?

17 Which engine builder was taken over by Audi in 1998?

18 Which motor manufacturer bought it later that year?

19 Who was deposed as Benetton boss midway through 1998?

20 Who took over?

Answers EQUIPMENT 1 *(see Quiz 96)*

1 1988. 2 AGS. 3 No. 4 Honda and Renault. 5 McLaren and Williams respectively. 6 V12.
7 Nomex. 8 A balaclava. 9 Driver aids, such as traction control. 10 Sauber. 11 McLaren.
12 Mecachrome. 13 Supertec. 14 Playlife. 15 Narrower. 16 Goodyear. 17 Bridgestone.
18 Telemetry. 19 McLaren. 20 Alessandro Zanardi.

1   Which bank backed Stewart in 1998?

2   Which major manufacturer bought Stewart during 1999?

3   Which American film star is preparing to make a film on Formula One?

4   Which team did designer Gary Anderson join after leaving Jordan?

5   Who controls Formula One's television rights?

6   Who was Formula One's best-paid driver in 1999?

7   Which team was refused permission to run its two cars in different liveries in 1999?

8   Who were the two sponsors?

9   These are brands of what?

10 If you want a mint to freshen your breath, which team would you go to in 1999?

11 What brand of fuel and oil does McLaren use?

12 Name the Malaysian state oil company that is a shareholder in Sauber?

13 Playstation sponsors which team?

14 Name the trading company formed by Arrows' owner Prince Malik in 1999?

15 What is made by Arrows' principal sponsor, Repsol?

16 What is made by Arrows' minor sponsor, Zepter?

17 What did Bernie Ecclestone launch in 1999?

18 Name the Spanish telecommunications company that sponsored Minardi.

19 Name the owner of Brands Hatch who made a bid for Silverstone.

20 What is the name of the team that was once Stewart?

Answers *THE CIRCUITS 4 (see Quiz 93)*

1 The Nordschleife. *2* Ayrton Senna. *3* Mauricio Gugelmin. *4* 1989 to 1991 inclusive. *5* Reims.
6 Thillois. *7* Silverstone. *8* Stowe. *9* Woodcote. *10* The Ardennes. *11* Eau Rouge. *12* La
Source. *13* Honda. *14* Damon Hill. *15* New York. *16* François Cevert. *17* Tarzan. *18* 1985.
19 Michele Alboreto. *20* Terlamenbocht.

1 Turbocharged engines were outlawed after the end of which season?

2 A W12 engine was scheduled to be used by which team in 1988?

3 Was it ever used?

4 Which two engine manufacturers introduced V10 engines to Formula One in 1989?

5 Which teams used these?

6 To what format of engine did Ferrari revert in 1989?

7 Of what material are drivers' fire-proof racesuits made?

8 What must drivers wear under their helmets?

9 What was or were outlawed at the end of the 1993 season?

10 Which team led the push for higher cockpit sides for 1995?

11 An extra wing on the top of the airbox was introduced by which team in 1995?

12 Renault stopped entering its engines as Renaults in 1997. What were they called?

13 The name changed again for 1998. To what?

14 What did Benetton call its engines in deference to a sponsor?

15 Was the tracking of the cars made wider or narrower for 1998?

16 Which tyre supplier pulled out of Formula One at the end of 1998?

17 This left which company as the sole tyre supplier?

18 What is the name of the system that allows data to be transferred via the airwaves from the car to a computer for analysis?

19 Which team built a state-of-the-art technical centre outside Woking in 1999?

20 Which driver reverted to using steel brakes in 1999?

Answers *THE BUSINESS OF FORMULA ONE 1 (see Quiz 94)*

1 James Hunt. **2** President Menem. **3** Marlboro. **4** An energy drink. **5** Larrousse. **6** Benson & Hedges. **7** Cesare Fiorio. **8** Asprey. **9** McLaren, Tyrrell and Williams. **10** Ross Brawn. **11** West. **12** Zakspeed. **13** Mastercard. **14** Lebanon. **15** Craig Pollock. **16** Winfield. **17** Cosworth. **18** Ford. **19** David Richards. **20** Rocco Benetton.

1 What does a yellow flag signal?

2 What does a green flag signal?

3 What does a red and yellow striped flag signal?

4 What does a blue flag signal?

5 What does a white flag signal?

6 What does a red flag signal?

7 What does the black and white chequered flag signal?

8 How does a marshal emphasize the message of a flag?

9 How did the regulation tyres change for 1999?

10 Is this for the front and the rear tyres, or both?

11 What has had to be secured to the chassis since the start of 1999?

12 What feature of the driver's seat also became mandatory for 1999?

13 Name Formula One's medical advisor who was involved in their design.

14 Name the company that builds these seats.

15 What's the maximum number of laps a driver is allowed in the qualifying session?

16 A driver must be within what percentage of pole time to qualify?

17 How many cars may each team field during qualifying?

18 What's the speed limit in the pit lane on practice days?

19 What's the speed limit in the pit lane during the race?

20 A driver must be able to vacate the cockpit of his car in less than how many seconds to be passed fit to race?

Answers *FAN CULTURE* (see Quiz 99)

1 Benetton. 2 Simtek. 3 Monaco. 4 Mika Hakkinen. 5 Mika Salo. 6 Flavio Briatore. 7 McLaren 8 David Coulthard, Mika Salo and Jacques Villeneuve. 9 Martin Brundle. 10 Stewart. 11 McLaren. 12 Williams. 13 Stowe. 14 Jordan. 15 A hornet. 16 Jordan, Melinda Messenger or Emma Noble. 17 Eddie Irvine. 18 600. 19 British American Racing. 20 Flavio Briatore.

1 What does the acronym FIA stand for?

2 Where is the FIA based?

3 Where was it based until 1998?

4 Who is the FIA president?

5 Name his predecessor as FIA president.

6 What team did the current FIA president launch in 1970?

7 Who is the FIA's vice-president for promotional affairs?

8 Which team did he run?

9 With which team was he involved in the 1950s?

10 Name Formula One's official race director in the 1990s.

11 Which British administrator made a bid to become FIA president in 1981?

12 The FISA Executive Committee changed its name to what in 1988?

13 The chief executive of the RAC Motor Sport Association died in a motorcycle accident on his way to the 1998 British Grand Prix. Who was he?

14 Name Formula One's race doctor.

15 Name the FIA official responsible for technical matters.

16 The Ayrton Senna trial was chaired by whom?

17 Name the European Commissioner who accused the FIA of breaching European competition laws.

18 Which company owned by Bernie Ecclestone controls Formula One's digital TV feed?

19 Which British driver has been in charge of the saftey car since 1997?

20 Which Brazilian now drives the medical car?

1 Which team pioneered the cut-off racesuit as a jacket for fans?

2 Which team's name was short for "simulated technology"?

3 At which 1994 grand prix were the first two grid positions left empty?

4 Which driver is famed for riding a unicycle?

5 Which driver is famed for rollerblading?

6 Which team boss liked to wear his cap back to front?

7 Which team has a showroom on London's Park Lane?

8 Three drivers shaved their heads after the 1996 Japanese Grand Prix. Who were they?

9 Which former driver appears alongside Murray Walker in the commentary box?

10 If you wore tartan trousers in the late 1990s, which team would you be supporting?

11 Which team had marble floors in its motorhome in the late 1990s?

12 Which team raced with a kangaroo emblem on its flanks in 1998 and 1999?

13 At which school near Silverstone is the annual British Grand Prix ball held?

14 Which team traditionally holds a music gig after the British Grand Prix?

15 What creature is depicted on the side of the Benson & Hedges Jordans of the late 1990s?

16 Name one of the British models often seen in Jordan colours in the late 1990s?

17 Who called Damon Hill "a sad old man" during 1998?

18 In 1998, Ferrari reached a special landmark of grands prix contested. How many?

19 Which team ran with a split colour scheme in 1999?

20 Which former team boss was seen stepping out with model Naomi Campbell in 1999?

Answers *RULES AND TACTICS* (see Quiz 97)

1 Danger ahead. **2** All clear, often after a hazard. **3** Slippery surface. **4** Driver approaching to overtake. **5** Slow-moving vehicle on track. **6** Race stopped immediately, often after a major accident. **7** The end of the race. **8** He or she waves it. **9** They gained an extra groove. **10** For the front tyres. **11** The wheels. **12** It had to be extractable. **13** Professor Sid Watkins. **14** Lear. **15** Twelve. **16** 107 per cent. **17** A maximum of three. **18** 80kph (50mph). **19** 120kph (75mph). **20** Five seconds.

1 Who hit a deer in qualifying for the 1987 Austrian Grand Prix?

2 At which track did Brands Hatch owner John Foulston die in 1987 testing a car?

3 Which partner of the Larrousse Calmels team was arrested after his wife was killed in Paris in 1989?

4 Which Swiss businessman who owned Brabham in 1989 and was detained for a $100 million fraud.

5 Why did Alain Prost and Ayrton Senna fall out after 1989's San Marino Grand Prix?

6 Which French driver caused ructions by signing for Ferrari *and* Williams for 1991?

7 Who was thrown from his smashed car in qualifying for 1990's Spanish Grand Prix?

8 Who had one of his arms severed in a helicopter accident in 1990?

9 "I think he honestly believes what he's saying. But then so did Hitler." Who said this of Ayrton Senna after the 1990 Japanese Grand Prix?

10 Which Williams team manager was abducted and beaten up in 1991?

11 Which driver was jailed in 1991 for spraying CS gas at a London taxi driver?

12 Who said the 1991 Australian Grand Prix should never have been started in conditions of torrential rain?

13 Who was Frank Williams accused of calling "a prat" at 1995's British Grand Prix?

14 Which two teams were accused in 1995 of running identical cars?

15 Frank Williams and five others were charged with manslaughter in 1996 for what?

16 What was Michael Schumacher's punishment for crashing into Jacques Villeneuve in the 1997 European Grand Prix?

17 Which team asked one of its drivers to slow down to let his team-mate win the 1998 Australian Grand Prix after the team-mate mistakenly drove into the pits?

18 Which team complained that a photographer crossed the circuit at Interlagos in 1998 to take a photo of its abandoned cars?

19 Which team's drivers collided when leading in the 1999 Austrian Grand Prix?

20 Which team's drivers collided when contesting the lead in the 1999 Belgian Grand Prix?

Answers ADMINISTRATORS *(see Quiz 98)*

1 Fédération International d'Automobiles. **2** Geneva. **3** Paris. **4** Max Mosley. **5** Jean-Marie Balestre. **6** March. **7** Bernie Ecclestone. **8** Brabham. **9** Connaught. **10** Roland Bruynseraede. **11** Basil Tye. **12** The World Motorsport Council. **13** Peter Hammond. **14** Professor Sid Watkins. **15** Charlie Whiting. **16** Maurizio Passarini. **17** Karel van Miert. **18** Formula One Holdings. **19** Oliver Gavin. **20** Alex Ribeiro.

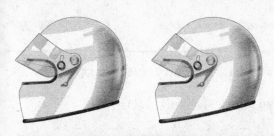

Medium Questions

Congratulations, you've fought your way through the easy questions and now you're preparing to move up a gear and tackle the medium ones. The tip is to think not just about the stars of the day, or of the top teams. Instead, look more towards the midfield. Certainly, all the stars are here – they won so often that there are still many more questions to be asked about their exploits.

Consider the circuits for a moment. The questions in this chapter won't just be on the Silverstones and Monzas but also on abandoned venues such as Clermont-Ferrand, Nivelles and Zeltweg.

Furthermore, rather than simply asking the obvious, I might occasionally have set a question that will require more than a moment's thought. The answer will not be the one you think of straightaway. So rack your brains if a question seems easier than those around it – it was probably the race when the regular driver was off duty due to injury or, bless me, a three-race ban. Crafty, yes, but how better to impress those fellow *aficionados* who dare to think that they know more than you.

When you've answered this second batch of 2,000 questions, you will be ready to tackle the race: the third chapter of difficult questions.

Prepare to qualify!

1   The Spanish Grand Prix moved to which circuit in 1926 and stayed there through the 1930s?
2   Where was the English Grand Prix held in 1926 and 1927?
3   Who won it?
4   Which British driver won the Monaco Grand Prix in 1928 and 1929?
5   Maserati scored its first win in the 1930 Italian Grand Prix with whom at the wheel?
6   Which Monegasque driver won his home grand prix in 1931?
7   What was unusual about three 1931 grands prix?
8   Which Italian driver won the first three grands prix of 1932?
9   What car was he driving?
10 Where was the Czech Grand Prix held in the 1930s?
11 Which driver who starred in the 1950 Formula One season won for Alfa Romeo in the 1933 Italian Grand Prix?
12 In 1934, which was the first German marque to win?
13 In which grand prix?
14 With which famous father of a famous son at the wheel?
15 Name the rival German marque that came good later in the year.
16 Where did they make their breakthrough?
17 Which politician financed the German racing programme as a whole?
18 Where was the German Grand Prix held in this era?
19 Which German driver scored four grands prix wins in 1935?
20 For which team?

Answers WORLD CHAMPIONSHIPS 1955–59 *(see Quiz 3)*

1 Jean Behra. 2 Maurice Trintignant. 3 Ferrari. 4 The Italian Grand Prix. 5 Monaco.
6 A Maserati. 7 Alfonso de Portago. 8 BRM. 9 Monaco (Mike Hawthorn, Peter Collins and Stirling Moss). 10 Pescara. 11 Stirling Moss. 12 His fifth. 13 Buenos Aires. 14 A Vanwall. 15 Zandvoort. 16 Morocco. 17 He had retired (and was later killed in a road accident). 18 Tony Brooks. 19 He ran out of fuel. 20 Bruce McLaren.

1 Which world famous family watched the 1950 British Grand Prix?

2 Who triggered the nine-car pile-up in the 1950 Monaco Grand Prix?

3 Who avoided it and went on to win the race?

4 At which circuit was the Swiss Grand Prix held in 1950?

5 Which famous grand prix was dropped from the calendar in 1951?

6 At which race did BRM make its world championship debut?

7 Which circuit hosted the first German world championship round?

8 Where was the Spanish Grand Prix held in 1951?

9 Who won the 1952 season's opening race, the Swiss Grand Prix?

10 Who was the only non-Ferrari driver to lead a grand prix in 1952?

11 What car was he driving?

12 How many successive wins did Alberto Ascari score in 1952?

13 In which country did the 1953 world championship kick off?

14 In 1953, Juan Manuel Fangio was back. What car was he driving?

15 Which Ferrari driver won the 1953 German Grand Prix?

16 Where did Maserati score its single 1953 victory?

17 Name two of Mercedes-Benz's three drivers for 1954.

18 Who became the first driver to die in a world championship event?

19 Alberto Ascari and Luigi Villoresi gave which marque its debut in the Spanish Grand Prix, the final race of the 1954 season?

20 Who won the race?

Answers WORLD CHAMPIONSHIP 1960 & 1961 *(see Quiz 4)*

1 Cliff Allison. **2** A Ferrari. **3** Rob Walker Racing. **4** Phil Hill. **5** Jack Brabham. **6** Cooper. **7** Innes Ireland. **8** Lotus. **9** US. **10** Riverside. **11** Stirling Moss. **12** Monaco. **13** Lotus. **14** Richie Ginther. **15** Phil Hill. **16** Dan Gurney. **17** A Porsche. **18** Stirling Moss. **19** A Lotus. **20** 12.

1   In 1955, who replaced Stirling Moss at Maserati?

2   Who won the 1955 Monaco Grand Prix?

3   For which team was he driving?

4   Which was the last grand prix in 1955 entered by Mercedes?

5   Where did Stirling Moss score his first 1956 win?

6   What car was he driving?

7   Peter Collins came second in the 1956 German Grand Prix with which Spanish driver?

8   Which British marque led for the first time in the 1956 British Grand Prix?

9   Three British drivers crashed out early in which 1957 grand prix?

10 Which Italian road circuit hosted a grand prix for the one and only time in 1957?

11 Who won the 1957 season's final two races to end the season as runner-up?

12 Juan Manuel Fangio became world champion again. What number title was this for the Argentinian?

13 In 1958, where did Stirling Moss give Cooper its first grand prix win?

14 Two races later, Moss won again in Holland. What car was he driving this time?

15 At which circuit was this?

16 In which country did the 1958 season's final race take place?

17 Why did 1958 world champion Mike Hawthorn not defend his title?

18 Which British driver won the 1959 French Grand Prix for Ferrari?

19 Why did Jack Brabham fail to win the 1959 season's closing race, the US Grand Prix?

20 Who was Brabham's team-mate who came through to win?

Answers THE ORIGINS OF FORMULA ONE *(see Quiz 1)*

1 San Sebastian. *2* Brooklands. *3* Robert Benoist. *4* W. Williams (aka William Grover-Williams). *5* Achille Varzi. *6* Louis Chiron. *7* They took 10 hours each. *8* Tazio Nuvolari. *9* An Alfa Romeo. *10* Brno. *11* Luigi Fagioli. *12* Auto Union. *13* German. *14* Hans Stuck. *15* Mercedes-Benz. *16* Monza. *17* Adolf Hitler. *18* Nürburgring. *19* Rudolf Caracciola. *20* Mercedes-Benz.

1 Bruce McLaren won the opening race of 1960 in Argentina. Which British driver finished second?

2 What car was he driving?

3 Stirling Moss won at Monaco in 1960. For which team was he driving?

4 Bruce McLaren was second there, but which Ferrari driver was third?

5 Who won five grands prix in a row in 1960?

6 For which works team was he driving?

7 The first of the five was the Dutch Grand Prix. Who finished second?

8 For which team was he driving?

9 The same driver finished second again later in the year. In which grand prix?

10 At which circuit was this held for the only time?

11 Who won the 1961 season's opening grand prix?

12 Where was this?

13 What chassis was he driving?

14 Which American led the race's early laps for Ferrari?

15 Which American won the third round in 1961, the Belgian Grand Prix, for Ferrari?

16 Which American was pipped to victory in the 1961 French Grand Prix?

17 What car was he driving?

18 Who won the 1961 German Grand Prix for Rob Walker Racing?

19 What car was he driving?

20 How many spectators were killed along with Wolfgang von Trips in the 1961 Italian Grand Prix?

Answers *WORLD CHAMPIONSHIPS 1950–54 (see Quiz 2)*
1 The British royal family. 2 Giuseppe Farina. 3 Juan Manuel Fangio. 4 Bremgarten. 5 Monaco.
6 The 1951 British Grand Prix. 7 Nürburgring. 8 Pedralbes. 9 Piero Taruffi. 10 Jean Behra.
11 A Gordini. 12 Six. 13 Argentina. 14 A Maserati. 15 Giuseppe Farina. 16 Monza. 17 Juan Manuel
Fangio, Hans Herrmann, Karl Kling. 18 Onofre Marimon (in practice for the 1954 German Grand
Prix). 19 Lancia. 20 Mike Hawthorn.

1 Name the Lotus driver who finished second in the 1962 season's opening Dutch Grand Prix.

2 A future racing car constructor won the 1962 Monaco Grand Prix. Name him.

3 In what make of car did Jim Clark win the 1962 Belgian Grand Prix?

4 Name the Belgian driver who led the 1962 Belgian Grand Prix for several laps.

5 Why did this driver retire from the race?

6 Which Cooper driver was second behind Dan Gurney in the 1962 French Grand Prix?

7 At which circuit was this?

8 Where was the German Grand Prix held in 1962?

9 Who won it for BRM?

10 Who completed the BRM one-two at Monza?

11 Which Lotus driver led the 1963 season's opening race, the Monaco Grand Prix?

12 Why did he retire?

13 Jim Clark lapped every driver bar one in the 1963 Belgian Grand Prix. Who was this?

14 What make of car was this individual driving?

15 Name the American driver who trailed Jim Clark in the 1963 Dutch Grand Prix.

16 What make of car was he driving?

17 Where was the British Grand Prix held in 1963?

18 Who won it?

19 What car was he driving?

20 Which country hosted the final race of 1963 on 28 December?

Answers WORLD CHAMPIONSHIP 1966 & 1967 *(see Quiz 7)*
1 Jackie Stewart. 2 BRM. 3 Jochen Rindt. 4 Maserati. 5 Mike Parkes. 6 Ferrari. 7 John Surtees. 8 Brabham. 9 Ludovico Scarfiotti. 10 Ferrari. 11 BRM. 12 Graham Hill. 13 Denny Hulme (Lorenzo Bandini was killed). 14 Brabham. 15 Jim Clark. 16 Silverstone. 17 Brabham (Denny Hulme and Jack Brabham). 18 Chris Amon. 19 John Surtees. 20 Honda.

1   Which Scottish driver led at Monaco in 1964 but retired?

2   Which team was thus left to score a one-two?

3   Who was the winning driver?

4   Lotus made amends at Zandvoort, but who was second for Ferrari?

5   Which Lotus driver finished third?

6   John Surtees boosted his title 1964 challenge by winning twice. Name either of the circuits at which he won.

7   Name the privateer who finished third in the 1964 Austrian Grand Prix.

8   What make of car was he driving?

9   Which future world champion made his debut in this race?

10   Which BRM driver boosted his title hopes by winning the 1964 US Grand Prix?

11   Who won the 1965 season's opening race, the South African Grand Prix?

12   Name his team-mate who finished fourth.

13   Another British driver finished sixth that day on his debut. Who was he?

14   For which team was he driving?

15   Why did Lotus miss the 1965 Monaco Grand Prix?

16   At which circuit did the French Grand Prix find a new home in 1965?

17   Who won the race?

18   For which team was he driving?

19   Why did Jim Clark retire from the 1965 US Grand Prix?

20   Who was left to win the race?

Answers *WORLD CHAMPIONSHIP 1968 & 1969* (see Quiz 8)

1 Graham Hill. **2** Spanish. **3** Jarama. **4** Richard Attwood. **5** BRM. **6** Jackie Stewart. **7** Matra.
8 Jo Schlesser. **9** Honda. **10** Jackie Stewart. **11** Ford Cosworth DFVs. **12** Jochen Rindt.
13 Lotus. **14** Jackie Stewart. **15** Piers Courage. **16** Brabham. **17** Jochen Rindt. **18** Jacky Ickx.
19 Jack Brabham. **20** Graham Hill.

1 Name the British driver who won the 1966 season's opening race at Monaco.
2 For which team was he driving?
3 Which Austrian driver finished second in the 1966 Belgian Grand Prix?
4 What make of engine was fitted to his Cooper?
5 Jack Brabham won the 1966 French Grand Prix, but which British driver came second?
6 For which team was this second placed driver racing?
7 Which British driver had quit the team and provided him with his chance?
8 Which team finished one-two in the 1966 British Grand Prix?
9 Name the Italian who scored his only win at the 1966 Italian Grand Prix.
10 For which team was he driving?
11 What make of engine did the Lotus team use at the start of 1967?
12 Which British driver joined Jim Clark in the Lotus line-up?
13 Who won the tragic 1967 Monaco Grand Prix?
14 For which team was he driving?
15 Which British driver won the 1967 British Grand Prix?
16 At which circuit was it held?
17 Which team scored a one-two in the 1967 German Grand Prix?
18 Which Ferrari driver chased them home in third?
19 Which British driver was triumphant at Monza?
20 What make of car was he driving?

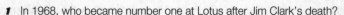
1 In 1968, who became number one at Lotus after Jim Clark's death?

2 At which grand prix did he put Lotus back on the winning trail?

3 At which circuit was this held?

4 Which British driver scored his best-ever result by coming second at Monaco in 1968?

5 For which team was he driving?

6 Who lost the 1968 Belgian Grand Prix when he ran out of fuel?

7 What make of car was he driving?

8 Which French driver was killed on his Formula One debut in the 1968 French Grand Prix?

9 For which team was he driving?

10 Who produced a stunning victory in the wet at Nürburgring in 1968?

11 Brabham swapped their Repcos for which engines in 1969?

12 Who crashed when leading the 1969 Spanish Grand Prix?

13 For which team was he driving?

14 Who went on to win?

15 Who finished second at Monaco in 1969 for Frank Williams?

16 What make of car was he driving?

17 Who was pipped by Jackie Stewart in the 1969 Italian Grand Prix?

18 Which Brabham driver won the 1969 Canadian Grand Prix?

19 Who finished second?

20 Which former world champion broke his legs in the 1969 US Grand Prix?

Answers **WORLD CHAMPIONSHIP 1964 & 1965** *(see Quiz 6)*
1 Jim Clark. **2** BRM. **3** Graham Hill. **4** John Surtees. **5** Peter Arundell. **6** Nürburgring, Monza. **7** Bob Anderson. **8** Brabham. **9** Jochen Rindt. **10** Graham Hill. **11** Jim Clark. **12** Mike Spence. **13** Jackie Stewart. **14** BRM. **15** Lotus entered the Indianapolis 500 instead. **16** Clermont-Ferrand. **17** Jim Clark. **18** Lotus. **19** Engine problems. **20** Graham Hill.

1 Which ever-unlucky driver chased Pedro Rodriguez home in the 1970 Belgian Grand Prix?

2 For which team was he driving?

3 Jochen Rindt won how many consecutive grands prix in 1970?

4 Where was the first of these?

5 Who died during this race?

6 What make of car was the driver who died driving?

7 In 1970, which Ferrari driver led the Dutch, French, British and German Grands Prix but won none of them?

8 Where did he make his breakthrough that year?

9 Name his team-mate who chased him home.

10 Ferrari ended the season with a one-two in which grand prix?

11 Who was the new Brabham team leader in 1971?

12 Which Swede was signed to lead March's attack in 1971?

13 At which circuit did Jackie Stewart give Tyrrell its first victory?

14 In 1971, which BRM driver was the meat in a Ferrari sandwich when he came second at Zandvoort?

15 Who won the 1971 French Grand Prix for Tyrrell?

16 Which future world champion made his debut in the 1971 Austrian Grand Prix?

17 What make of car was he driving?

18 Peter Gethin won the 1971 Italian Grand Prix. Name the other BRM driver in the points that day.

19 Who scored his first grand prix win at Watkins Glen in 1971?

20 For which team was he driving?

Answers WORLD CHAMPIONSHIP 1974 & 1975 *(see Quiz 11)*

1 Lotus. *2* Denny Hulme. *3* Carlos Reutemann. *4* Emerson Fittipaldi. *5* Jean-Pierre Beltoise. *6* Jarama. *7* Ronnie Peterson. *8* Dijon-Prenois. *9* Watkins Glen. *10* Brabham (Carlos Reutemann and Carlos Pace). *11* Hesketh. *12* Brazilian. *13* Brabham. *14* Montjuich Park (five spectators were killed). *15* A Hill. *16* Niki Lauda. *17* Heavy rain. *18* Emerson Fittipaldi. *19* Clay Regazzoni. *20* Niki Lauda.

1   Who was the new Lotus sponsor in 1972?

2   What colours did the team paint its cars?

3   Which team entered as many as five cars in some grands prix in 1972?

4   Who won the 1972 season's opening race in Buenos Aires?

5   Lotus won the 1972 Belgian Grand Prix. Who was the winning driver?

6   Jackie Stewart won the 1972 French Grand Prix at which circuit?

7   Which Ferrari driver led the 1972 British Grand Prix from pole but retired?

8   Name the former motorcycle champion who finished second at Monza in 1972?

9   For which team was he driving?

10 Which American driver finished second for McLaren in the 1972 Canadian Grand Prix?

11 Clay Regazzoni left Ferrari for which team in 1973?

12 Which former world champion fielded his own team for the first time in 1973?

13 Who set the 1973 season rolling by winning the opening race in Argentina?

14 Who won for Tyrrell in South Africa in 1973?

15 During that race, who had to be rescued from his flaming car?

16 Who helped him?

17 Which track broke up under the cars in 1973?

18 In 1973, at which circuit did Ronnie Peterson finally score his first grand prix win?

19 What car was he driving?

20 Which McLaren driver won the 1973 British Grand Prix at Silverstone?

Answers **WORLD CHAMPIONSHIP 1976 & 1977** *(see Quiz 12)*

1 Brabham. **2** James Hunt. **3** Ferrari. **4** It was a six-wheeler. **5** Tyrrell. **6** James Hunt. **7** Guy
Edwards, Harald Ertl, Brett Lunger and Arturo Merzario. **8** Jody Scheckter. **9** Lotus. **10** Third.
11 Tyrrell. **12** Ronnie Peterson. **13** Kyalami. **14** Tom Pryce. **15** Shadow. **16** Mario Andretti.
17 Jody Scheckter's. **18** John Watson. **19** Brabham. **20** James Hunt.

1   Which team did Emerson Fittipaldi quit in 1974 to join McLaren?
2   Name his team-mate who won the season's opening race in Argentina.
3   Which local hero led that race until he ran out of fuel?
4   A local hero did win the 1974 Brazilian Grand Prix. Who was he?
5   Who finished second for BRM in the 1974 South African Grand Prix?
6   When Ferrari's Niki Lauda and Clay Regazzoni finished one-two in the 1974 Spanish Grand Prix, at which circuit were they racing?
7   Name the Lotus driver who won the 1974 Monaco Grand Prix.
8   Which circuit hosted the 1974 French Grand Prix?
9   Where was the 1974 season's closing grand prix held?
10 Which team's drivers finished one-two?
11 For which team did James Hunt finish second in the 1975 season's opening race in Argentina?
12 At which grand prix did Carlos Pace score his only win in 1975?
13 What make of car was he driving?
14 Which circuit hosted the troubled 1975 Spanish Grand Prix?
15 What make of car was Rolf Stommelen driving when he crashed out of the lead?
16 Who chased James Hunt all the way to the finish line in the 1975 Dutch Grand Prix?
17 Why was the 1975 British Grand Prix at Silverstone stopped prematurely?
18 Who was leading at the time?
19 Who gave Ferrari a home win at Monza in 1975?
20 Who wrapped up the title that day with third place?

1   Which top team swapped Ford for Alfa Romeo engines in 1976?

2   Who was signed up to replace Emerson Fittipaldi at McLaren that year?

3   Which team won the 1976 season's first three grands prix?

4   The Tyrrell P34 made its first appearance at the 1976 Spanish Grand Prix. What was unusual about it?

5   Which team repeated its 1974 result by scoring a one-two in the 1976 Swedish Grand Prix?

6   Who won the 1976 British Grand Prix but was later disqualified?

7   Name any of the four drivers who helped exticate Niki Lauda from his burning Ferrari in the 1976 German Grand Prix.

8   Which Tyrrell driver made James Hunt work hard for his win in the 1976 US Grand Prix?

9   Mario Andretti won the 1976 season's closing race, the Japanese Grand Prix, for which team?

10   What finishing position in this race was enough to make James Hunt champion?

11   From which team did Jody Scheckter join Wolf in 1977?

12   Who replaced him there?

13   At which circuit did Niki Lauda score his first win since his 1976 accident?

14   Which driver was killed during this race?

15   For what team was he driving when he was killed?

16   Who won the 1977 US West Grand Prix at Long Beach for Lotus?

17   Whose puncture let him through to win?

18   Who ran out of fuel on the final lap of the 1977 French Grand Prix to hand victory to Mario Andretti?

19   For which team was he driving?

20   Who won the second and final grand prix at Fuji?

Answers *WORLD CHMAPIONSHIP 1972 & 1973* (see Quiz 10)

1 John Player. **2** Black and gold. **3** BRM. **4** Jackie Stewart. **5** Emerson Fittipaldi. **6** Clermont-Ferrand. **7** Jacky Ickx. **8** Mike Hailwood. **9** Surtees. **10** Peter Revson. **11** BRM. **12** Graham Hill. **13** Emerson Fittipaldi. **14** Jackie Stewart. **15** Clay Regazzoni. **16** Mike Hailwood. **17** Zolder. **18** Paul Ricard. **19** A Lotus. **20** Peter Revson.

1 In 1978, who was the driver for the new Arrows team?

2 Who would have been its driver if he hadn't been diagnosed as having cancer?

3 Name this driver's former team-mate who won the 1978 season's opening race in Argentina.

4 Who won the 1978 South African Grand Prix for Lotus?

5 Who won the 1978 British Grand Prix at Brands Hatch?

6 Who did he pass to take the lead?

7 Who were they lapping at the time?

8 Why were the first two finishers in the 1978 Italian Grand Prix penalized a minute?

9 Which Canadian driver won the 1978 Canadian Grand Prix for Ferrari?

10 Which circuit was hosting this race for the first time?

11 Who joined Jean-Pierre Jabouille in the Renault line-up in 1979?

12 To which team had Carlos Reutemann moved?

13 Jacques Laffite dominated the 1979 South American grands prix for which team?

14 Name his team-mate.

15 Who won the 1979 Belgian Grand Prix for Ferrari?

16 Name one of the two drivers fighting over second place in the closing laps of the 1979 French Grand Prix.

17 At which circuit was this?

18 In 1979, Alan Jones scored three consecutive wins for which team?

19 What part of Gilles Villeneuve's Ferrari blew to cost him the lead of the 1979 Dutch Grand Prix?

20 Who claimed the 1979 world championship title for Ferrari at Monza?

1 In 1980, which famous marque returned in its own right?

2 Which two teams merged?

3 Who won the 1980 season's opener in Argentina for Williams?

4 Which Lotus driver finished second behind René Arnoux in Brazil?

5 Name the Brazilian who scored his first win at Long Beach in 1980?

6 For which team was he racing?

7 Carlos Reutemann won the 1980 Monaco Grand Prix for which team?

8 Which driver crashed fatally in testing at Hockenheim in 1980?

9 Which circuit hosted the 1980 Italian Grand Prix for the only time?

10 Who lost the 1980 Canadian Grand Prix because of a jump start penalty?

11 In 1981, which team was the first to follow Renault down the turbo route?

12 Which team scored a one-two in the opening race of 1981 at Long Beach?

13 Who won the 1981 Argentinian Grand Prix for Brabham?

14 In 1981, the San Marino Grand Prix was held for the first time. At which circuit was this?

15 What was the nationality of the winning driver?

16 Name the French Ferrari driver who led the 1981 Belgian Grand Prix.

17 Name his team-mate who won next time out at Monaco.

18 Which French driver scored his first win in the 1981 French Grand Prix?

19 For which team was he driving?

20 Which French driver won the 1981 Austrian Grand Prix for Ligier?

Answers *WORLD CHAMPIONSHIP 1984 AND 1985* (see Quiz 16)
1 Patrick Tambay and Derek Warwick. *2* Stefan Bellof and Martin Brundle. *3* Michele Alboreto. *4* Ayrton Senna. *5* Nelson Piquet. *6* Nigel Mansell. *7* Martin Brundle. *8* Their cars had lead balls in the water tanks, which was adjudged to be moveable ballast. *9* Dallas. *10* Keke Rosberg. *11* Nigel Mansell. *12* Renault. *13* René Arnoux. *14* Stefan Johansson. *15* Ayrton Senna. *16* Lotus. *17* Alain Prost. *18* McLaren. *19* Nigel Mansell. *20* Kyalami.

1 Which Italian driver joined Nelson Piquet at Brabham in 1982?
2 Why were Nelson Piquet and Keke Rosberg disqualified from first and second in the 1982 Brazilian Grand Prix?
3 For which team was Rosberg driving?
4 Name the McLaren driver who won at Long Beach in 1982.
5 Only the grandee teams turned out at Imola that year. Who won for Ferrari?
6 Who finished a disgruntled second?
7 John Watson won the 1982 Belgian Grand Prix for which team?
8 Where was this held?
9 Which Italian novice died on the grid at the 1982 Canadian Grand Prix?
10 For which team was he driving?
11 Renault succeeded again in the 1983 French Grand Prix. Which of its drivers won?
12 Which circuit hosted the 1983 Belgian Grand Prix for the first time since 1970?
13 Name the Italian who led the race for Alfa Romeo.
14 Which Ferrari driver won the 1983 Canadian Grand Prix?
15 Name the American Renault number two who followed him home.
16 Which Brazilian boosted his title hopes by winning the 1983 Italian and European Grands Prix?
17 Which circuit hosted the second of these races?
18 Who finished third on home ground for Lotus?
19 For which team was Nelson Piquet driving when he clinched the 1983 title at Kyalami?
20 Name his team-mate who won this final race.

Answers WORLD CHAMPIONSHIP 1978 & 1979 *(see Quiz 13)*

1 Riccardo Patrese. 2 Gunnar Nilsson. 3 Mario Andretti. 4 Ronnie Peterson. 5 Carlos Reutemann. 6 Niki Lauda. 7 Bruno Giacomelli. 8 For jumping the start (Mario Andretti and Gilles Villeneuve). 9 Gilles Villeneuve. 10 Montreal. 11 René Arnoux. 12 Lotus. 13 Ligier. 14 Patrick Depailler. 15 Jody Scheckter. 16 René Arnoux, Gilles Villeneuve. 17 Dijon-Prenois. 18 Williams. 19 A tyre. 20 Jody Scheckter.

1 Who were the two new Renault drivers for 1984?

2 Whose were the two new faces at Tyrrell?

3 Which Italian Ferrari driver spun out of the lead of the 1984 Brazilian Grand Prix?

4 Who scored his first point for Toleman in the 1984 South African Grand Prix?

5 Who burned his feet on his car's oil radiator while winning in Canada?

6 Which British driver was blamed for the shunt that forced a restart in Detroit?

7 Which of his compatriots finished second for Tyrrell?

8 The Tyrrell drivers were later disqualified from the 1984 season's results for what reason?

9 Which American oil city hosted a grand prix for the one and only time in 1984?

10 Who won it?

11 Who left Lotus to join Williams in 1985?

12 With what make of turbo engine did Tyrrell finally race?

13 Which Ferrari driver lost his ride after the 1985 Brazilian Grand Prix?

14 Who replaced him for the remainder of the season?

15 Which Brazilian qualified on pole position at Imola in 1985, led, then ran out of fuel?

16 For which team was he driving?

17 Who won the 1985 title with two races still to run?

18 For which team was he driving?

19 Who finally won a grand prix when the European Grand Prix came to Brands Hatch in 1985?

20 Where did he win again before the year was out?

Answers *WORLD CHAMPIONSHIP 1980 & 1981 (see Quiz 14)*

1 Alfa Romeo. *2* Fittipaldi and Wolf. *3* Alan Jones. *4* Elio de Angelis. *5* Nelson Piquet. *6* Brabham. *7* Williams. *8* Patrick Depailler. *9* Imola. *10* Didier Pironi. *11* Ferrari. *12* Williams. *13* Nelson Piquet. *14* Imola. *15* Brazilian (Nelson Piquet). *16* Didier Pironi. *17* Gilles Villeneuve. *18* Alain Prost. *19* Renault. *20* Jacques Laffite.

1 In 1986, who was blocked from joining Lotus?

2 At whose insistence was he barred?

3 Who filled the vacant seat?

4 In 1986, at which circuit was the Spanish Grand Prix held for the first time?

5 McLaren won the third and fourth races of 1986 with which of its drivers triumphant?

6 Who died testing for Brabham at Paul Ricard?

7 Which British driver replaced him?

8 Which British driver scored his third win of 1986 at the French Grand Prix?

9 Who won the first ever Hungarian Grand Prix?

10 Who was forced by a puncture to retire when leading the 1986 Australian Grand Prix?

11 In 1987, which driver had left Benetton for Ferrari?

12 Who took his place at Benetton?

13 Which Williams driver was not allowed to start the 1987 San Marino Grand Prix?

14 Why not?

15 Who retired from the lead of the 1987 Monaco Grand Prix?

16 Why did Nigel Mansell drop from the lead at Detroit?

17 Which British driver had a huge crash in the 1987 Mexican Grand Prix?

18 For which team was he driving?

19 What was the name of the cup competed for by drivers of cars without turbo engines?

20 Who won it?

1 McLaren dominated the 1988 season. Which of its drivers won the season's first race in Brazil?

2 And the second at Imola?

3 Name either of the Ferrari drivers who finished second and third at Monaco in 1988.

4 Which British driver finished second to Ayrton Senna in the 1988 British Grand Prix?

5 For which team was he driving?

6 Which Benetton driver finished third at Silverstone?

7 Why were the Benettons disqualified from third and fourth places in the 1988 Belgian Grand Prix?

8 Who finished third for Arrows at Monza in 1988?

9 Who pushed Alain Prost hardest for victory in Portugal that year?

10 For which team was he driving?

11 In 1989, which team had swapped its Judd engines for a new deal with Renault?

12 Name either of this team's two drivers.

13 Which French driver broke his neck in a testing accident before the 1989 Brazilian Grand Prix?

14 For which team was he driving?

15 Which McLaren driver apparently broke a pre-race agreement at Imola?

16 Which Tyrrell driver finished third in Mexico in 1989?

17 Which driver was fired by Benetton after the 1989 US Grand Prix at Phoenix?

18 Name his replacement.

19 Who cartwheeled at the start of the 1989 French Grand Prix?

20 Which McLaren driver ended 1989 as champion for the third time?

Answers WORLD CHAMPIONSHIP 1991 (see Quiz 20)

1 Jean Alesi. *2* Stefano Modena. *3* Riccardo Patrese. *4* Williams. *5* Nigel Mansell. *6* Alain Prost.
7 Riccardo Patrese. *8* Second. *9* Jordan. *10* Andrea de Cesaris, Bertrand Gachot. *11* Green. *12* Riccardo Patrese. *13* Nigel Mansell. *14* Ayrton Senna (fuel pressure problems). *15* Michael Schumacher. *16* Benetton. *17* Roberto Moreno. *18* Nigel Mansell (illegal pit stop). *19* The track was flooded. *20* Ayrton Senna.

1 Who was accused by Ayrton Senna of fixing the 1989 title?

2 What was his position?

3 Who collided with Ayrton Senna and cost him his first victory on home ground in the 1990 Brazilian Grand Prix?

4 For which team was this driver racing?

5 Name his team-mate who chased Ayrton Senna home at Monaco that year?

6 Who won the Canadian Grand Prix after his team-mate was docked a minute for jumping the start?

7 This elevated which Brazilian driver to second place?

8 For which team was he driving?

9 Which two drivers banged wheels at the Peralta corner in the Mexican Grand Prix?

10 Who won the French Grand Prix after being pushed very hard by the Leyton House team?

11 At which circuit was this race held?

12 Who did Ayrton Senna take off in the Hungarian Grand Prix?

13 Who rolled at the end of the first lap of the Italian Grand Prix?

14 For which team was he driving?

15 What did he do when the red flags came out?

16 Who failed to help his Ferrari team-mate's title hopes at Estoril?

17 Which British driver suffered life-threatening injuries in a car-shattering accident at Jerez?

18 Where was the season's final race held?

19 Who won it?

20 For which team was he driving?

1 Who replaced Nigel Mansell at Ferrari?

2 Who, in turn, filled his old seat at Tyrrell?

3 Ayrton Senna led every lap of the season's first two races. Who headed him at the start of the third race, at Imola?

4 For which team was this driver racing?

5 Name his team-mate.

6 Which former world champion fell off on the parade lap at Imola?

7 Who was caught out when Stefano Modena's engine blew right in front of him at Monaco?

8 Over which position were they fighting at the time?

9 Which new team scored points for the first time in the Canadian Grand Prix?

10 Name either of its two drivers.

11 What colour was the team's livery?

12 Who won the Mexican Grand Prix?

13 Name his team-mate who won the French Grand Prix.

14 Who stopped on the last lap at Silverstone when second?

15 Who made his Formula One debut for Jordan at the Belgian Grand Prix?

16 For which team was he driving by the following race?

17 Which driver was made to move the opposite way to fill his seat at Jordan?

18 Who was disqualified from the Portuguese Grand Prix?

19 Why was the Australian Grand Prix stopped after 14 of the scheduled 81 laps?

20 Who was in front when the race was stopped?

Answers **WORLD CHAMPIONSHIP 1988 & 1989** *(see Quiz 18)*
1 Alain Prost. **2** Ayrton Senna. **3** Gerhard Berger, Michele Alboreto. **4** Nigel Mansell. **5** Williams.
6 Alessandro Nannini. **7** Fuel irregularities. **8** Eddie Cheever. **9** Ivan Capelli. **10** Leyton House.
11 Williams. **12** Thierry Boutsen or Riccardo Patrese. **13** Philippe Streiff. **14** AGS. **15** Ayrton
Senna. **16** Michele Alboreto. **17** Johnny Herbert. **18** Emanuele Pirro. **19** Mauricio Gugelmin.
20 Alain Prost.

1 Who joined Michael Schumacher at Benetton?

2 Name Jordan's two new drivers for 1992.

3 Jordan changed engines too. To what?

4 Who chased his team-mate home in the season's opening race at Kyalami?

5 Who chased the Williams drivers home in Mexico for his first podium visit?

6 Who was so exhausted after finishing third at Imola that he stayed in his car for 20 minutes after the race?

7 Which team broke Williams's winning run at Monaco?

8 Who was right on the winner's tail in the closing laps?

9 Name the Austrian who won the Canadian Grand Prix.

10 Who was the Austrian who finished fourth?

11 For which team was the fourth-placed driver racing?

12 Who had to wave his team-mate through to victory in the French Grand Prix?

13 Who did Martin Brundle beat when he finished third in the British Grand Prix?

14 Who won the Hungarian Grand Prix on the day that Nigel Mansell became champion?

15 In which position did Nigel Mansell finish in that race?

16 Who guessed wrongly and stayed out on slicks during the Belgian Grand Prix?

17 Who guessed correctly and took his first win?

18 Who did Nigel Mansell wave through into the lead at the Italian Grand Prix?

19 Who won the race?

20 Who did Ayrton Senna hit when he was trying to take the lead in Australia?

1 Nigel Mansell was absent from Formula One in 1993. In which championship was he racing?

2 Who won first time out for Williams?

3 Where was this?

4 Ayrton Senna was second, but who was third for Ligier?

5 Who finished second behind Ayrton Senna in the Brazilian Grand Prix?

6 Lotus had an unusually good race in Brazil. Which of their drivers finished fourth?

7 Who won the European Grand Prix?

8 Which Minardi driver finished sixth at Donington and also at Imola next time out?

9 Who was the only other driver to complete the same number of laps as winner Alain Prost at Imola?

10 For which team was he driving?

11 Who scored his first points in the Spanish Grand Prix?

12 Who was given a stop-go penalty at Monaco and then stalled in the pits?

13 Who finished third behind Alain Prost and Michael Schumacher at Silverstone?

14 For which team was he driving?

15 Winning the German Grand Prix took Alain Prost to a landmark number of wins. How many was it?

16 Why did Damon Hill lose the lead in that race?

17 Why did Alain Prost have to start from the rear of the grid in Hungary?

18 What did Alain Prost do on clinching the world title at Estoril?

19 Who made his first podium visit at Suzuka?

20 For which team was he driving?

Answers **WORLD CHAMPIONSHIP 1995** *(see Quiz 24)*
1 Michael Schumacher. **2** Benetton. **3** Fuel irregularities. **4** Jean Alesi. **5** Ferrari. **6** Williams.
7 Damon Hill. **8** Rubens Barrichello. **9** Eddie Irvine. **10** Speeding in the pit lane. **11** Damon Hill.
12 Michael Schumacher. **13** Michael Schumacher. **14** David Coulthard. **15** Heinz-Harald
Frentzen (third). **16** Sauber. **17** Jean Alesi. **18** Michael Schumacher. **19** Mika Hakkinen. **20** Jan
Magnussen.

1 Who replaced Ayrton Senna at McLaren?

2 For which team had he been driving in 1993?

3 Name either of this team's two new drivers.

4 What activity had become a prerequisite part of every driver's race?

5 Which circuit hosted the season's opening race?

6 Who won the season's second race at the TI Circuit?

7 Who survived a massive accident in practice for the San Marino Grand Prix?

8 For which team was he driving?

9 Who won the Spanish Grand Prix to restore morale at Williams?

10 Why was Michael Schumacher slowed in this race?

11 Which British driver was third for Tyrrell?

12 Which British driver scored his first points in the Canadian Grand Prix?

13 For which team was he driving?

14 Who was blamed for triggering a first-corner shunt that affected almost half the field in the German Grand Prix?

15 Which team avoided the trouble to break its 58-race losing streak?

16 Who was its winning driver?

17 Which team claimed second and third places that day?

18 Who finished on the podium for the first time in the Hungarian Grand Prix?

19 Who was disqualified from the Belgian Grand Prix because the plank on the bottom of his car was too worn away?

20 How many points clear of Damon Hill was Michael Schumacher when they headed to the Adelaide finale?

Answers WORLD CHAMPIONSHIP 1992 *(see Quiz 21)*

1 Martin Brundle. **2** Mauricio Gugelmin and Stefano Modena. **3** Yamaha. **4** Riccardo Patrese (his team-mate was Nigel Mansell). **5** Michael Schumacher (third). **6** Ayrton Senna. **7** McLaren (Ayrton Senna). **8** Nigel Mansell. **9** Gerhard Berger. **10** Karl Wendlinger. **11** March. **12** Riccardo Patrese. **13** Michael Schumacher. **14** Ayrton Senna. **15** Second. **16** Ayrton Senna. **17** Michael Schumacher. **18** Riccardo Patrese (his team-mate). **19** Ayrton Senna. **20** Nigel Mansell.

1   Who won the opening race of 1995 at Interlagos?

2   For which team was he driving?

3   Why were he and second-placed David Coulthard temporarily disqualified?

4   In Argentina, who triggered an accident that forced a restart and yet went on to finish second?

5   For which team was he driving?

6   Which team won on the return to Imola one year on from the death of Ayrton Senna?

7   Who fell from second to fourth place on the last lap of the Spanish Grand Prix?

8   Who finished second in the Canadian Grand Prix behind Jean Alesi?

9   Who finished third for the same team?

10   Why was David Coulthard given a stop-go penalty at the British Grand Prix?

11   Who was the focus of the crowd's vilification at Hockenheim?

12   Who was their hero?

13   Who won the German Grand Prix?

14   Who dominated the Belgian Grand Prix until his gearbox failed?

15   Who reached the podium for the first time at the Italian Grand Prix?

16   For which team was he driving?

17   Who starred in the damp European Grand Prix at the Nürburgring?

18   Who wrapped up the title with two races still to run?

19   Who bounced back from an appendectomy to finish second at Suzuka?

20   Who had stood in for him at the Pacific Grand Prix?

1 David Coulthard moved to which team for 1996?

2 Who replaced him at Williams?

3 Who were the two new drivers at Ferrari?

4 Which team employed the outgoing Ferrari drivers?

5 Which race was at the start of the calendar for the first time?

6 The second race was in Brazil. Who won it?

7 Who won the third race, in Argentina?

8 Who chased Jacques Villeneuve all the way to the line at the Nürburgring?

9 Who finished third in the rain-hit Monaco Grand Prix?

10 For which team was he driving?

11 Michael Schumacher won the Spanish Grand Prix. Which Benetton driver was second?

12 Who failed to start the French Grand Prix after his car broke down on the parade lap?

13 Who offered to resign as a result of this?

14 Who won the British Grand Prix?

15 Which Benetton driver was second?

16 Who finished third for McLaren?

17 Which leading team almost had both of its drivers in the pits for tyres at the same time in the Belgian Grand Prix?

18 Who won that race despite having a huge shunt in untimed practice?

19 Who crashed out of the lead in the Italian Grand Prix?

20 Who ended the year as runner-up to Damon Hill?

Answers WORLD CHAMPIONSHIP 1998 *(see Quiz 27)*

1 Jordan. 2 Ralf Schumacher. 3 David Coulthard. 4 Heinz-Harald Frentzen. 5 Mika Hakkinen.
6 Michael Schumacher. 7 David Coulthard. 8 X-wings. 9 Alexander Wurz. 10 Jarno Trulli's.
11 Michael Schumacher. 12 Damon Hill. 13 Heinz-Harald Frentzen. 14 Jos Verstappen. 15 Mika
Hakkinen. 16 Purple. 17 David Coulthard. 18 The German Grand Prix – he was third. 19 He
crashed into the back of David Coulthard. 20 The Italian Grand Prix – Michael was first and Ralf
third.

1 Whose 1997 season began with a failure to start the opening race in Melbourne?

2 For which team was he driving?

3 Who had qualified on pole position, but was taken off at the first corner?

4 Who took him off?

5 Who lost second place in the closing laps when a brake disc exploded?

6 Which team failed to go out to practice in Brazil and subsequently folded?

7 Who were its two unfortunate drivers?

8 Who pressed Heinz-Harald Frentzen at Imola?

9 What were the weather conditions during the Monaco Grand Prix?

10 Whose fluffed pit stop cost him victory in the Canadian Grand Prix?

11 Who slid off in the wet at Magny-Cours but hung on to win?

12 Which Benetton driver finished second in the British Grand Prix?

13 Who won the race?

14 Who was the only driver to head Gerhard Berger during the German Grand Prix?

15 From whom did Jacques Villeneuve steal victory on the final lap of the Hungarian Grand Prix?

16 Which Sauber driver finished third?

17 At which grand prix was the safety car used to lead the cars away at the start for the first time?

18 Who overcame Jean Alesi to win the Italian Grand Prix?

19 The Austrian Grand Prix was back on the calendar. What is the name of the revised track on which the race was held?

20 Which novice led the first half of the race for Prost?

Answers **WORLD CHAMPIONSHIP 1999** *(see Quiz 28)*

1 Rubens Barrichello. **2** His car caught fire at the first start. **3** Stephane Sarrazin. **4** He crashed. **5** Michael Schumacher. **6** Mika Salo. **7** Mirabeau. **8** Jacques Villeneuve. **9** David Coulthard and Eddie Irvine. **10** Giancarlo Fisichella. **11** Benetton. **12** Stewart. **13** David Coulthard. **14** Damon Hill. **15** David Coulthard and Mika Hakkinen. **16** He crashed after suffering a puncture. **17** BAR. **18** Heinz-Harald Frentzen. **19** Michael Schumacher. **20** Ferrari's.

1   To which team did Damon Hill transfer for 1998?

2   Who was his team-mate?

3   Who slowed to allow his team-mate through to win in the Australian Grand Prix?

4   Who was the third driver on the podium?

5   Who stormed to victory in the Brazilian Grand Prix?

6   Who was the third driver on the podium this time?

7   Who quietened the *tifosi* by heading the Ferraris home at the San Marino Grand Prix?

8   What feature became prevalent at the same meeting?

9   Which relative novice refused to be intimidated by Michael Schumacher at Monaco?

10   Whose Prost collided with Jean Alesi's Sauber at both starts in Canada?

11   Who had a stop-go penalty in Canada and still won?

12   Who did he accuse of dangerous tactics?

13   Who did he himself take out of the race?

14   From the French Grand Prix, who replaced Jan Magnussen in the Stewart team?

15   Who thought he would win the British Grand Prix because Michael Schumacher would be disqualified?

16   What colour did Jacques Villeneuve dye his hair before the Austrian Grand Prix?

17   Who pulled into the pits for a new nose on the opening lap in Austria and yet fought through to second place?

18   In which grand prix did Jacques Villeneuve make his first podium appearance of 1998?

19   Why did Michael Schumacher retire from the lead of the Belgian Grand Prix?

20   At which grand prix were both Schumachers on the podium?

Answers WORLD CHAMPIONSHIP 1996 *(see Quiz 25)*

1 McLaren. *2* Jacques Villeneuve. *3* Michael Schumacher and Eddie Irvine. *4* Benetton (Jean Alesi and Gerhard Berger). *5* The Australian Grand Prix. *6* Damon Hill. *7* Damon Hill. *8* Michael Schumacher. *9* Johnny Herbert. *10* Sauber. *11* Jean Alesi. *12* Michael Schumacher. *13* Jean Todt. *14* Jacques Villeneuve. *15* Gerhard Berger. *16* Mika Hakkinen. *17* Williams. *18* Michael Schumacher. *19* Damon Hill. *20* Jacques Villeneuve.

1   Which Stewart driver started from the back of the grid at the Australian Grand Prix?

2   Why?

3   Who replaced the injured Luca Badoer at Minardi for the Brazilian Grand Prix?

4   How did he fare in the race?

5   Who raced to victory in the San Marino Grand Prix?

6   Who drove the second BAR entry at Imola?

7   At which corner did Mika Hakkinen run up an escape road at Monaco?

8   Who kept Michael Schumacher in his wake by running third early in the Spanish Grand Prix?

9   Which two British drivers clashed over second place in the Canadian Grand Prix?

10   Who moved up to second with four laps to go?

11   For which team was he driving?

12   Which team claimed pole for the French Grand Prix?

13   Name the McLaren driver who retired from the lead?

14   Which British driver led the British Grand Prix for one lap?

15   Name the two team-mates who clashed at the second corner of the Austrian Grand Prix.

16   Why did Mika Hakkinen retire from the German Grand Prix?

17   Which team had both of its cars destroyed in qualifying for the Belgian Grand Prix?

18   Who inherited victory in the Italian Grand Prix?

19   Who qualified on pole for the Malaysian Grand Prix?

20   Which team's cars were temporarily disqualified after the Malaysian Grand Prix?

Answers WORLD CHAMPIONSHIP 1997 *(see Quiz 26)*

1 Damon Hill. 2 Arrows. 3 Jacques Villeneuve. 4 Eddie Irvine. 5 Heinz-Harald Frentzen. 6 Lola
7 Ricardo Rosset and Vincenzo Sospiri. 8 Michael Schumacher. 9 Wet. 10 David Coulthard.
11 Michael Schumacher. 12 Jean Alesi. 13 Jacques Villeneuve. 14 Giancarlo Fisichella.
15 Damon Hill. 16 Johnny Herbert. 17 Belgian. 18 David Coulthard. 19 The A1-Ring. 20 Jarno
Trulli.

1 Name the British marque that came third in the 1958 Constructors' Cup.

2 With what make of engines?

3 Which team was second for the second time in 1959?

4 Which British team improved to third in 1959?

5 Where did Ferrari rank in 1960?

6 Which was the best-placed British marque behind Ferrari in 1961?

7 Which German marque was best of the rest?

8 British marques filled the top four places in 1962. Which one was fourth?

9 Who scored their points?

10 Which British marque slipped to second behind Lotus in 1963?

11 Where did Lotus rank in 1964?

12 Which marque scored most points, but was placed second in 1965?

13 Which marque finished runner-up to Brabham in 1966?

14 What engines did third-placed Cooper use?

15 To which engines did Lotus swap during 1967?

16 Which American-owned marque was placed seventh in 1967?

17 Name the French marque that was third overall in 1968?

18 Who scored most of their points?

19 What make of engines did the 1969 champions use?

20 Which new British marque ranked third in 1970?

Answers THE CONSTRUCTORS' CUP 3 *(see Quiz 31)*
1 Williams. 2 Ford Cosworth DFVs. 3 Ligier. 4 McLaren. 5 Renault. 6 Toleman. 7 Hart. 8 TAG. Porsche. 9 Renault. 10 Renault, Ligier and Tyrrell. 11 Second. 12 McLaren. 13 Second. 14 Ford. 15 Thierry Boutsen and Teo Fabi. 16 Alain Prost and Ayrton Senna. 17 Ferrari. 18 Ferrari. 19 Benetton. 20 Benetton.

1 Which new team entered by a former world champion scored its first points in 1970?

2 Which resurgent British marque was second in 1971?

3 March ranked equal third with Ferrari in 1971. Who scored all their points?

4 Where did Tyrrell rank in 1972?

5 Which team came third?

6 Where did Tyrrell rank in 1973?

7 Which team came third?

8 Which team finished second behind McLaren in 1974?

9 Who scored the bulk of McLaren's points?

10 In 1975, which team won its first title since 1964?

11 Who was its main points scorer?

12 Which French marque made its debut in 1976?

13 Which American marque achieved its one and only win?

14 Which French marque made its debut in 1977?

15 In 1977, which team made it three titles in a row?

16 Which British marque came third in 1978?

17 What engines did its cars use?

18 How did Ligier rank overall in 1979?

19 Who was its chief points scorer?

20 Who scored the bulk of Williams's points in 1980?

Answers **THE CONSTRUCTORS' CUP 4** *(see Quiz 32)*

1 Ford (Benetton). 2 Fifth. 3 Tyrrell. 4 McLaren. 5 Benetton. 6 Alain Prost. 7 McLaren.
8 Michael Schumacher. 9 Damon Hill, David Coulthard and Nigel Mansell. 10 Mercedes.
11 Renault. 12 Ferrari. 13 Benetton. 14 Second. 15 Michael Schumacher. 16 Michael
Schumacher. 17 Williams. 18 Mugen Honda. 19 Playlife 20 Petronas.

LEVEL 2

1   Which team won the 1981 Constructors' Cup?
2   With what engines?
3   Which French marque won two rounds and yet ended up fourth overall?
4   Which British marque came second in 1982?
5   Which French marque came third?
6   Name the British marque that scored its first points in 1983.
7   With what engines?
8   What engines did champions McLaren use in 1984?
9   What engines did Lotus use to come third?
10 In 1985, which three other teams used the same engines as Lotus?
11 Where did Ferrari finish?
12 Alain Prost thwarted the Williams drivers to become champion for which team in 1986?
13 Where did his team end up in the Constructors' Cup?
14 Benetton progressed to fifth in the Constructors' Cup in 1987 using which engines?
15 Who were Benetton's two drivers.
16 Name McLaren's two drivers for 1988.
17 Which team ended up a distant second behind McLaren?
18 Which team did Williams overhaul to be ranked second in 1989?
19 Which team was fourth?
20 Which team moved past Williams in the final two races to finish third in 1990?

Answers THE CONSTRUCTORS' CUP 1 *(see Quiz 29)*

1 Cooper. *2* Climax. *3* Ferrari. *4* BRM. *5* Third. *6* Lotus (second). *7* Porsche. *8* Lola. *9* John Surtees. *10* BRM. *11* Third. *12* BRM. *13* Ferrari. *14* Maserati. *15* Ford Cosworth DFV. *16* Eagle. *17* Matra. *18* Jackie Stewart. *19* Ford (Matra). *20* March.

1 What engines did the third-placed team use in 1990?

2 Where did newcomers Jordan finish in 1991?

3 Which long-standing British team did they beat by a point?

4 Which team finished second in 1992?

5 Which team finished third in 1992?

6 Who was the Williams team's top scorer in 1993?

7 Which team finished the year second overall?

8 Who was Benetton's top-scoring world champion in 1994?

9 Which drivers scored Williams's points in 1994?

10 What engine did McLaren use to come fourth in 1995?

11 What engine did champions Benetton use?

12 Which team grabbed second place at the final round in 1996?

13 Which team did they overhaul?

14 Where did Ferrari finish in 1997?

15 Who was Ferrari's top points scorer?

16 Who led Ferrari's challenge in 1998?

17 Which team grabbed third place in the final round?

18 What engine did the Jordans use in 1999?

19 What was the name given to the Mecachrome engines used by Benetton?

20 What was the name given to the Ferrari engines used by Sauber?

Answers *THE CONSTRUCTORS' CUP 2 (see Quiz 30)*

1 Surtees. **2** BRM. **3** Ronnie Peterson. **4** Second. **5** McLaren. **6** Second. **7** McLaren. **8** Ferrari. **9** Emerson Fittipaldi. **10** Ferrari. **11** Niki Lauda. **12** Ligier. **13** Penske (Austrian Grand Prix). **14** Renault. **15** Ferrari. **16** Brabham. **17** Alfa Romeo. **18** Third. **19** Jacques Laffite. **20** Alan Jones.

1 What is the full name of the team for which AGS is the acronym?

2 Who founded the team?

3 Which Italian driver raced for the team for three years?

4 In 1980, which grand prix did Bruno Giacomelli lead for Alfa Romeo, during the team's second spell in Formula One?

5 Another driver led the 1983 Belgian Grand Prix for the marque. Who was he?

6 Name either of the drivers who raced for Alfa Romeo in 1984 and 1985.

7 Who were the two main players in the group that founded Arrows?

8 Who was the sponsor, the "A" of Arrows?

9 Who was the first driver to race for the German ATS team in 1977?

10 What chassis did the team use?

11 In which country was the original ATS team based?

12 Which designer did the team tempt away from Ferrari?

13 Who founded British American Racing?

14 Who was his number two driver in 1999?

15 Who stood in because of injury for three races?

16 Who built the chassis entered by Beatrice on its arrival in 1986?

17 Which American Indycar entrant was the force behind the team?

18 Name the Italian who managed Benetton through the early 1990s.

19 Who took over from him?

20 In which year did Benetton win its only Constructors' Cup to date?

Answers *THE TEAMS 3* (see Quiz 35)

1 Weslake. *2* US sportscars. *3* Toyota. *4* Building caravans. *5* Rikky von Opel. *6* Marc Surer.
7 Theodore. *8* Jose Froilan Gonzalez. *9* Silverstone. *10* 1961. *11* Harvey Postlethwaite.
12 John Barnard. *13* Rory Byrne. *14* Ingo Hoffman. *15* Keke Rosberg. *16* Olivier Grouillard.
17 Fomet. *18* Arrows. *19* Aguri Suzuki. *20* Red and white.

1 Which French driver raced for Benetton in 1997.

2 Name Benetton's drivers for 1998 and 1999.

3 Who was the second Brabham driver to become world champion?

4 Who was the third Brabham driver to do so?

5 In what year was that?

6 Which British world champion made his Formula One debut with Brabham?

7 Who was BRM's designer from 1962 to 1969?.

8 What marque had BRM founder Raymond Mays previously created?

9 Who took over BRM from the original owner?

10 Who later took it over from him?

11 Which driver achieved Connaught's highest ever finish, third in the 1956 Italian Grand Prix?

12 Who was the last driver to win a grand prix in a Cooper?

13 In which race was that?

14 What engine powered him to this success?

15 What was the name of the Brazilian state sugar company that gave its name to the Fittipaldi team in the mid 1970s?

16 What was the main colour of the Fittipaldi livery when the team arrived in Formula One?

17 To what colour did this change in 1977?

18 No longer in Formula One, for what racing category does Dallara build the most cars?

19 In which American series do Dallara chassis race?

20 In which year did Eagle hit the grand prix circus?

Answers THE TEAMS 4 (see Quiz 36)

1 Ken Wharton. *2* Robert Manzon, Maurice Trintignant. *3* Simca. *4* Harvey Postlethwaite.
5 Brett Lunger. *6* Anthony "Bubbles" Horsley. *7* 1973. *8* Shadow. *9* Lola. *10* Tony Brise.
11 Lola. *12* John Surtees. *13* Monza. *14* Frank Williams. *15* Howden Ganley. *16* Yamaha.
17 Gary Anderson. *18* Mike Gascoyne. *19* Rubens Barrichello in the 1994 Belgian Grand Prix.
20 Kojima.

1   Which make of engine did Eagle use through most of its spell in Formula One?

2   In what category of racing did Dan Gurney's Eagles shine in the late 1980s?

3   With which manufacturer was he closely involved in this period?

4   The Eifelland team ran a modified March in 1972. What was Eifelland's core business?

5   Who was the first driver to race an Ensign in Formula One?

6   The marque's best result was fourth in the 1981 Brazilian Grand Prix. Name the driver.

7   With which marque did Ensign merge in 1982?

8   Who gave Ferrari its first Formula One victory in 1951?

9   Where did he achieve this?

10   In which year did Ferrari first win the Constructors' Cup?

11   Who was the first British designer to lead the Ferrari design team?

12   Name the British designer who arrived at Ferrari in 1987 and later insisted on working from a base in England.

13   Who is currently in charge of the design team?

14   Name the driver who appeared for Fittipaldi once, alongside Emerson Fittipaldi in 1976.

15   Who was Emerson Fittipaldi's regular team-mate in 1980?

16   Who was the main driver for Fondmetal in 1991?

17   What abbreviation was used for the team's chassis that year?

18   Footwork had a spell in charge of which team from 1991 to 1993?

19   Name the Japanese driver who raced for the team in 1992 and 1993.

20   What colour were their cars?

Answers THE TEAMS 1 *(see Quiz 33)*

1 Automobiles Gonfaronaises Sportive. *2* Henri Julien. *3* Gabriele Tarquini. *4* US. *5* Andrea de Cesaris. *6* Eddie Cheever, Riccardo Patrese. *7* Jackie Oliver and Alan Rees. *8* Franco Ambrosio. *9* Jean-Pierre Jarier. *10* Penske. *11* Italy. *12* Carlo Chiti. *13* Craig Pollock. *14* Ricardo Zonta. *15* Mika Salo. *16* Lola. *17* Carl Haas. *18* Flavio Briatore. *19* David Richards. *20* 1995.

1 Who was Frazer Nash's most successful driver?

2 Name either of the two French drivers who raced for Gordini between 1950 and 1952.

3 With which French manufacturer was Gordini linked?

4 Who was the designer for the Hesketh team?

5 Which American drove the team's second car in 1975?

6 Who took over the running of the team after Lord Hesketh quit at the end of 1975?

7 In which year did the Hill team hit the grids?

8 What chassis did the team use in its first year?

9 What chassis did the team use in its second year?

10 Who was Graham Hill's protégé?

11 Which British marque built Honda's RA300 chassis in 1967?

12 Which British driver raced this to its only win?

13 Where did he do this?

14 Who entered his cars as Iso Marlboros in 1973 and 1974?

15 Name the team's lead driver for 1973.

16 Jordan's second season was a weak one. What engines were the team using?

17 Who designed the chassis?

18 Which designer took over when Anderson left for Stewart in 1998?

19 Who was the first driver to lead a grand prix for Jordan?

20 With which Japanese chassis did Masahiro Hasemi set the fastest lap in the 1976 Japanese Grand Prix?

Answers *THE TEAMS 2* (see Quiz 34)

1 Jean Alesi. **2** Giancarlo Fisichella and Alexander Wurz. **3** Denny Hulme. **4** Nelson Piquet. **5** 1981. **6** Damon Hill. **7** Tony Rudd. **8** ERA. **9** Alfred Owen. **10** Louis Stanley. **11** Ron Flockhart. **12** Pedro Rodriguez. **13** The 1967 South African Grand Prix. **14** A Maserati. **15** Copersucar. **16** Silver. **17** Yellow. **18** Formula Three. **19** The Indy Racing League. **20** 1966.

Quiz 37 *THE TEAMS 5*

 LEVEL 2

1 Who designed the Lancia D50?
2 In what branch of motor sport did Gerard Larrousse begin his competitive career?
3 What was the name of Larrousse's title sponsor in 1992?
4 Which French driver raced for the team in 1993 and 1994?
5 What was the best result for a Leyton House chassis?
6 Name the driver.
7 In which year did Ligier win the opening two races of the season?
8 Name the team's number two driver who won that year's Spanish Grand Prix.
9 Name the finance company that brought Lola into Formula One in 1962.
10 Which Indycar team owner ran Lola chassis in Formula One in 1985/86?
11 Which former sportscar ace ran a Lola chassis from 1987 to 1991?
12 Who was Emerson Fittipaldi's team-mate at Lotus in 1973?
13 Who was Nigel Mansell's team-mate in 1982?
14 Which was Lotus's final year in Formula One?
15 Who was its lead driver that year?
16 Name March's first designer.
17 Who scored half a point for March in 1975?
18 Who gave March its final Formula One win?
19 Which successful French single-seater manufacturer had a shot at Formula One in 1978?
20 Name the team's driver.

Answers *THE TEAMS 7* (see Quiz 39)

1 Parnelli Jones. 2 Mario Andretti. 3 1974. 4 Mark Donohue. 5 True. 6 Jo Bonnier. 7 Loic Bigois. 8 Shinji Nakano. 9 Brabham. 10 Kenneth Acheson, Eliseo Salazar. 11 Jean-Pierre Jabouille. 12 Yellow, black and white. 13 Alain Prost. 14 Michel Tetu. 15 Derek Warwick. 16 Hans-Gunther Schmid. 17 ATS. 18 Gustav Brunner. 19 Peter Sauber. 20 Sportscar racing.

1 Which family took control of Maserati in the late 1930s?

2 Who gave Maserati its first win in 1953?

3 Who gave Matra its first win in 1968?

4 Who led that year's Monaco Grand Prix for Matra?

5 In which year did the first McLaren chassis appear in Formula One?

6 Who drove it?

7 Who was the next driver to race a McLaren?

8 Who designed the landmark McLaren MP4?

9 Who is the ex-Williams designer who helped them to the 1998 title?

10 In which grand prix in 1999 did McLaren's cars run first and second throughout, except for one lap during the pitstop sequence?

11 Name the designer of the Mercedes W196.

12 What colour was the Mercedes Formula One livery?

13 Minardi pulled off a coup by using what engine in 1991?

14 Who became the team's main shareholder in the late 1990s?

15 What nationality was Peter Monteverdi?

16 Which team did he take over in 1990?

17 What team was formed by the Maserati brothers after the Second World War?

18 Who drove Osella to its best-ever result, fourth in the 1982 San Marino Grand Prix?

19 Which team took over Osella in 1990?

20 Who was the Pacific number two in its debut season, 1994?

Answers THE TEAMS 8 *(see Quiz 40)*

1 Mercedes. **2** Jean Alesi. **3** Don Nicols. **4** Black. **5** Jean-Pierre Jarier. **6** Andrea Montermini. **7** Jean-Marc Gounon. **8** Jos Verstappen. **9** John Wickham. **10** Gordon Coppuck. **11** Ford. **12** Jos Verstappen. **13** Johnny Herbert. **14** Alan Jenkins. **15** Edenbridge, Kent. **16** Rolf Stommelen. **17** Matchbox. **18** John Watson. **19** Vittorio Brambilla. **20** Louis Rosier.

1 Which legendary Indycar racer founded the Parnelli team?

2 Who drove the team's car between 1974 and 1976?

3 In which year did Penske arrive in Formula One?

4 Who was the driver until his death in the team's second season?

5 True or false: Porsche entered Formula One with a Formula Two class car?

6 Who was Dan Gurney's team-mate at Porsche in 1961 and 1962?

7 Name the French designer who was responsible for the Prost AP01.

8 Who was Olivier Panis's team-mate at Prost in 1997?

9 What chassis did RAM enter on its Formula One debut in 1976?

10 Name either of the drivers who raced for RAM in 1983, its first season as a constructor.

11 Who was Renault's driver when they entered Formula One in 1977?

12 What were the three colours on the livery of every Formula One Renault?

13 Who became the team's number one in 1981?

14 Who designed all of the Renaults during the 1980s?

15 Which British driver joined the team in 1984?

16 Name the founder of the Rial marque.

17 What team had this German previously entered in Formula One?

18 Who designed his first chassis in 1988?

19 Name the boss of Sauber?

20 In which branch of motor racing had Sauber made its name?

Answers THE TEAMS 5 *(see Quiz 37)*

1 Vittorio Jano. *2* Rallying. *3* Venturi. *4* Erik Comas. *5* Second place in the 1990 French Grand Prix. *6* Ivan Capelli. *7* 1979. *8* Patrick Depailler. *9* Yeoman Credit. *10* Carl Haas. *11* Gerard Larrousse. *12* Ronnie Peterson. *13* Elio de Angelis. *14* 1994. *15* Johnny Herbert. *16* Robin Herd. *17* Lella Lombardi (Spanish Grand Prix). *18* Ronnie Peterson (1976). *19* Martini. *20* René Arnoux.

1 With which manufacturer was Sauber linked prior to entering Formula One?

2 Who quit Sauber after a troubled 1999 season?

3 Name the founder of the Shadow team.

4 What colour were its cars from 1973 to 1975?

5 Which French driver drove for the team during this period?

6 Who drove the second Simtek in 1994 after Roland Ratzenberger's death?

7 Which French driver took over later in the year?

8 Who was the Simtek team leader in 1995?

9 Who was Spirit's team manager?

10 Who was Spirit's designer?

11 With which motor manufacturer was Stewart tied up from its inception?

12 Who replaced Jan Magnussen at Stewart midway through 1998?

13 Who replaced him as the team's number two for 1999?

14 Which designer quit the team before the start of the 1999 season?

15 Where was the Surtees team headquarters?

16 Who was the first driver to race for Surtees after John Surtees?

17 Which model car builder sponsored Surtees in 1975?

18 Who drove the car that year?

19 Who brought Beta sponsorship in 1977?

20 Who was Talbot's most successful driver in 1950?

1 From which country did Tecno originate?

2 Which drinks company sponsored the team?

3 Who was Tecno's driver on its debut in 1972?

4 Which driver had Theodore founder Teddy Yip run in Formula One in 1977 before the team built its own cars?

5 Which racing-car builder produced the first Theodore chassis?

6 With which chassis was this replaced?

7 Which industrialist was behind the Thin Wall Specials?

8 On which chassis were the Thin Wall Specials based?

9 Which current team owner was involved with the Token?

10 Name either of the two drivers who raced a Token.

11 What was Token renamed in 1975, when it was entered in non-championship races only?

12 Who designed the early Toleman chassis?

13 What engines powered the Tolemans from 1981 to 1985?

14 Which British driver was with the team from 1981 to 1983?

15 Who was his team-mate for the first season?

16 Who designed the first Tyrrell chassis?

17 Who took over from him in 1978?

18 Who was the team's first number two in 1971?

19 Name the two drivers who took over in 1974.

20 Who were Tyrrell's last two drivers?

Answers THE DRIVERS 1 (see Quiz 43)

1 European Formula Three. 2 Alain Prost. 3 Larrousse. 4 Footwork Arrows. 5 Lola. 6 1989. 7 European Formula 3000. 8 Eddie Jordan. 9 Alain Prost. 10 Prost. 11 Ligier. 12 McLaren. 13 Because he had raced Peugeot sportscars and McLaren used Peugeot engines. 14 Lotus. 15 UDT Laystall Racing Team. 16 He broke his legs. 17 Reg Parnell Racing. 18 Lola. 19 He pulled his visor off instead of just a tear-off strip. 20 He got a puncture.

1 Whose death prompted the closure of Vanwall?

2 Which was the first grand prix won by a Vanwall?

3 Name either of the drivers who shared the car.

4 Venturi Larrousse was the name given to the Larrousse team in which year?

5 Name either of the team's drivers that year.

6 What was the first year that Frank Williams entered a car bearing his own name?

7 Who was the first driver to score points in one?

8 Name the driver who gave Williams its first win.

9 At which grand prix was this?

10 Who swapped seats with Heinz-Harald Frentzen for 1999?

11 Who designed the Wolf chassis?

12 At which circuit did they make their breakthrough in 1977?

13 Who was the team manager?

14 Who were the two partners in the Wolf Williams team?

15 Which was the only year that the team ran in Formula One?

16 Name one of its three drivers?

17 Who founded the Zakspeed team?

18 Which Dutch driver joined Jonathan Palmer in the team's 1986 line-up?

19 Name the German who drove for the team in 1988 and 1989.

20 To what form of racing did Zakspeed return when it quit Formula One?

Answers *THE DRIVERS 2 (see Quiz 44)*

1 Motorcycles. **2** DW Racing Enterprises. **3** The 1976 Japanese Grand Prix. **4** Gunnar Nilsson. **5** Italian. **6** Alfa Romeo. **7** Ferrari. **8** The Indycar title. **9** Monza. **10** Mika Hakkinen. **11** Surtees. **12** Jean-Pierre Jabouille. **13** Interlagos. **14** Ligier. **15** DAMS. **16** Monaco (third in 1964). **17** Reims. **18** German. **19** He won all of the grands prix he contested. **20** The Mille Miglia.

1 What championship did Michele Alboreto win in 1980?

2 Who beat Alboreto to the 1985 world title?

3 Alboreto returned to Tyrrell in 1989 but left mid season to race for which team?

4 Which team did he move to from there?

5 With which chassis did he occasionally fail to qualify in 1993?

6 In which year did Jean Alesi make his Formula One debut?

7 What championship did he win that year?

8 For which future Formula One team owner?

9 Who was his team-mate during his first year at Ferrari in 1991?

10 For which team will Alesi race in 2000?

11 Which team offered Philippe Alliot a ride midway through 1986 when its lead driver broke his legs?

12 With which British team did Alliot have a one-off outing in 1994?

13 Why was he picked for this?

14 Cliff Allison made his Formula One debut with which team in 1958?

15 After ending his Ferrari career, with which team did Allison sign up for 1961?

16 What ended his career at Spa-Francorchamps that year?

17 With which team did Chris Amon make his Formula One debut in 1963?

18 In what chassis did he make his debut?

19 Why did he lose the 1971 Italian Grand Prix?

20 Why did he lose the 1972 French Grand Prix?

---

1 What did Bob Anderson race until he was almost 30?

2 Under what team name were his cars entered throughout his Formula One career?

3 Which was the first grand prix that Mario Andretti won for Lotus?

4 Who was his team-mate in 1977?

5 At which grand prix did Andretti clinch his 1978 world title?

6 Which team did Andretti join in 1981 when he quit Lotus?

7 For which team did he pop up to take pole position at Monza in 1982?

8 What title did Andretti win in 1984?

9 At which circuit did Michael Andretti score his best result, third in 1993?

10 Who replaced him for the remainder of the season?

11 Which team did René Arnoux join at the end of his maiden Formula One season, 1978?

12 Who was his team-mate at Renault in 1979?

13 Where did Arnoux score his first grand prix win, in 1980?

14 Which French team brought Arnoux back to Formula One in 1986?

15 Of which Formula 3000 team was Arnoux a founding partner?

16 Where did Peter Arundell first stand on a Formula One podium?

17 In 1964, at which circuit did he suffer injuries in a Formula Two race that kept him out of the cockpit until 1966?

18 In which 1951 grand prix did Alberto Ascari score his first win?

19 What was notable about his title-winning 1952 season?

20 What Italian road race did Ascari win in 1954?

Answers THE TEAMS 10 *(see Quiz 42)*

1 Stuart Lewis-Evans's. *2* The 1957 British Grand Prix. *3* Tony Brooks, Stirling Moss. *4* 1992.
5 Bertrand Gachot, Ukyo Katayama. *6* 1975. *7* Jacques Laffite. *8* Clay Regazzoni. *9* The 1979
British Grand Prix. *10* Ralf Schumacher. *11* Harvey Postlethwaite. *12* Buenos Aires. *13* Peter
Warr. *14* Walter Wolf and Frank Williams. *15* 1976. *16* Jacky Ickx, Michele Leclere, Arturo
Merzario. *17* Erich Zakowski. *18* Huub Rothengatter. *19* Bernd Schneider. *20* Touring cars.

1 With which team did Richard Attwood have his first full season of Formula One in 1965?

2 Whose death opened the way for Attwood to join BRM in 1968?

3 For which manufacturer did Attwood win the 1970 Le Mans 24 Hours?

4 What chassis did Luca Badoer drive for BMS Scuderia Italia in 1993?

5 Who was his experienced team-mate that year?

6 What team brought Badoer back to Formula One in 1995?

7 Name either of the non-championship races that Giancarlo Baghetti won before making his world championship debut.

8 Which Italian team did Baghetti join after his spell at Ferrari?

9 Baghetti drove a BRM in 1964 for which team?

10 For which team did Julian Bailey race in 1988?

11 At which circuit did he score his only point in 1991?

12 Victory in which Formula Three race launched Mauro Baldi's career in 1980?

13 Which championship did Baldi win the following year?

14 After spells at Arrows and Alfa Romeo, for which team did Baldi drive in 1984?

15 For which team did Lorenzo Bandini make his Formula One debut in 1961?

16 What chassis did he race for the team?

17 Which 1966 grand prix did he lose when his throttle cable snapped?

18 Fabrizio Barbazza failed to qualify for a single 1991 grand prix for which team?

19 With which team did Barbazza bounce back in 1993 to score twice?

20 At which circuit did he suffer terrible injuries in 1995?

1 Name the American driver who now runs a successful racing school?

2 What chassis did he race on his six Formula One outings?

3 From the manufacture of what foodstuff did Paolo Barilla's family make a fortune?

4 With which works sportscar team did Barilla make his name?

5 With which Formula One team did he spend the 1990 season?

6 What racing title did Rubens Barrichello win in 1991?

7 Barrichello beat a current rival to that title. Who is he?

8 At which grand prix did Barrichello first visit the podium?

9 Who was Barrichello's team-mate for the majority of his time at Jordan?

10 In which year did Barrichello lead his home grand prix?

11 Name the East German driver who raced in five German grands prix.

12 Name his son who went on to win the Le Mans 24 Hours in 1977.

13 In which 1954 grand prix did Elie Bayol score points?

14 For which works team was he driving?

15 Jean Behra finished third on his debut at which grand prix in 1952?

16 To which British team did Behra move in 1958?

17 To which Italian team did he move in 1959?

18 Why did he leave the team after three grands prix?

19 Derek Bell scored just one point in Formula One. For which team was he driving?

20 For which Italian team did Bell race in 1972?

Answers *THE DRIVERS 6* (see Quiz 48)

1 March. 2 Spanish. 3 Ralph Clarke, David Mordaunt, Jack Durlacher, Alistair Guthrie.
4 Belgian. 5 Ecurie Nationale Belge. 6 Austrian. 7 Surtees. 8 Maserati. 9 Gordini. 10 Williams.
11 The Le Mans 24 Hours. 12 McLaren. 13 Mauricio Gugelmin. 14 March. 15 Ligier. 16 Jaguar.
17 Ferrari. 18 A BRM. 19 Maserati. 20 Third (1951 Italian Grand Prix with Guiseppe Farina;
1953 Dutch Grand Prix with Jose Froilan Gonzalez).

1 What nationality was Stefan Bellof?

2 For which team was he a race winner in Formula Two in 1982?

3 In which year did Bellof win the World Endurance Championship for Porsche?

4 Who was Bellof's most frequent sportscar partner?

5 Which championship did Jean-Pierre Beltoise win in 1968?

6 He was second that same year for Matra in which grand prix?

7 In which 1970 grand prix did he lose the lead because of a mechanical problem?

8 For which new team did Beltoise hope to race in 1976 until the drive went to someone else?

9 Who was Olivier Beretta's team-mate at Larrousse in 1994?

10 In which racing category has Beretta been a champion since quitting Formula One?

11 What nationality is Allen Berg?

12 With which team did he spend the 1986 season?

13 In which grand prix did Gerhard Berger score his first world championship points, in 1985?

14 Who was his team-mate at Arrows that year?

15 Where did Berger score his first grand prix win, in 1986?

16 Where did he suffer burns to his hands in 1989?

17 Which grand prix did Berger win when he came back from a lay-off in 1997?

18 Who was Eric Bernard's team-mate at Larrousse in 1990?

19 What sidelined Bernard in 1992?

20 At which grand prix did Bernard finish third in 1994?

1   What make of chassis did Mike Beuttler race throughout his Formula One career?

2   His best result was a seventh place in which 1973 grand prix?

3   Name two of the four backers who entered Beuttler's March in 1973.

4   Lucien Bianchi scored his first world championship point in which 1960 grand prix?

5   Bianchi was driving a Cooper that day for which team?

6   What nationality is Hans Binder?

7   For which Formula One team did he race through most of 1977?

8   With what make of car did "B Bira" enter the first world championship round at Silverstone in 1950?

9   He swapped to which French make two years later?

10 For which team was Mark Blundell test driver before making his Formula One debut for another team?

11 Which big race did Blundell win while without a Formula One drive in 1992.

12 Which team snapped Blundell up after Tyrrell dropped him at the end of 1994?

13 Which former Formula One driver has been Blundell's Indycar team-mate?

14 Which works team ran Raul Boesel in his maiden Formula One season in 1982?

15 For which team did Boesel drive in his second, and last, season?

16 For which manufacturer did Boesel become World Sports-Prototype Champion in 1987?

17 With which famous Italian team did Bob Bondurant make his debut in 1965?

18 Bondurant scored his only points when he came fourth at Monaco in 1966. What car was he driving?

19 Felice Bonetto was given his world championship chance by Scuderia Milano in 1950 in what make of chassis?

20 What was Bonetto's highest grand prix finish, achieved once in 1951 and once in 1953?

Answers *THE DRIVERS 4 (see Quiz 46)*

1 Skip Barber. **2** March. **3** Pasta. **4** Lancia. **5** Minardi. **6** British Formula Three. **7** David Coulthard. **8** The 1995 Canadian Grand Prix (second). **9** Eddie Irvine. **10** 1999. **11** Edgar Barth. **12** Jurgen Barth. **13** Argentinian. **14** Gordini. **15** Swiss. **16** BRM. **17** Ferrari. **18** He had a fight with the team manager. **19** Surtees (sixth in the 1970 US Grand Prix). **20** Tecno.

1 What chassis did Joakim Bonnier drive on his Formula One debut in 1956?

2 Bonnier turned to which German works team in 1961?

3 His final season was 1971. What chassis did he drive?

4 At what circuit did Bonnier die the following summer?

5 With which famous pop group was Slim Borgudd the drummer?

6 In what racing discipline has Borgudd since been world champion?

7 Which championship did Jean-Christophe Boullion win in 1994 *en route* to Formula One?

8 Whose seat did Boullion take at Sauber midway through 1995?

9 Who was Thierry Boutsen's team-mate in his first season with Arrows in 1983?

10 To which team did Thierry turn in 1991 after being kicked out of Williams?

11 Which was the last team he raced for in Formula One in 1993?

12 In which year did David Brabham break into Formula One?

13 What championship had he won the previous year?

14 In what year did Jack Brabham make his Formula One debut?

15 What was the first car he raced in Formula One for the Brabham Racing Organization?

16 At which track did Jack Brabham score his 14th and final grand prix win in 1970?

17 Apart from David, name Jack Brabham's other two sons who have raced?

18 Which sponsor helped Vittorio Brambilla into Formula One in 1974?

19 At which grand prix did he take a surprise pole position in 1975?

20 After leaving March, for which team did Brambilla race in 1977 and 1978?

Answers THE DRIVERS 9 *(see Quiz 51)*

1 OSCA. 2 Scuderia Castellotti. 3 Monaco. 4 Andrea Moda. 5 Luis Perez Sala. 6 Touring cars. 7 European Formula Three. 8 Tyrrell. 9 Australian. 10 AGS. 11 French. 12 The Mille Miglia. 13 Modena. 14 Long Beach. 15 Ayrton Senna. 16 Tecno. 17 Jean-Pierre Beltoise. 18 Johnny Servoz-Gavin. 19 Paul Ricard (second). 20 Lago-Talbot.

1   Who gave Tony Brise his Formula One break in 1975?

2   At which 1975 grand prix did he score his only point?

3   For which team did Chris Bristow race a Cooper in 1960?

4   At which circuit did he crash to his death that summer?

5   With which make of chassis did Tony Brooks make his Formula One breakthrough in 1955?

6   With which team did he make his world championship debut in 1956?

7   Brooks won two grands prix for Ferrari in 1959. At which tracks did he score these wins?

8   Brooks's final season was with BRM in 1961. He bowed out with third place at which circuit?

9   Under what banner did Alan Brown enter his Cooper in 1952?

10 Brown scored points on his debut. In which grand prix was this?

11 Who was Martin Brundle's team-mate when he raced an Audi in the 1981 British Saloon Car series?

12 Brundle's second stab at Formula One came in 1989 with which team?

13 In which year did he partner Mika Hakkinen at McLaren?

14 Who is Brundle's partner in the ITV commentary booth?

15 Who was Ronnie Bucknum's team-mate at Honda in 1965?

16 In what branch of racing did Bucknum excel after quitting Formula One?

17 With which team did Ivor Bueb make his Formula One debut in 1957?

18 What big race did Bueb win that year for the second time?

19 Who was Bueb's partner and what make of car were they driving?

20 Which team's Maserati did Ian Burgess race to sixth in the 1959 German Grand Prix?

Answers *THE DRIVERS 10* (see Quiz 52)

1 South African. **2** Lotus. **3** Coloni. **4** Osella. **5** Renault. **6** Alfa Romeo. **7** Swiss. **8** Fondmetal.
9 The Monte Carlo Rally. **10** Monaco. **11** Ecurie Belge. **12** Tuberculosis. **13** Scotland.
14 British. **15** 1965. **16** Lotus. **17** HWM. **18** Ferrari. **19** French. **20** French.

1 Which sportscar team entered its regular driver Giulio Cabianca in one of its cars in the 1958 Monaco Grand Prix?

2 Cabianca was fourth in the 1960 Italian Grand Prix driving a Ferrari-engined Cooper for which team?

3 Fourth place in which 1989 grand prix was Alex Caffi's best result?

4 A failed attempt to qualify what chassis in 1992 marked the end of Caffi's Formula One career?

5 Who was Adrian Campos's compatriot and team-mate at Minardi in 1988?

6 In what category of racing did Campos go on to compete in the 1990s?

7 Which European title did Ivan Capelli win in 1984?

8 With which team did Capelli make his Formula One debut in 1985?

9 In which grand prix did he score his first points at the end of that year?

10 Capelli had only two outings in 1986. With which team was this?

11 In which 1956 grand prix did Eugenio Castellotti finish second?

12 Which road race did he win for Ferrari that same year?

13 At which circuit was Castellotti killed in 1957?

14 Johnny Cecotto finished sixth on his second Formula One outing in 1983 at which circuit?

15 Who was his team-mate at Toleman in 1984?

16 With which team did François Cevert make his world championship debut with a Formula Two car in 1969?

17 His brother-in-law also raced in Formula One. Who was he?

18 Whose sudden retirement from Formula One gave Cevert his break with Tyrrell in 1970?

19 Cevert made his first visit to a Formula One podium at which circuit in 1971?

20 Eugene Chaboud finished fifth in the 1950 French Grand Prix in what chassis?

Answers *THE DRIVERS 7 (see Quiz 49)*

1 Maserati. *2* Porsche. *3* McLaren. *4* Le Mans. *5* Abba. *6* Truck racing. *7* European Formula 3000. *8* Karl Wendlinger. *9* Marc Surer. *10* Ligier. *11* Jordan. *12* 1990. *13* British Formula Three. *14* 1955. *15* Lotus (1962). *16* Kyalami. *17* Gary and Geoff. *18* Beta Tools. *19* Swedish. *20* Surtees.

1   What nationality is Dave Charlton?

2   What chassis did he race when he came to Europe in 1971?

3   For what team did Pedro Chaves draw a blank by failing to qualify even once in 1991?

4   With which team did Eddie Cheever have his first full season of Formula One in 1980?

5   Which French team did Cheever join for 1983?

6   With which team did Cheever spend 1984 and 1985?

7   What nationality is Andrea Chiesa?

8   For which team did he race in 1992?

9   Which famous rally did Louis Chiron win in 1954?

10   After Chiron's retirement from the cockpit, which grand prix did he help run until 1979?

11   Which team entered Johnny Claes through most of his Formula One career?

12   Of what disease did he die at the age of 39?

13   From which country did Jim Clark hail?

14   Which grand prix did Clark win four years running?

15   In which year did he become world champion for the second time?

16   Clark won the 1965 Indianapolis 500 for which team?

17   Which team gave Peter Collins his Formula One debut in 1952?

18   For which team did he score all three of his grand prix wins?

19   What nationality is Erik Comas?

20   Comas's best-ever finish was fifth place in which 1992 grand prix?

Answers *THE DRIVERS 8* (see Quiz 50)

1 Frank Williams. *2* Swedish. *3* Yeoman Credit Racing. *4* Spa-Francorchamps. *5* Connaught.
6 BRM. *7* Reims and Avus. *8* Watkins Glen. *9* Ecurie Richmond. *10* Swiss (fifth). *11* Stirling
Moss. *12* Brabham. *13* 1994. *14* Murray Walker. *15* Richie Ginther. *16* Sportscars.
17 Connaught. *18* The Le Mans 24 Hours. *19* Ron Flockhart, a Jaguar. *20* Scuderia Centro
Sud.

1 Where did David Coulthard finish in his first full season of Formula One in 1995?

2 At which circuit did Coulthard set the 1997 season rolling in style?

3 Where did he score his only win of 1998?

4 Which former driver helps guide Coulthard's career?

5 Who gave Piers Courage his first full season of Formula One in 1968?

6 What make of chassis did he drive that year?

7 His best result that year was fourth in which grand prix?

8 With which team did Yannick Dalmas make his mark in Formula One?

9 A move to which other French team led to disappointment in 1989?

10 Which famous sportscar race has Dalmas won four times?

11 With which team did Derek Daly attempt to make his Formula One debut in 1978?

12 A move to which team put him on the grid for the first time?

13 Which team did Daly join from Tyrrell in 1981?

14 Christian Danner was the inaugural winner of which championship?

15 Name either of the two teams for which Danner raced in 1986.

16 Andrea de Adamich scored his best finish, sixth place, at which 1972 grand prix?

17 What make of car was he driving?

18 Which 1985 grand prix was awarded to Elio de Angelis after winner Alain Prost was disqualified?

19 For which team was de Angelis driving at the time?

20 In which year did de Angelis finish a career-best third overall?

Answers THE DRIVERS 13 (see Quiz 55)

1 Northern Ireland. 2 Eddie Jordan. 3 Mosport Park. 4 CanAm. 5 Penske. 6 Ivan Capelli.
7 Australian. 8 Jaguar. 9 Canadian. 10 BRM. 11 Graham Hill. 12 Penthouse. 13 Lotus.
14 French. 15 Colin Crabbe. 16 ATS. 17 Austrian. 18 Hesketh. 19 Ensign. 20 In a light aircraft crash.

1 Under which banner did Carel Godin de Beaufort enter his cars?

2 What colour was his car painted?

3 With which team did Andrea de Cesaris make his Formula One debut in 1980?

4 For what team was he driving when he barrel-rolled in Austria in 1985?

5 For which new team did de Cesaris score points in 1991?

6 What nationality is Emmanuel de Graffenried?

7 At which grand prix did Pedro de la Rosa score a point at the start of 1999?

8 Who was his team-mate at Arrows in that race?

9 What nationality is Jean-Denis Deletraz?

10 With which team did he make his Formula One debut in the 1994 Australian Grand Prix?

11 Who was Patrick Depailler's team-mate at Tyrrell in 1974 and 1975?

12 In which grand prix did he finish second behind this team-mate in 1974 and 1976?

13 Where in 1979 did Depailler score his second grand prix win?

14 Why did he miss the majority of that season?

15 What nationality was Alfonso de Portago?

16 Name one of the other sports at which de Portago competed at international level alongside car racing.

17 Emilio de Villota raced what privately entered chassis in 1977?

18 He went on to win which Formula One championship in 1980?

19 Which reigning world champion was Pedro Diniz's team-mate in 1997?

20 For which team was this?

Answers *THE DRIVERS 14 (see Quiz 56)*

1 BRM. *2* 1975. *3* Purple. *4* 1982. *5* Osella. *6* Brabham. *7* His brother Teo Fabi. *8* US (third in Detroit). *9* 1986. *10* AGS. *11* The 1951 French Grand Prix. *12* Juan Manuel Fangio. *13* 1948. *14* Alfa Romeo. *15* Monaco. *16* Maserati. *17* Tazio Nuvolari. *18* Juan Manuel Fangio. *19* Alberto Ascari. *20* In a road accident.

1 From which country does Martin Donnelly hail?

2 Which future Formula One team owner ran him in Formula 3000?

3 Mark Donohue burst on to the Formula One scene by finishing third on his debut at which circuit in 1971?

4 Which North American championship did Donohue win in 1973?

5 What make of car did Donohue race in Formula One in 1974 and 1975?

6 Who beat Johnny Dumfries to the 1984 European Formula Three title?

7 Dumfries's final points finish for Lotus in 1986 was sixth place in which grand prix?

8 For which works team did he win the 1988 Le Mans 24 Hours?

9 What nationality is George Eaton?

10 What chassis did he race throughout his Formula One career from 1969 to 1971?

11 Which former world champion gave Guy Edwards his Formula One break?

12 Famed for his sponsorship-hunting skills, which sponsor did Edwards take to Hesketh in 1976?

13 Edwards later became sponsorship consultant for which top team?

14 Vic Elford's best Formula One result was fourth place for Cooper in which 1968 grand prix?

15 Elford also scored points in 1969 in a McLaren entered by whom?

16 Elford went on to manage which team in 1977?

17 What nationality was Harald Ertl?

18 For which team did Ertl drive in 1976 and 1977?

19 A change of teams meant he raced what chassis in 1978?

20 How did Ertl die in 1982?

Answers THE DRIVERS 11 (see Quiz 53)

1 Third. 2 Melbourne. 3 Imola. 4 Martin Brundle. 5 Reg Parnell. 6 BRM. 7 Italian. 8 Larrousse.
9 AGS. 10 The Le Mans 24 Hours. 11 Hesketh. 12 Ensign. 13 March. 14 Formula 3000.
15 Osella, Arrows. 16 Spanish. 17 Surtees. 18 San Marino. 19 Lotus. 20 1984.

1 With which team did Bob Evans spend his maiden season of Formula One?

2 Which year was that?

3 What colour was Evans's helmet?

4 In what year was Corrado Fabi European Formula Two champion?

5 Which team did he join for his first year in Formula One?

6 Fabi moved on to which team?

7 He had three grands prix as stand-in for whom?

8 Teo Fabi's first Formula One podium finish was at which 1984 grand prix?

9 In which year did he twice qualify in pole position for Benetton?

10 Pascal Fabre spent only the 1987 season in Formula One. With which team?

11 Luigi Fagioli won just one grand prix. Which one was it?

12 Fagioli shared his winning Alfa Romeo with whom?

13 In what year did Juan Manuel Fangio first come to race in Europe?

14 For which team did he race in the inaugural world championship in 1950?

15 At which circuit did Fangio score his first win that year?

16 With which team did he return in 1953 after taking a year to recover from injury?

17 Which pre-war great acted as Giuseppe Farina's tutor at Alfa Romeo?

18 Which Alfa Romeo team-mate overshadowed Farina in 1951?

19 Which Ferrari team-mate overshadowed him in 1952?

20 How did Farina die in 1966?

Answers *THE DRIVERS 12* (see Quiz 54)

1 Ecurie Maarsbergen. *2* Orange. *3* Alfa Romeo. *4* Ligier. *5* Jordan. *6* Swiss. *7* Australian. *8* Toranosuke Takagi. *9* Swiss. *10* Larrousse. *11* Jody Scheckter. *12* Swedish. *13* Jarama. *14* He broke his legs in a hang-gliding accident. *15* Spanish. *16* Bobsleigh, swimming, horse racing. *17* McLaren. *18* The British championship. *19* Damon Hill. *20* Arrows.

1 Rudi Fischer raced which make of chassis throughout his two-year Formula One career?

2 Fischer's best result was second place in which 1952 grand prix?

3 In what championship did Giancarlo Fisichella race in 1995?

4 Which manufacturer ran him in that championship?

5 Which team gave Fisichella his Formula One break?

6 In which 1999 grand prix did he finish second?

7 Christian Fittipaldi was South American Formula Three champion in 1990. True or false?

8 In which 1992 grand prix did he score his first championship point?

9 In which 1993 grand prix did Christian Fittipaldi flip across the finish line?

10 Whose car had he clipped?

11 At which circuit did Emerson Fittipaldi score his first win, in 1970?

12 In what year did he become world champion for the first time?

13 In what year did he become world champion for the second time?

14 What was his best result for the Fittipaldi team?

15 Who were Wilson Fittipaldi's Brabham team-mates in his maiden season in 1972?

16 In what year did he start racing a Fittipaldi?

17 Did he ever score any points in this car?

18 How did Ron Flockhart die?

19 With which team did Gregor Foitek attempt to make his Formula One debut in 1989?

20 Foitek's best result, achieved in 1990, proved to be seventh at Monaco driving an Onyx for which compatriot?

Answers THE DRIVERS 17 *(see Quiz 59)*

1 Maserati. *2* The Buenos Aires circuit. *3* BRM. *4* Watkins Glen. *5* Tim Schenken. *6* John Willment. *7* British Saloon Cars. *8* British Formula 5000. *9* Osella. *10* Monza. *11* Giacomo Russo. *12* Belgian. *13* Reims. *14* Yeoman Credit Racing. *15* Formula Open Fortuna. *16* Spain. *17* ERA. *18* Cooper. *19* Maserati. *20* Scuderia Centro Sud.

1 At which 1973 grand prix did George Follmer finish on the podium?

2 At which circuit was it held that year?

3 What nationality is Norberto Fontana?

4 For which team did he make his Formula One debut in 1997?

5 Heinz-Harald Frentzen came fifth on his second Formula One outing, in 1994. In which grand prix was this?

6 The following year Frentzen made his first visit the podium at which circuit?

7 Who was Frentzen's team-mate at Williams in 1997 and 1998?

8 At which circuit did Frentzen score his first win for Jordan in 1999?

9 For which British team did Paul Frere finish fifth on his debut in 1952?

10 Frere raced for a French works team in 1954. Which one?

11 However, it was in the Le Mans 24 Hours that Frere achieved his best results. In which year did he win it?

12 Who beat Bertrand Gachot to the 1987 British Formula Three crown?

13 Who was Gachot's team-mate at Onyx in 1989?

14 With which team did Gachot score his first points in 1991?

15 For which team did Patrick Gaillard turn out at five grands prix in 1979?

16 What nationality is Divina Galica?

17 In what sport had she excelled before turning to car racing?

18 With which car did she twice attempt to qualify in 1978?

19 With which works team did Nanni Galli race in 1971?

20 With which works team did Nanni Galli race in 1972?

Answers **THE DRIVERS 18** *(see Quiz 60)*

1 British Formula 5000. 2 McLaren. 3 Bruce McLaren's. 4 Toleman. 5 Zakspeed. 6 Alfa Romeo. 7 US. 8 Orange. 9 American. 10 Eagle. 11 Lago-Talbot. 12 Belgian. 13 Ferrari. 14 Buenos Aires. 15 Maserati. 16 Chico. 17 1951. 18 Maserati. 19 British. 20 Maurice Trintignant.

1 Oscar Galvez scored points for fifth on his only grand prix outing in 1953. Which team did he drive for?

2 What is now named after him?

3 Which team gave Howden Ganley his Formula One break in 1971?

4 Ganley rounded off that maiden season with fourth place at which circuit?

5 With which fellow Formula One racer did Ganley form the Tiga racing car construction company?

6 Who entered Frank Gardner in a Brabham in 1964 and 1965?

7 After quitting Formula One, Gardner went on to win which title three times?

8 Which major single-seater series did Gardner also win?

9 Which team gave Jo Gartner his Formula One break in 1984?

10 At which circuit did Gartner score his only points, finishing fifth?

11 "Geki" was the pseudonym of which Italian driver?

12 What nationality was Olivier Gendebien?

13 His best Formula One result was second in a Cooper in the 1960 French Grand Prix. At which circuit was this?

14 For which team was Gendebien driving?

15 What championship did Marc Gene win in 1998 before graduating to Formula One?

16 In which country was that championship based?

17 Bob Gerard finished sixth on both of his 1950 grand prix outings. What car was he driving?

18 Gerard replaced this with a car he would race through until 1956. What car was this?

19 Gerino Gerini finished fourth on his Formula One debut in Argentina for which works team in 1956?

20 Which team entered Gerini in a Maserati in 1958?

Answers THE DRIVERS 15 (see Quiz 57)

1 Ferrari. 2 Swiss. 3 International Touring Cars. 4 Alfa Romeo. 5 Minardi. 6 Canadian. 7 True. 8 Japanese. 9 Italian. 10 Team-mate Pierluigi Martini's. 11 Watkins Glen. 12 1972. 13 1974. 14 Second (in the 1978 Brazilian Grand Prix). 15 Graham Hill and Carlos Reutemann. 16 1975. 17 No. 18 He crashed his light aircraft. 19 EuroBrun. 20 Peter Monteverdi.

1. What championship did Peter Gethin win in 1969?
2. With which team did he make his Formula One debut in 1970?
3. Whose death gave him this ride?
4. Which team did Piercarlo Ghinzani join midway through 1985?
5. Ghinzani moved to which German team in 1988?
6. Bruno Giacomelli joined which Formula One team in 1979?
7. Which grand prix did he lead in 1980 until his electrics failed?
8. What was the main colour of Giacomelli's helmet?
9. What nationality was Richie Ginther?
10. Which American car did Ginther try to qualify for his final grand prix at Monaco in 1967?
11. What car did Yves Giraud-Cabantous race to fourth place in the first-ever world championship grand prix at Silverstone in 1950?
12. Ignazio Giunti finished fourth on his Formula One debut at which 1970 grand prix?
13. For which team was he driving?
14. Giunti was killed in a sportscar race at which circuit in 1971?
15. Francesco Godia finished fourth in two 1956 grands prix for which works team?
16. By which diminutive version of his first name was he often known?
17. In which year did Jose Froilan Gonzalez score his first grand prix win?
18. Gonzalez moved to which rival Italian team in 1952?
19. His second win came in which grand prix in 1954?
20. Who shared Gonzalez's Ferrari when he won the Le Mans 24 Hours in 1954?

1 Horace Gould scored points just once by finishing fifth in which 1956 grand prix?

2 What make of car was he racing?

3 With which team did Jean-Marc Gounon make his Formula One debut at the end of 1993?

4 For which team did Gounon drive in the second half of 1994?

5 In which grand prix did Masten Gregory finish third on his debut in 1957?

6 Masten's best-ever finish was second in which 1959 grand prix?

7 Which American team fielded Masten in a Cooper in 1961?

8 Olivier Grouillard finished runner-up to whom in the 1988 Formula 3000 series?

9 With which team did Grouillard fail to qualify for almost all of the 1991 grands prix?

10 In which branch of racing did Grouillard shine after qutting Formula One?

11 What nationality is Miguel Angel Guerra?

12 With which Italian team did Guerra spend a brief spell in 1981?

13 Who beat Roberto Guerrero to the 1980 British Formula Three title?

14 Which British team owner spotted Guerrero's potential in Formula Two?

15 With which team did Mauricio Gugelmin progress to Formula 3000 after winning the British Formula Three title with them?

16 In what year did Gugelmin make his Formula One debut?

17 At which circuit did Gugelmin cartwheel his Leyton House in 1989?

18 Dan Gurney was second in only his second grand prix for Ferrari in 1959. Where was this?

19 A move to which British team in 1960 was a disappointment for Gurney?

20 With which team did Gurney bring his Formula One career to an end in 1970?

Answers THE DRIVERS 21 (see Quiz 63)

1 Swiss (third). 2 Avus. 3 Ligier. 4 Brabham. 5 British. 6 Alain Prost. 7 Hungaroring. 8 Arrows. 9 London Rowing Club. 10 Dutch. 11 Monaco. 12 Watkins Glen. 13 1958. 14 Ferrari. 15 Olivier Gendebien. 16 McLaren. 17 Mike Hailwood. 18 Monaco. 19 CanAm. 20 Argentinian.

1 What chassis was Mike Hailwood driving when he finished sixth at Monaco in 1964?

2 Which team ran Hailwood in his final year of Formula One, 1974?

3 Which famous team guided Mika Hakkinen to the 1990 British Formula Three title?

4 Who was Hakkinen's team-mate at Lotus in 1992?

5 Hakkinen had to wait until who was dropped so that he could race for McLaren in 1993?

6 How did Hakkinen exit the 1999 Italian Grand Prix?

7 British privateer Bruce Halford raced what make of car in 1956 and 1957?

8 What type of car did Jim Hall campaign for the British Racing Partnership in 1963?

9 Hall's best result was fifth at which grand prix that year?

10 Walt Hansgen had a best result of fifth, which he achieved in the 1964 US Grand Prix. For which team was he guesting?

11 What nationality was Paul Hawkins?

12 Where did Hawkins drive his DW Racing Enterprises Lotus in the 1965 Monaco Grand Prix?

13 Mike Hawthorn made his Formula One debut in 1952 in what car?

14 His best result that year was third place in which grand prix?

15 Name Hawthorn's team-mate who slowed to let him finish second in the Moroccan Grand Prix so that he could claim the 1958 title?

16 Under which team banner did Brian Henton enter a March in 1977?

17 With which team did he start the 1982 season before moving to Tyrrell?

18 In which points-scoring position did Johnny Herbert finish his first grand prix in 1989?

19 At which circuit was that?

20 To which team was Herbert farmed out when Lotus chased paying drivers at the end of 1994?

Answers *THE DRIVERS 22 (see Quiz 64)*

1 March. **2** International Trophy. **3** Jochen Mass. **4** Wolf. **5** Lotus. **6** Frank Williams. **7** Six. **8** Simtek. **9** Footwork (Arrows). **10** Lotus. **11** UDT Laystall Racing. **12** BRP. **13** Interlagos. **14** Canadian (third). **15** 1996. **16** Michael Schumacher. **17** Reg Parnell. **18** BRM. **19** European Formula Two. **20** Austria.

1 Hans Herrmann first mounted a Formula One podium at which grand prix in 1954?

2 Herrmann is famous for being thrown from his BRM at which circuit in 1959?

3 With which team did François Hesnault surprisingly land a ride in 1984?

4 Hesnault had a disappointing spell with which British team the following year?

5 In which 1992 grand prix did Damon Hill make his first race start?

6 Who was his team-mate in his first season at Williams?

7 At which circuit did Damon Hill score his first grand prix win in 1993?

8 To which team did he move in 1997?

9 Graham Hill carried the colours of what sporting club on his helmet?

10 In which 1962 grand prix did Graham Hill score his first win?

11 Which grand prix did Graham Hill win five times?

12 At which circuit did Graham Hill suffer serious leg injuries in 1969?

13 In which year did Phil Hill make his grand prix debut?

14 For which team did he achieve his first win, the 1960 Italian Grand Prix?

15 Phil Hill won the Le Mans 24 Hours three times, sharing with which driver?

16 For which team did David Hobbs make a couple of outings in 1974?

17 Hobbs was standing in for which injured driver?

18 Denny Hulme scored his first grand prix win at which circuit in 1967?

19 Which North American sportscar title did Hulme win in 1968?

20 Which grand prix provided his final win at the start of 1974?

Answers THE DRIVERS 19 (see Quiz 61)
1 British. *2* Maserati. *3* Minardi. *4* Simtek. *5* Monaco. *6* Portuguese. *7* Camoradi International. *8* Roberto Moreno. *9* Fondmetal. *10* Sportscars. *11* Argentinian. *12* Osella. *13* Stefan Johansson. *14* Mo Nunn. *15* West Surrey Racing. *16* 1988. *17* Paul Ricard. *18* Avus. *19* BRM. *20* McLaren.

1 What was the first chassis that James Hunt raced in Formula One?

2 Which non-championship race did Hunt win in 1974?

3 Who was Hunt's team-mate at McLaren in 1976 and 1977?

4 For which team did Hunt drive in 1979, his final year in Formula One?

5 Which team did Jacky Ickx join in 1974 after a spell at Ferrari?

6 In 1976, Ickx moved on to start the season racing for whom?

7 How many times has Ickx won the Le Mans 24 Hours?

8 With which team did Taki Inoue make his Formula One debut in 1994?

9 Inoue had a full season with which team in 1995?

10 With which team did Innes Ireland break into Formula One in 1959?

11 For which team did Ireland race in 1962 after losing his Lotus seat?

12 Ireland's final points came in 1964 driving what chassis for the British Racing Partnership?

13 At which circuit in 1994 did Eddie Irvine get involved in a multiple crash for which he was blamed?

14 At which 1995 grand prix did Irvine claim his first top-three finish?

15 In which year did Irvine move from Jordan to Ferrari?

16 Who was Irvine's team-mate throughout his Ferrari career?

17 Which British entrant gave Chris Irwin his only full season of Formula One in 1967?

18 What chassis did Irwin drive?

19 Which championship did Jean-Pierre Jabouille win in 1976 before graduating to Formula One?

20 Jabouille's first win was in France, but where did he score his only other grand prix win in 1980?

Answers *THE DRIVERS 20 (see Quiz 62)*

1 Lotus. **2** McLaren. **3** West Surrey Racing. **4** Johnny Herbert. **5** Michael Andretti. **6** He spun off. **7** Maserati. **8** Lotus. **9** German. **10** Lotus. **11** Australian. **12** Into the harbour. **13** Cooper. **14** British. **15** Phil Hill. **16** British Formula One Racing Team. **17** Arrows. **18** Fourth. **19** Jacarepagua (Brazil). **20** Ligier.

1 Who was Jean-Pierre Jarier's team-mate at Shadow between 1974 and 1976?
2 To which team did Jarier move for the 1977 season?
3 For which British team did Jarier finish third in the 1979 South African Grand Prix?
4 With which team did Stefan Johansson attempt to start his Formula One career in 1980?
5 Johansson scored his first points in the 1984 Italian Grand Prix with which team?
6 Having joined Onyx in 1989, at which grand prix did Johansson peak with third place?
7 Name Alan Jones's famous racing father.
8 With which team did Alan Jones make a one-off comeback in 1983?
9 With which team did he make a more concerted comeback in 1985?
10 What championship did Ukyo Katayama win in 1991 before arriving in Formula One?
11 What make of engine powered his Tyrrell from 1993 to 1995?
12 What was the highest finishing position that Katayama achieved in a grand prix?
13 Rupert Keegan made his Formula One debut in 1977 with which team?
14 He jumped ship to join which team for the following year?
15 Keegan returned in 1980 with what chassis with little success?
16 David Kennedy tried and failed to qualify seven times in 1980 for which team?
17 Karl Kling finished second on his Formula One debut in which 1954 grand prix?
18 In which 1975 grand prix did Jacques Laffite finish a surprise second?
19 Laffite became the first driver for which new team in 1976?
20 To which British team did Laffite move after his spell there?

Answers THE DRIVERS 25 *(see Quiz 67)*

1 Wolf Williams. *2* South African. *3* Tyrrell. *4* Shadow. *5* Keke Rosberg. *6* The Le Mans 24 Hours. *7* Lago-Talbot. *8* 1955. *9* Italian. *10* Cooper. *11* Monaco. *12* Connaught. *13* Vanwall. *14* Zimbabwe (Rhodesia as it was then). *15* James Hunt. *16* Chesterfield. *17* HWM. *18* International Trophy. *19* 1961. *20* Scuderia Centro Sud.

---

1 Jan Lammers quit ATS midway through 1980 to join which team?

2 Lammers had a miserable time with which team in 1982?

3 In 1994, Lammers drove an estate car for which manufacturer in the British Touring Car Championship?

4 Which Formula Three series did Pedro Lamy win on his way to Formula One?

5 Which team did Lamy join from Lotus in 1995?

6 Francisco Landi scored his only points when he finished fourth in which 1956 grand prix?

7 For which works team was Landi driving?

8 Was Hermann Lang in his thirties or forties when he made his Formula One debut?

9 For which team did Lang finish fifth in the 1953 Swiss Grand Prix?

10 Claudio Langes spent the entire 1990 season failing to qualify for which team?

11 Nicola Larini moved from Osella to which team for 1990?

12 Which Italian team signed Larini for 1991?

13 What nationality is Oscar Larrauri?

14 With which team did Larrauri spend his 18 month Formula One career?

15 At which circuit did Niki Lauda score his first grand prix win in 1974?

16 To which team did Lauda move for 1978?

17 With which team did he return in 1982?

18 In which year did Lauda win his third world title?

19 Giovanni Lavaggi turned out for which team in 1995?

20 For which team did he turn out in 1996?

Answers **THE DRIVERS 26** *(see Quiz 68)*

1 Italian. **2** Jose Froilan Gonzalez. **3** Canadian. **4** Jos Verstappen. **5** Trevor Taylor.
6 Nürburgring. **7** Belgian. **8** Elio de Angelis. **9** Keke Rosberg. **10** Jacarepagua (Brazil).
11 Maserati. **12** Nürburgring, Bremgarten. **13** Reims. **14** Louis Rosier. **15** Belgian.
16 Silverstone. **17** BRM. **18** A flying stone blinded him in one eye. **19** Brazilian. **20** Argentinian.

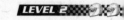
1 Michel Leclere raced for which team in 1976?

2 Which was the only grand prix entered by Neville Lederle?

3 Geoff Lees finished seventh in a one-off outing for which team in the 1979 German Grand Prix?

4 With which team did Lees start the 1980 season?

5 Which former world champion guided JJ Lehto's early career?

6 Which big sportscar race did JJ win in 1995?

7 What make of chassis did Pierre Levegh race through his two-year Formula One career?

8 In which year was he killed when he crashed into the crowd at Le Mans?

9 Jack Lewis raced to fourth place at which 1961 grand prix?

10 What chassis was Lewis driving that day for the H & L Motors team?

11 Stuart Lewis-Evans finished fourth on his Formula One debut in 1957 at which circuit?

12 For which team was Lewis-Evans driving that day?

13 Which team immediately snapped up his services?

14 From which country did John Love hail?

15 Who was Brett Lunger's team-mate when he arrived in Formula One in 1975?

16 Which cigarette company backed Lunger's 1977 campaign?

17 Lance Macklin raced for which team for almost his entire Formula One career?

18 Macklin's only top result was victory in 1952 in which non-championship Formula One race?

19 In what year did Tony Maggs make his Formula One debut?

20 Which team entered Maggs in a BRM in 1964?

Answers THE DRIVERS 23 *(see Quiz 65)*

1 Tom Pryce. **2** ATS. **3** Tyrrell. **4** Shadow. **5** Toleman. **6** Portuguese. **7** Stan Jones. **8** Arrows. **9** Team Haas. **10** Japanese Formula 3000. **11** Yamaha. **12** Fifth (twice – in the Brazilian and San Marino Grands Prix). **13** Hesketh. **14** Surtees. **15** Williams. **16** Shadow. **17** French. **18** German. **19** Ligier. **20** Williams.

1   Umberto Maglioli's best-ever Formula One result was third in which 1954 grand prix?

2   With whom did Maglioli share his Ferrari in that race?

3   In which 1998 grand prix did Jan Magnussen score his only point?

4   Who replaced Magnussen at Stewart for the following race?

5   With which British driver did Willy Mairesse tangle in the 1962 Belgian Grand Prix?

6   In 1965, at which circuit did Mairesse incur injuries that effectively ended his Formula One career?

7   Nigel Mansell scored his first points with third place in which 1981 grand prix?

8   Who was Mansell's team-mate at Lotus from 1980 to 1984?

9   Who was Mansell's team-mate when he joined Williams in 1985?

10   Mansell won his first grand prix for Ferrari at which circuit in 1989?

11   For which works team did Sergio Mantovani race throughout his Formula One career?

12   Mantovani's best result was fifth. Name one of the two circuits at which he achieved this in 1954.

13   Robert Manzon's best result in 1950 was fourth in the French Grand Prix. Where was this held?

14   In 1954, Manzon raced a Ferrari entered by which fellow Formula One driver?

15   Onofre Marimon marked his debut for Maserati by finishing third in which 1953 grand prix?

16   Marimon was third again the following year at which circuit?

17   With what chassis did Helmut Marko contest each of his nine grands prix?

18   How did Marko's career end?

19   What nationality is Tarso Marques?

20   In which 1996 grand prix did he clash with Martin Brundle?

Answers *THE DRIVERS 24* (see Quiz 66)

1 Ensign. 2 Theodore. 3 Volvo. 4 German. 5 Minardi. 6 Argentinian. 7 Maserati. 8 Forties. 9 Maserati. 10 EuroBrun. 11 Ligier. 12 Modena Team. 13 Argentinian. 14 EuroBrun. 15 Jarama. 16 Brabham. 17 McLaren. 18 1984. 19 Pacific. 20 Minardi.

1 With which team did Pierluigi Martini make an abortive attempt to break into Formula One in 1984?

2 After a four-year run with Minardi, to which rival Italian team did Martini move in 1992?

3 What nationality is Jochen Mass?

4 Who was Mass's team-mate in his first year with McLaren?

5 To which team did Mass move in 1978?

6 In what industry did Ken McAlpine's family make a fortune?

7 McAlpine was a benefactor of which team, whose chassis he raced in Formula One?

8 What make of chassis did Bruce McLaren race for the first eight years of his Formula One career?

9 At which circuit did McLaren win his first grand prix, the 1959 US?

10 McLaren won just once in 1962. Which grand prix was that?

11 Carlos Menditeguy was third in his native grand prix in 1957. At which circuit was this?

12 Menditeguy finished fourth there in 1960, driving a Cooper for which team?

13 Arturo Merzario was a star for which works sportscar team in 1975?

14 Merzario raced for which Formula One team in the first half of 1976?

15 With which team did Merzario see out the season?

16 Roberto Mieres replaced which injured French driver at Gordini in 1953?

17 Mieres moved to Maserati midway through 1954 and was fourth first time out in which grand prix?

18 François Migault took part in two grands prix in 1975 for which British team?

19 John Miles scored his only points for fifth in which 1970 grand prix?

20 Miles later became an engineering consultant for which sportscar company?

Answers THE DRIVERS 29 (see Quiz 71)

1 Ferrari. **2** Juan Manuel Fangio. **3** Lotus. **4** Nelson Piquet. **5** Toranosuke Takagi. **6** Canadian. **7** Olivier Panis or Jarno Trulli. **8** Minardi. **9** British (third). **10** Suzuka. **11** March. **12** Jordan. **13** Ensign. **14** TV broadcaster. **15** Belgian. **16** Frank Williams. **17** British Formula Three. **18** Mario Andretti. **19** Arrows. **20** Larrousse.

1 Which top Formula One team entered Gerhard Mitter in the German Grand Prix in 1964 and 1965?

2 Which Italian road race did Mitter win in 1969?

3 In 1988, Stefano Modena struggled in his first full season of Formula One with which team?

4 After a two-year spell with Brabham, to which team did Modena move in 1991?

5 Modena scored his best result, second place, in which grand prix?

6 Why did Andrea Montermini fail to qualify his Simtek for the 1994 Spanish Grand Prix?

7 Which team fielded Montermini in 1995?

8 Gianni Morbidelli raced for which team in 1991?

9 With which team did Morbidelli make his comeback in 1994?

10 In which 1995 grand prix did Morbidelli race to a shock third place?

11 Roberto Moreno had a second crack at Formula One with which team in 1987?

12 Benetton swapped Moreno for a driver from which team after the 1991 Belgian Grand Prix?

13 Moreno raced alongside compatriot Pedro Diniz at which new team in 1995?

14 What nationality was Silvio Moser?

15 What privately entered chassis did Moser guide to fifth in the 1968 Dutch Grand Prix?

16 Moser raced which chassis in 1970 and 1971?

17 For which team did Stirling Moss make his Formula One debut in 1951?

18 What works team snapped him up for 1956 after Mercedes quit?

19 Which British team secured Moss's services for 1957?

20 Moss won the 1958 Argentinian Grand Prix in what Rob Walker-entered chassis?

Answers *THE DRIVERS 30* (see Quiz 72)

1 British. *2* Mexican. *3* Jacky Ickx. *4* Surtees. *5* Carlos Reutemann. *6* An arrow. *7* Osella.
8 Montreal. *9* Williams. *10* RAM. *11* Australian. *12* Eric Bernard. *13* Australian. *14* Jarno Trulli.
15 Footwork. *16* Italian. *17* French. *18* Monza. *19* In a road accident in 1977. *20* Yeoman
Credit Racing, Bowmaker.

1   For which Italian team did Luigi Musso race in 1956?

2 . To whom did Musso refuse to hand over his car in the 1956 Italian Grand Prix?

3   Satoru Nakajima scored a point for which team on his second Formula One
     outing?

4   Who was Nakajima's team-mate in 1988?

5   Who is Nakajima's protégé?

6   In which 1997 grand prix did Shinji Nakano score his first point?

7   Name either of his team-mates that year.

8   With which team did Alessandro Nannini make his Formula One debut in
     1986?

9   Nannini joined Benetton in 1988 and was on the podium for the first time at
     which grand prix that year?

10   At which circuit did Nannini achieve his only grand prix win in 1989?

11   Emanuele Naspetti jumped into Formula One with which team midway through
     1992?

12   Naspetti's only further outing was with which team in 1993?

13   Which team gave Tiff Needell his Formula One opportunity in 1980?

14   What career has Needell followed in the 1990s?

15   What nationality is Patrick Neve?

16   Who entered Neve in a March in 1977?

17   What championship did Gunnar Nilsson win in 1975?

18   Who was Nilsson's team-mate at Lotus in 1976 and 1977?

19   For which new team was Nilsson signed to drive in 1978?

20   With which team did Hideki Noda have three Formula One outings in 1994?

Answers THE DRIVERS 27 *(see Quiz 69)*

1 Toleman. **2** Scuderia Italia. **3** German. **4** Emerson Fittipaldi. **5** ATS. **6** Civil engineering.
7 Connaught. **8** Cooper. **9** Sebring. **10** Monaco. **11** Buenos Aires. **12** Scuderia Centro Sud.
13 Alfa Romeo. **14** March. **15** Wolf Williams. **16** Jean Behra. **17** Swiss. **18** Hill (Embassy
Racing). **19** South African. **20** Lotus.

---

1   Jackie Oliver led which grand prix in his maiden season, 1968?

2   Oliver rounded off that first Formula One season by finishing third in which grand prix?

3   Who partnered Oliver to victory in a Ford GT40 in the 1969 Le Mans 24 Hours?

4   With which team did Carlos Pace spend 1973, his second season in Formula One?

5   Who was Pace's team-mate at Brabham from 1974 to 1976?

6   What was the shape of the design on the top of his helmet?

7   For which team did Riccardo Paletti drive in 1982?

8   At which circuit was he killed?

9   Which team gave Jonathan Palmer his Formula One break in 1983?

10   Palmer's first full season, 1984, was spent with which team?

11   Palmer's best-ever finish was fourth in which 1987 grand prix?

12   Who was Olivier Panis's team-mate in 1994, his first season with Ligier?

13   In which 1995 grand prix did Panis score a surprise second place?

14   Who was Panis's team-mate at Prost in 1999?

15   For which team did Massimiliano Papis race in 1995?

16   Papis missed out on a point by one place in which 1995 grand prix?

17   Mike Parkes finished second in which 1966 grand prix on his Ferrari debut?

18   Parkes was second again at which circuit later that season?

19   How did Parkes die?

20   Name one of the two Formula One teams that Reg Parnell ran before forming his own.

Answers *THE DRIVERS 28* (see Quiz 70)
1 Lotus. *2* Targa Florio. *3* EuroBrun. *4* Tyrrell. *5* Canadian (1991). *6* He broke his ankles in qualifying. *7* Pacific. *8* Minardi. *9* Footwork. *10* Australian. *11* AGS. *12* Jordan (Michael Schumacher). *13* Forti. *14* Swiss. *15* Brabham. *16* Bellasi. *17* HWM. *18* Maserati. *19* Vanwall. *20* Cooper.

1   Which compatriot did Riccardo Patrese displace when Shadow gave him his Formula One break in 1977?

2   Which grand prix did Patrese lead for Arrows in 1978?

3   What team did Patrese join after his first spell with Brabham?

4   Which team gave Patrese his final season of Formula One in 1993?

5   Cesare Perdisa scored his second third place finish in which 1956 grand prix?

6   Who took over Perdisa's Maserati during that race?

7   With which chassis did Larry Perkins start his 1976 campaign?

8   Perkins was drafted into which top team mid season in 1976?

9   Henri Pescarolo made his Formula One debut with which team in 1968?

10 Who ran Pescarolo in a March in 1971?

11 Pescarolo teamed up with two other French drivers to race for which team in 1974?

12 Who entered Ronnie Peterson's March in his first season of Formula One in 1970?

13 Which years did Peterson's first spell at Lotus span?

14 Which grand prix did Peterson win for March in 1976?

15 Andre Pilette scored his only points by finishing fifth in the 1954 Belgian Grand Prix for which team?

16 What buisness did Pilette set up after his retirement from the cockpit?

17 What car did Nelson Piquet drive in his second, third and fourth grands prix in 1978?

18 Piquet scored his first win at which American circuit in 1980?

19 In which year did Piquet become world champion for the first time?

20 In which year did Piquet become world champion for the second time?

Answers THE DRIVERS 33 *(see Quiz 75)*

1 Hesketh. 2 1979. 3 Fourth in the 1981 San Marino, German and Dutch Grands Prix.
4 Cooper. 5 McLaren (fifth). 6 US Formula 5000. 7 Gianclaudio. 8 Switzerland. 9 Ensign.
10 Shadow. 11 Pole position. 12 Kyalami. 13 Belgium. 14 Revlon. 15 Mosport Park. 16
Hesketh. 17 Ian Scheckter. 18 Rob Walker. 19 Jack Brabham. 20 Four.

1   When Didier Pironi made his debut with Tyrrell in 1978, who was his team-mate?
2   In which year did Pironi join Ferrari?
3   Who was his team-mate there?
4   By winning which 1982 grand prix did Pironi infuriate his team-mate?
5   Who was Emanuele Pirro's team-mate at Benetton in 1989?
6   For which team had Pirro been test driver earlier that year?
7   What championship did Alain Prost win in 1979 before graduating to Formula One?
8   Who was Prost's team-mate at McLaren in 1980?
9   In what year did Prost clinch his third world title for McLaren?
10 Which team did Prost take over at the start of 1997?
11 In which year did Tom Pryce win the Monaco Formula Three race?
12 In what make of chassis did Pryce make his Formula One debut that same year?
13 Which 1975 grand prix did Pryce start from pole position?
14 David Purley's first Formula One outings in 1973 were in what make of chassis?
15 Who did Purley attempt to rescue from a burning car in that year's Dutch Grand Prix?
16 With which team did Bobby Rahal enter two grands prix in 1978?
17 Rahal is better known for winning which major championship?
18 For which French team did Nano da Silva Ramos finish fifth in the 1956 Monaco Grand Prix?
19 With which team did Roland Ratzenberger make his Formula One breakthrough in 1994?
20 At which circuit did Ratzenberger crash to his death in qualifying?

Answers *THE DRIVERS 34* (see Quiz 76)

1 Lotus. 2 Ferrari. 3 Spa-Francorchamps. 4 Motorcycles. 5 Belgian. 6 ATS. 7 Emerson Fittipaldi. 8 Honda. 9 McLaren. 10 Adelaide. 11 Swiss, Belgian. 12 Ferrari. 13 Brazilian. 14 Tyrrell. 15 Toranosuke Takagi. 16 Toleman. 17 Zakspeed. 18 Jonathan Palmer. 19 British. 20 Touring cars.

1 What was the first Formula One chassis raced by Hector Rebaque in 1977?

2 In which season did Rebaque enter his own chassis?

3 What was his highest ever Formula One finish, a result he achieved three times?

4 Brian Redman raced to third place at Monaco in 1968 for which team?

5 Redman scored there again in 1972 for which team?

6 Which single-seater title did Redman win each year from 1974 to 1976?

7 What is the full version of Clay Regazzoni's first name?

8 From which country does he come?

9 Which team did Regazzoni join from Ferrari for 1977?

10 He moved on to which team for 1978?

11 In which grid position did Carlos Reutemann qualify for his world championship debut in 1972?

12 Reutemann's first win came in 1974 at which circuit?

13 Where did Reutemann score his 12th and final grand prix win in 1981?

14 Which cosmetic brand made Peter Revson's family fortune?

15 Revson won the 1973 Canadian Grand Prix at which circuit?

16 With what chassis did Alex Ribeiro make his Formula One debut in 1976?

17 Who was Ribeiro's team-mate at March in 1977?

18 Which British entrant gave Jochen Rindt his Formula One break in the 1964 Austrian Grand Prix?

19 Who was Rindt's team-mate at Brabham in 1968?

20 When Rindt won the 1970 German Grand Prix, how many wins in a row did that make?

Answers THE DRIVERS 31 (see Quiz 73)

1 Renzo Zorzi. 2 South African. 3 Alfa Romeo. 4 Benetton. 5 Belgian. 6 Stirling Moss. 7 Boro Ensign. 8 Brabham. 9 Matra. 10 Frank Williams. 11 BRM. 12 Colin Crabbe. 13 1973 and 1976 (he joined March after the first race of 1976). 14 Italian. 15 Gordini. 16 A racing school. 17 A privately entered McLaren. 18 Long Beach. 19 1981. 20 1983.

1 Which top team entered Pedro Rodriguez in two grands prix in 1963?

2 Which other top team entered him in a handful of races in 1964 and 1965, and later in 1969?

3 At which circuit did Pedro Rodriguez win in 1970?

4 What did Ricardo Rodriguez race until he was 14?

5 His best Formula One result was fourth in which 1962 grand prix?

6 Which was the second Formula One team for which Keke Rosberg drove in 1978?

7 Which former world champion was Rosberg's team-mate in 1980?

8 Rosberg sampled turbo power in 1984 with which make of engine?

9 With which team did Rosberg spend 1986, his final season?

10 Rosberg led the final race until getting a puncture. At which circuit was that?

11 Name either of the two 1950 grands prix in which Louis Rosier finished third.

12 Which Italian make of chassis did Rosier race from 1952 to 1954?

13 What nationality is Ricardo Rosset?

14 Which team did Rosset join in 1998?

15 Name the team-mate who outpaced him there?

16 With what chassis did Huub Rothengatter win a Formula Two race in 1980?

17 Rothengatter joined his third Formula One team in 1986. Which team was this?

18 Who was his team-mate that year?

19 Luis Perez Sala's best Formula One result was sixth in which 1989 grand prix?

20 In what form of racing did Sala shine after quitting Formula One?

Answers *THE DRIVERS 32* (see Quiz 74)

1 Patrick Depailler. *2* 1981. *3* Gilles Villeneuve. *4* San Marino. *5* Alessandro Nannini.
6 McLaren. *7* European Formula Three. *8* John Watson. *9* 1989. *10* Ligier. *11* 1974. *12* Token.
13 British. *14* March. *15* Roger Williamson. *16* Wolf. *17* Indycar. *18* Gordini. *19* Simtek.
20 Imola.

Quiz 77 THE DRIVERS 35

Answers – see page 192

1 Which team gave Eliseo Salazar his Formula One break in 1981?

2 Salazar moved mid season to which other team?

3 Who was Salazar's team-mate at ATS in 1982?

4 The 1983 season proved to be Salazar's last in Formula One. Who did he drive for?

5 At the end of which season did Mika Salo make his Formula One debut?

6 With which team was that?

7 What cost Salo points on his first appearance for Tyrrell in 1995?

8 At which circuit does Salo score points more often than not?

9 In which 1999 grand prix did Salo cede the lead to Ferrari team-mate Eddie Irvine?

10 Which British team entered Roy Salvadori in five 1953 grands prix?

11 In Salvadori's best season he was placed fourth overall. Which year was that?

12 Which sportscar manufacturer entered a Formula One team in 1959 for which Salvadori raced?

13 Salvadori scored his final points in a Cooper for which team in 1961?

14 For which works team did Consalvo Sanesi race in 1950 and 1951?

15 Sanesi's best result was a fourth place in which 1951 grand prix?

16 At which circuit was this held?

17 Ludovico Scarfiotti scored a point on his debut at which 1963 grand prix?

18 After leaving Ferrari, what chassis did Scarfiotti race in the 1967 Italian Grand Prix?

19 In which 1957 grand prix did Giorgio Scarlatti finish a career-best fifth?

20 Who shared Scarlatti's Maserati that day?

Answers THE DRIVERS 37 (see Quiz 79)

1 Piercarlo Ghinzani. 2 Below. 3 Arrows. 4 Willi Weber. 5 Spanish. 6 Damon Hill. 7 Montreal. 8 Silverstone. 9 1996. 10 Spa-Francorchamps. 11 Heinz-Harald Frentzen. 12 Yellow, red and black. 13 German. 14 Porsche. 15 Targa Florio. 16 Lotus. 17 British Formula Three. 18 Six. 19 Alain Prost. 20 The 1993 Australian Grand Prix.

1 Is Ian Scheckter older or younger than his brother Jody?

2 Ian Scheckter made his Formula One debut with what privately entered chassis?

3 In what year's South African Grand Prix was that?

4 Ian Scheckter had only one full-time campaign in Formula One, in 1977. With which works team was that?

5 What colour band was wrapped around Jody Scheckter's white helmet?

6 In what year did Jody Scheckter make his Formula One debut?

7 What team did he join in 1974?

8 A move to which new team brought victory first time out in 1977?

9 How many grands prix did Jody Scheckter win *en route* to becoming world champion in 1979?

10 How many did he win for Ferrari the following year?

11 What make of chassis did Harry Schell race in 1954 before joining the works team in 1955?

12 Schell joined which British team later that year?

13 Who was Schell's team-mate at BRM in 1958?

14 What nationality is Tim Schenken?

15 With which team did Schenken run the 1972 season?

16 With which fellow antipodean did he form the Tiga racing-car building concern?

17 What is the abbreviated version of Domenico Schiattarella's first name?

18 For which team did Schiattarella make his handful of Formula One outings?

19 Jo Schlesser made his world championship debut in a Formula Two Matra at which 1966 Grand Prix?

20 At which circuit did Schlesser die in 1968?

1 Who was Bernd Schneider's team-mate at Zakspeed in 1989?

2 Did Schneider qualify for above or below 50 per cent of that year's races?

3 Schneider was summoned by which team for two outings in 1990?

4 Who has been Michael Schumacher's manager throughout his career?

5 At which 1994 grand prix did Schumacher get jammed in fifth gear and yet still finish second?

6 With whom did Schumacher collide in the 1994 title shoot-out?

7 Where did Schumacher crash out of the lead in 1999?

8 At which circuit did Schumacher break a leg in 1999?

9 In which year did Ralf Schumacher win the Formula Nippon title?

10 At which circuit did Ralf Schumacher finish second in 1998?

11 Who did Ralf Schumacher chase home in the 1999 Italian Grand Prix?

12 What are the three main colours on Ralf Schumacher's helmet?

13 Vern Schuppan's best Formula One result was seventh in which 1977 grand prix?

14 For which manufacturer did Schuppan win the Le Mans 24 Hours in 1983?

15 Which major Italian race did Wolfgang Seidel win in 1959?

16 What make of car did Seidel race for Scuderia Colonia in 1961?

17 Which championship did Ayrton Senna win in 1983?

18 How many times did Senna win the Monaco Grand Prix?

19 Who was Senna's team-mate at McLaren when he won the 1988 world title?

20 Which was Senna's last grand prix win?

Answers THE DRIVERS 35 *(see Quiz 77)*

1 March. *2* Ensign. *3* Manfred Winkelhock. *4* RAM. *5* 1994. *6* Lotus. *7* Cramp. *8* Monaco. *9* German. *10* Connaught. *11* 1958. *12* Aston Martin. *13* Yeoman Credit Racing. *14* Alfa Romeo. *15* Swiss. *16* Bremgarten. *17* Dutch. *18* Eagle. *19* Italian. *20* Harry Schell.

1   What is the full version of Chico Serra's first name?

2   Serra scored his only point, for Fittipaldi, at which circuit?

3   What was Johnny Servoz-Gavin's real first name?

4   An injury to whom gave Servoz-Gavin his break with Matra in 1968?

5   Why did Servoz-Gavin quit Formula One in 1970?

6   Sportscar ace Carroll Shelby finished fourth in the 1958 Italian Grand Prix in what make of car?

7   Which team had entered it?

8   For which team did Shelby race in 1959?

9   What major race did Shelby win for the team that same year?

10 What make of chassis did Jo Siffert race in his first two seasons in Formula One?

11 Siffert's first works ride was with which team in 1970?

12 He raced for a further works team the following year. Which one?

13 Which grand prix did Siffert win for them?

14 With which team did Andre Simon make his Formula One debut in 1951?

15 For which injured driver did he stand in at the 1955 German Grand Prix?

16 Alex Soler-Roig began his Formula One career with what chassis?

17 In what year was that?

18 Soler-Roig had a short spell with which works team?

19 Raymond Sommer scored his second Le Mans win in 1933 sharing with which legendary pre-war driver?

20 After driving a Ferrari in the opening races of 1950, what chassis did Sommer race after that?

Answers *THE DRIVERS 36 (see Quiz 78)*

1 Older. *2* Lotus. *3* 1974. *4* March. *5* Orange. *6* 1972. *7* Tyrrell. *8* Wolf. *9* Three. *10* None.
11 Maserati. *12* Vanwall. *13* Joakim Bonnier. *14* Australian. *15* Surtees. *16* Howden Ganley.
17 Mimmo. *18* Simtek. *19* German. *20* Rouen-les-Essarts.

1. In which 1964 grand prix did Mike Spence finish fourth?
2. Spence went one better and finished third in which 1965 grand prix?
3. For which team did Spence race in 1967?
4. Whose departure from Lotus opened the door for Alan Stacey in 1960?
5. Who was his number one there that season?
6. Jackie Stewart finished third in his second grand prix. Where was this?
7. Who was Stewart's BRM team-mate that year?
8. Why had Stewart turned down the chance to join Lotus?
9. In what year did Stewart move on to race for Matra?
10. With which chassis did Stewart start the 1970 season?
11. From which country does Siegfried Stohr hail?
12. Stohr raced for just one season in Formula One, 1981. With which team?
13. Who was Rolf Stommelen's team-mate at Brabham in 1970?
14. In which 1975 grand prix did Stommelen crash out of the lead when his rear wing flew off?
15. What car was he driving that day?
16. Which French team fielded Philippe Streiff in 1985?
17. For which team was Streiff driving when he had his career-ending accident?
18. At which 1977 grand prix did Hans-Joachim Stuck crash out of the lead?
19. What car was he driving that day?
20. Which team did Stuck move to in 1978?

Answers THE DRIVERS 41 *(see Quiz 83)*
1 Karting. *2* Fondmetal. *3* Tyrrell. *4* Mercedes. *5* The Mille Miglia. *6* Jim Clark. *7* Willy Mairesse.
8 Formula 5000. *9* Arrows. *10* Formula Two. *11* RAM (Canadian Grand Prix). *12* Teacher.
13 British. *14* Connaught. *15* Maki. *16* McLaren. *17* Vanwall. *18* Bugatti. *19* Scuderia
Serenissima. *20* BRM.

1   What was Danny Sullivan's nickname?

2   Who was his Tyrrell team-mate in 1983?

3   With which team did Marc Surer make his Formula One debut in 1979?

4   A move to which team midway through 1981 put his points collecting on hold?

5   For which team did Surer drive in 1985?

6   For which team did John Surtees race a Cooper in 1961?

7   In which year did Surtees score his first grand prix win for Ferrari?

8   Surtees quit Ferrari after two grands prix in 1966. Which team did he join?

9   Surtees won which grand prix before the end of that season?

10   For which Japanese manufacturer did Surtees then race?

11   With which team did Aguri Suzuki spend his first full season in Formula One?

12   In what year did he move to Larrousse?

13   For which team did Suzuki race in 1992 and 1993?

14   What nationality is Jacques Swaters?

15   What team entered Swaters's Ferrari in 1953 and 1954?

16   Which team gave Patrick Tambay his Formula One debut in 1977?

17   Tambay raced an Ensign for which team for the remainder of that year?

18   Which top team signed Tambay for 1982?

19   Who was he replacing?

20   At which circuit did Tambay score his first win that year?

Answers *THE DRIVERS 42* *(see Quiz 84)*
1 German Formula Three. *2* Ukyo Katayama. *3* Prost. *4* Sixth – in the Belgian Grand Prix.
5 Brabham. *6* Damon Hill. *7* Surtees. *8* Dutch. *9* Frank Williams. *10* Dutch. *11* Hungarian.
12 Arrows. *13* Snowmobile racing. *14* Trois Rivieres. *15* Carlos Reutemann. *16* Jody
Scheckter. *17* Spanish. *18* Melbourne. *19* Nürburgring. *20* Seven.

1   Gabriele Tarquini was world champion in what racing discipline in 1984?

2   For which team did Tarquini race in 1992?

3   Which British team gave Tarquini a one-off outing in 1995?

4   For which team did Piero Taruffi finish second in the 1955 Italian Grand Prix?

5   Which Italian road race did Taruffi win for Ferrari in 1957?

6   Who was Trevor Taylor's team-mate at Lotus in 1962?

7   Taylor had a big accident with which driver in the 1962 Belgian Grand Prix?

8   In what category did Taylor subsequently feature?

9   With which team did Mike Thackwell take his first crack at Formula One in 1980?

10   Thackwell won which championship in 1984 before he returned to Formula One?

11   For which team did he make his only Formula One start in 1984?

12   Thackwell turned his back on racing in 1988. What is his current profession?

13   Eric Thompson scored points on his only Formula One outing. In which 1952 grand prix was this?

14   For which team was Thompson driving?

15   Tony Trimmer attempted to make his Formula One debut with what Japanese chassis in 1975?

16   Trimmer's final attempt to qualify came in 1978 with which chassis?

17   Which British team signed up Maurice Trintignant for 1956?

18   Trintignant gave which French marque its only ever Formula One outing that year?

19   Which Italian team fielded Trintignant in a Cooper in 1961?

20   Which chassis did Trintignant use in 1964, his final season?

Answers THE DRIVERS 39 *(see Quiz 81)*

1 Mexican. *2* Mexican. *3* BRM. *4* Graham Hill. *5* Innes Ireland. *6* Monaco. *7* Graham Hill. *8* He didn't feel ready to take on Jim Clark. *9* 1968. *10* March. *11* Italy. *12* Arrows. *13* Jack Brabham. *14* Spanish. *15* Hill. *16* Ligier. *17* AGS. *18* US. *19* Brabham. *20* Shadow.

1 Which championship did Jarno Trulli win in 1996?

2 Who was Trulli's team-mate at Minardi in 1997?

3 Trulli moved to which French team in 1998?

4 What was his best finish that year?

5 Which British team fielded Eric van de Poele in 1992?

6 Who was his team-mate?

7 Gijs van Lennep made his Formula One debut in 1971 in what chassis?

8 Van Lennep scored his only point in which 1973 grand prix?

9 Who entered his car in that event?

10 What nationality is Jos Verstappen?

11 At which 1994 grand prix did he finish third for the first time?

12 Which team ran him in 1996?

13 In what form of racing did Gilles Villeneuve start his competition career?

14 Gilles Villeneuve burst on to the scene in 1976 by beating James Hunt and Jacques Laffite in a Formula Atlantic race where?

15 Who was his team-mate in 1978, his first year at Ferrari?

16 Which team-mate did Gilles Villeneuve help to the 1979 title?

17 Which 1981 grand prix did Gilles Villeneuve win at the head of a procession of cars that all finished within 1.25 seconds of each other?

18 Jacques Villeneuve started his Formula One career by leading his first race at which circuit?

19 At which circuit did he score his first Formula One win, in 1996?

20 How many grands prix did Jacques Villeneuve win *en route* to his world title in 1997?

Answers *THE DRIVERS 40 (see Quiz 82)*

1 The Kentucky Kid. *2* Michele Alboreto. *3* Ensign. *4* Theodore. *5* Brabham. *6* Yeoman Credit Racing. *7* 1963. *8* Cooper. *9* Mexican. *10* Honda. *11* Zakspeed. *12* 1990. *13* Footwork. *14* Belgian. *15* Ecurie Francorchamps. *16* Surtees. *17* Theodore. *18* Ferrari. *19* Gilles Villeneuve. *20* Hockenheim.

Quiz 85 THE DRIVERS 43

Answers – see page 200

1. Who was Jacques Villeneuve's team-mate at Williams in 1998?
2. For which team did Jacques Villeneuve race in 1999?
3. What nationality was Luigi Villoresi?
4. Villoresi finished second twice for which team in 1953?
5. In which year did Villoresi win the Mille Miglia?
6. How did Rikky von Opel's family make a fortune?
7. Which team did von Opel commission to build a Formula One car for the 1973 season?
8. Von Opel raced for which team in the first half of the 1974 season?
9. Wolfgang von Trips first climbed a Formula One podium at which 1957 grand prix?
10. Von Trips first win came for Ferrari at which 1961 grand prix?
11. What film was made in the late 1990s by Chris Rea with Wolfgang von Trips as its hero?
12. What nationality is Dave Walker?
13. Which team gave him his Formula One break?
14. Who was Walker's team-mate in 1972?
15. Who was Derek Warwick's Toleman team-mate in 1981?
16. In which 1982 grand prix did Warwick hold second place?
17. Which was Warwick's third team in Formula One?
18. Warwick joined his fourth Formula One team in 1987. Which was this?
19. From which country does John Watson hail?
20. Which team did Watson join in 1977?

Answers THE DRIVERS 45 *(see Quiz 87)*

1 Watkins Glen (third in 1970 US Grand Prix). *2* Emerson Fittipaldi. *3* BRM. *4* Austrian. *5* The Le Mans 24 Hours. *6* No. *7* Giancarlo Fisichella. *8* Christian Fittipaldi. *9* Minardi. *10* Lotus. *11* Ralf Schumacher. *12* Brazil. *13* FIA GT. *14* Jacques Villeneuve. *15* Mika Salo. *16* Italian. *17* 1975. *18* Shadow. *19* Brabham. *20* Niki Lauda.

1 Who was John Watson's team-mate in his first season with McLaren?
2 Name either of the circuits on which Watson won grands prix in 1982.
3 Volker Weidler failed to qualify for which team in 1989?
4 What medical problem forced Weidler to retire from racing several years later?
5 At which grand prix did Karl Wendlinger first score points, in 1992?
6 For which team was he driving?
7 During which year did Wendlinger make his comeback?
8 Ken Wharton finished fourth on his Formula One debut in which 1952 grand prix?
9 Wharton entered what chassis for himself the following year?
10 In what country was Wharton killed when racing at the start of 1957?
11 With which make of chassis did Peter Whitehead make his name before the Second World War?
12 To what category of racing did Whitehead turn when he quit Formula One in 1954?
13 Who was driving the Ferrari in which Whitehead was killed in 1958?
14 From which country did Roger Williamson hail?
15 Which championship did Williamson win in 1972?
16 With which team did Joachim Winkelhock fail ever to get through pre-qualifying in 1989?
17 Which touring car championship did Winkelhock win in 1993?
18 What relation of Joachim Winkelhock's was Manfred Winkelhock?
19 Manfred Winkelhock's only points came for fifth place at which 1982 grand prix?
20 At which circuit did Manfred Winkelhock crash to his death in a sportscar race in 1985?

Answers *THE GREAT RACES 1 (see Quiz 88)*
1 Niki Lauda. 2 Ferrari. 3 It was raining heavily and he couldn't see because of the spray. 4 Mario Andretti. 5 Lotus. 6 Third place. 7 Teddy Mayer. 8 Masahiro Hasemi. 9 Kojima. 10 Patrick Depailler. 11 Niki Lauda. 12 Brabham. 13 Mario Andretti. 14 Jody Scheckter. 15 Riccardo Patrese. 16 Engine failure. 17 Patrick Depailler. 18 Ronnie Peterson. 19 Patrick Depailler. 20 John Watson.

1   At which circuit did Reine Wisell score his first Formula One points?

2   Who was Wisell's team-mate at Lotus in 1971?

3   Which team ran Wisell in 1972?

4   What nationality is Alexander Wurz?

5   What big race did Wurz win in 1996?

6   Did Wurz appear on a grand prix podium in 1998?

7   Who was Wurz's Benetton team-mate in 1998 and 1999?

8   Who beat Alessandro Zanardi to the 1991 Formula 3000 title?

9   Which Italian team ran Zanardi in 1992?

10 For which team did he race in 1994 before leaving for Indycars in 1996?

11 Who was Zanardi's team-mate on his return to Formula One in 1999?

12 From which country does Ricardo Zonta hail?

13 Which international championship did Zonta win immediately before graduating to Formula One?

14 Who was Zonta's team-mate at British American Racing in 1999?

15 Who was Zonta's stand-in when he missed three grands prix through injury?

16 What nationality is Renzo Zorzi?

17 In which year did Zorzi win the Monaco Formula Three race?

18 For which team did he race in the first third of the 1977 season?

19 Ricardo Zunino made his Formula One debut with which team in 1979?

20 Who quit the sport to give Zunino this opportunity?

Answers THE DRIVERS 43 *(see Quiz 85)*

1 Heinz-Harald Frentzen. **2** British American Racing. **3** Italian. **4** Ferrari (Argentine and Belgian Grands Prix). **5** 1951. **6** Car manufacturing (Opel). **7** Ensign. **8** Brabham. **9** Italian (third). **10** Dutch. **11** "La Passione". **12** Australian. **13** Lotus. **14** Emerson Fittipaldi. **15** Brian Henton. **16** British. **17** Brabham. **18** Arrows. **19** Northern Ireland. **20** Brabham.

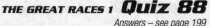

---

1 Who arrived at the 1976 Japanese Grand Prix leading the title race?

2 For which team was he driving?

3 Why did he pull off at the end of the second lap?

4 Who took the lead with 10 laps to go and went on to win?

5 For which team was he driving?

6 Which position was just enough to clinch James Hunt the title?

7 Name the McLaren team boss who had to convince Hunt he'd done enough.

8 Which Japanese driver set the race's fastest lap?

9 What make of car was he driving?

10 Who finished second in a Tyrrell?

11 Who started the 1978 South African Grand Prix in pole position?

12 For which team was he driving?

13 Who led the early laps?

14 Name the local hero who took the lead for Wolf.

15 Which driver then took the lead for Arrows?

16 Why did he retire?

17 Who took over the lead?

18 Who nipped past on the final lap to win?

19 Which Tyrrell driver finished second?

20 And which Brabam driver finished third?

Answers *THE DRIVERS 44 (see Quiz 86)*

1 Patrick Tambay. **2** Zolder, Detroit. **3** Rial. **4** An ear problem. **5** Canadian. **6** March. **7** 1995.
8 Swiss. **9** Cooper. **10** New Zealand. **11** ERA. **12** Sportscars. **13** His half-brother Graham.
14 England. **15** British Formula Three. **16** AGS. **17** British. **18** Brother. **19** Brazilian.
20 Mosport Park.

1   Who led the 1982 Monaco Grand Prix until three laps from the end?

2   For which team was he driving?

3   Why did he retire?

4   Who took over the lead?

5   For which team was he driving?

6   Who took over the lead when he spun?

7   Who should have won but stopped in the tunnel on the final lap?

8   Name the Irish driver who brieldly looked set to come through to win.

9   For which team was he driving?

10 After all this, who came through to win?

11 Who qualified in pole position for the 1985 Portuguese Grand Prix and led every lap?

12 What were the weather conditions before the start of the race?

13 For which team was he driving?

14 What engine powered him to success?

15 Name the team manager who greeted him on his return to the pits.

16 Who was driving for Ferrari as replacement for René Arnoux?

17 Name his team-mate who came second.

18 Who finished third for Renault?

19 Which Italian driver ran in second place behind his team-mate in the early laps?

20 Who was the first driver home – in sixth place – in a non-turbo car?

Answers THE CIRCUITS 1 *(see Quiz 91)*

1 Alexander Wurz's. 2 Damon Hill. 3 Aintree. 4 Liverpool. 5 Sweden. 6 It's not by the start/finish line. 7 Jean Behra. 8 Dell. 9 Stirling's Bend. 10 Switzerland. 11 Overhanging trees. 12 Ascari. 13 Giancarlo Fisichella. 14 Clermont-Ferrand. 15 Charade. 16 Dallas. 17 Fair Park. 18 1982. 19 The Renaissance Center. 20 René Arnoux and Gilles Villeneuve.

1 Who led the early laps of the 1986 Australian Grand Prix?

2 What make of car was he driving?

3 Who took the lead for McLaren?

4 Who was running a safe third and set for the title?

5 Why did he fail?

6 Why was his team-mate called into the pits?

7 Who came through to win the race and the title?

8 The Ferrari driver who finished third was a lap down. Who was he?

9 Which British team had both its drivers in the points?

10 Which British driver rounded out his only season of Formula One with sixth place?

11 Where was the 1968 German Grand Prix held?

12 What was the prevalent weather condition?

13 Who started in pole position in a Brabham?

14 Who took the lead on the opening lap and went on to score a famous win?

15 What make of car was he driving?

16 What handicap was the race-winner carrying?

17 Who finished second for Lotus?

18 Who challenged for Ferrari, but spun out?

19 Which driver finished third?

20 For which team was he driving?

Answers THE CIRCUITS 2 *(see Quiz 92)*

1 Parabolique. 2 Donington Park. 3 East London. 4 Jim Clark. 5 It was blown off in a storm.
6 The circuit was considered unsafe. 7 Gilles Villeneuve. 8 A volcano. 9 1970. 10 Eddie Irvine.
11 Budapest. 12 Damon Hill. 13 1980. 14 Tosa. 15 2000. 16 Fera Dura. 17 Mika Hakkinen.
18 Reclaimed marshland. 19 Nelson Piquet. 20 Gilles Villeneuve.

1 Which Formula One driver's family was involved in the creation of the A1-Ring?
2 Who was the last driver to win an Australian Grand Prix in Adelaide?
3 Which British circuit is more famous for horse racing?
4 In the outskirts of which city is it located?
5 In which country would you find Anderstorp?
6 What's unusual about its pit lane?
7 Which French driver was killed when he flew over the banking at Avus?
8 Complete the name of this corner at Brands Hatch. Dingle ----?
9 What's the name of the corner that follows it?
10 In which country would you find Bremgarten?
11 What made its track surface treacherous?
12 Name the corner at the end of the back straight at Buenos Aires.
13 Who survived a huge shunt when testing at Catalunya in 1998?
14 Which former grand prix circuit is located in France's Massif central?
15 By what shortened name is it now known?
16 Which Texan city hosted a grand prix in 1984?
17 By what name was the circuit known?
18 In what year did Detroit first host a grand prix?
19 What was the name of the huge building that overlooked the circuit?
20 Which two drivers had a famous scrap for second at Dijon-Prenois in 1979?

Answers THE GREAT RACES 2 *(see Quiz 89)*

1 Alain Prost. 2 Renault. 3 He crashed. 4 Riccardo Patrese. 5 Brabham. 6 Didier Pironi.
7 Andrea de Cesaris. 8 Derek Daly. 9 Williams. 10 Riccardo Patrese. 11 Ayrton Senna. 12 Torrential rain. 13 Lotus. 14 Renault. 15 Peter Warr. 16 Stefan Johansson. 17 Michele Alboreto.
18 Patrick Tambay. 19 Elio di Angelis. 20 Stefan Bellof.

1   At Dijon-Prenois, name the corner at the end of the loop added in 1977.
2   Which British circuit hosted the Auto Union and Mercedes teams in the late 1930s?
3   Which South African circuit was built in a seaside park?
4   Who won two of the three world championship rounds held there?
5   What happened to the roof of the main grandstand at Estoril?
6   Why was Estoril dropped from the Formula One calendar in 1997?
7   Who flew over Ronnie Peterson's car and into an officials' area at Fuji in 1977?
8   The circuit at Fuji is built on the slopes of what?
9   In which year did Hockenheim first host the German Grand Prix?
10 Who won there for Ferrari in 1999?
11 Outside which Hungarian city would you find the Hungaroring?
12 Which driver came within half of a lap of winning the 1997 race there?
13 In what year did Imola host the Italian Grand Prix for the only time?
14 What's the name of Imola's first hairpin?
15 In which year will the Indianapolis Motor Speedway first host a proper Formula One race?
16 What is the name of the uphill right-hander behind the pits at Interlagos?
17 Who won the Brazilian Grand Prix at Interlagos for the second year in succession in 1999?
18 On what sort of land was Rio's Jacarepagua circuit built?
19 This circuit is now renamed in honour of which Brazilian hero?
20 The Spanish Grand Prix was held at Jarama for the last time in 1981. Who held up a procession of cars to win?

Answers THE GREAT RACES 3 (see Quiz 90)

1 Nelson Piquet. 2 Williams. 3 Keke Rosberg. 4 Nigel Mansell. 5 His Williams had a tyre blow-out. 6 For a precautionary check on his tyres. 7 Alain Prost. 8 Stefan Johansson. 9 Tyrrell. 10 Johnny Dumfries. 11 Nurburgring. 12 Heavy Rain. 13 Jacky Ickx. 14 Jackie Stewart. 15 Matra. 16 A broken wrist (suffered in a Formula Two race). 17 Graham Hill. 18 Chris Amon. 19 Jochen Rindt. 20 Brabham.

1   Why was a chicane built before the fast right behind the paddock at Jerez in 1992?

2   Who scored his first win there in the 1997 title shoot-out?

3   What was the name of the corner at the end of the main straight on the original Kyalami layout?

4   Which American gambling city held a grand prix in 1981 and 1982?

5   The temporary circuit was in the car park of which famous hotel and casino?

6   Which famous French circuit has hosted only one grand prix?

7   What was the name of the version of the circuit used?

8   What was the name of the bending waterfront start/finish straight at Long Beach?

9   Who was crippled when he crashed into a car parked in the escape road at the end of this straight in 1980?

10   After which circuit is the second corner at Magny-Cours named?

11   Name the right-hander near the end of the lap that was suitably named for the wet 1999 race?

12   Is the first corner at Melbourne a right-left or a left-right ess?

13   Who destroyed his car at Melbourne's second corner in 1996?

14   Name the tight hairpin at Monaco.

15   Who crashed in Monaco's tunnel in 1998?

16   In which Spanish city would you find Montjuich Park?

17   Whose car vaulted the barriers and killed four onlookers in 1975?

18   The Circuit Gilles Villeneuve in Montreal is located on the banks of the which river?

19   What's the name of the fast right-hander after the first chicane at Monza?

20   What's the name of the chicane after the track has dipped under the old track?

Answers THE BUSINESS OF FORMULA ONE 1 (see Quiz 95)

1 Moscow. **2** Arrows (Nordica). **3** Australian. **4** Toleman. **5** Coffee. **6** Benetton. **7** Brabham. **8** Williams (Canon). **9** AGS. **10** USF&G. **11** Leyton House. **12** Coloni. **13** Minardi. **14** Peter Collins. **15** Onyx. **16** Nigel Mansell. **17** March. **18** Tyrrell (Braun). **19** Seven-Up. **20** Fuji Film.

1 What weather conditions tended to be predominant at Mosport Park?

2 Name the circuit near Brussels that hosted the Belgian Grand Prix in 1972 and 1974.

3 Who won both of those races?

4 In which region of Germany would you find the Nürburgring?

5 At which point on the old circuit were cars expected to take off, according to its name?

6 From the production of what did Paul Ricard raise the money to build his circuit?

7 What's the name of the circuit's back straight?

8 What is the full name of the Rouen circuit?

9 The first US Grand Prix was hosted at which circuit in 1959?

10 What is Sebring's primary use?

11 In which English county is Silverstone located?

12 Name the first corner.

13 What's the closest Belgian city to Spa-Francorchamps?

14 What's the name of the circuit's artificial chicane at the end of the lap?

15 Name the first corner at Suzuka.

16 What's the name of the corner before Suzuka's start/finish straight?

17 In what year did Watkins Glen host the US Grand Prix for the last time?

18 Does the circuit's first corner turn left or right?

19 What is the prevalent language in the district of Belgium where Zolder is located?

20 After which Belgian driver is Zolder's final chicane named?

Answers *THE BUSINESS OF FORMULA ONE 2 (see Quiz 96)*

1 Keke Rosberg. 2 Jaguar. 3 Sasol. 4 Alain Prost. 5 Bravo. 6 Cyril de Rouvre. 7 Klaus Waltz. 8 England. 9 The Belgian Grand Prix in 1992. 10 Simtek. 11 March (Uliveto). 12 Tom Walkinshaw. 13 Ayrton Senna. 14 Williams. 15 March. 16 Huub Rothengatter. 17 Minardi and Scuderia Italia. 18 Lotus (Loctite). 19 Mild Seven. 20 Camel.

1   Bernie Ecclestone visited which capital city in 1982 to discuss the possibility of hosting a grand prix?

2   If you wanted ski boots in 1983, which team would have sprung to mind?

3   What was the clothing company that backed Spirit in the mid 1980s?

4   Which team was backed by Segafredo in 1984?

5   What does Segafredo make?

6   The Toleman team was backed by which Italian clothing company in 1985?

7   If you wanted an Olivetti typewriter in the mid 1980s, which team would you have approached?

8   But if it was a photocopier or camera, to which team would you have turned?

9   Which team was sponsored by Charro in 1986 and 1987?

10 Arrows was sponsored by which finance house in the late 1980s?

11 Which Japanese company backed March in the late 1980s?

12 The Himont company backed which team in the late 1980s?

13 Which team was backed by Spanish jeans manufacturer Lois in the late 1980s?

14 Which Benetton team manager resigned in 1989?

15 Belgian financier Jean-Pierre van Rossem backed which team with his Moneytron company in 1989?

16 Which driver opened a Ferrari dealership in Dorset?

17 Which team moved into financial services with disastrous consequences?

18 If you wanted an electric razor in 1991, to which team would you have looked?

19 Which soft drinks company sponsored Jordan in 1991, its maiden season?

20 And which camera film manufacturer was a co-sponsor of Jordan?

Answers THE CIRCUITS 3 *(see Quiz 93)*

1 Because of Martin Donnelly's accident there in 1990. *2* Mika Hakkinen. *3* Crowthorne. *4* Las Vegas. *5* Caesar's Palace. *6* Le Mans in 1967. *7* Bugatti. *8* Shoreline Drive. *9* Clay Regazzoni. *10* Estoril. *11* Chateau d'Eau. *12* Right-left. *13* Martin Brundle. *14* Loews. *15* Alexander Wurz. *16* Barcelona. *17* Rolf Stommelen's. *18* St Lawrence. *19* Curva Grande. *20* Ascari.

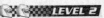
1   Which former world champion helped Mika Hakkinen into Formula One?

2   Which sportscar manufacturer is to have its name on a Formula One team for the first time in 2000?

3   Which South African oil company became Jordan's main sponsor in 1992?

4   Name the former world champion who took a year's sabbatical from driving.

5   Name the proposed Spanish Formula One team that failed when Jean-François Mosnier died?

6   To whom did Guy Ligier sell the Ligier team at the end of 1992?

7   Name the Larrousse team partner who shot himself after a police siege in Germany.

8   In what country did John Barnard base his GTO design agency that worked for Ferrari?

9   At which race was Andrea Moda boss Andrea Sassetti arrested and his cars impounded?

10 Music television channel MTV backed which team in the mid 1990s?

11 If you wanted a drink of mineral water in 1992, which team would you have approached?

12 Which team boss was voted off the board of the British Racing Drivers' Club in 1992?

13 Which driver offered his services to Frank Williams for free for 1993?

14 Rothmans sponsored which team from 1994 to 1997?

15 With which Formula One team had Rothmans previously been involved?

16 Jos Verstappen reached Formula One thanks to the managerial efforts of which former Formula One racer?

17 Which two teams merged for 1994?

18 If you wanted glue in 1994, which team would you approach?

19 Which Japanese tobacco company took over as Benetton's main sponsor in 1994?

20 Which tobacco company did it take over from?

Answers *THE CIRCUITS 4* (see Quiz 94)

1 Rain. *2* Nivelles. *3* Emerson Fittipaldi. *4* Eifel. *5* The Flugplatz. *6* Pastis. *7* Mistral. *8* Rouen-les-Essarts. *9* Sebring. *10* It's an airfield. *11* Northamptonshire. *12* Copse. *13* Liège. *14* Bus Stop. *15* Spoon Curve. *16* Casio Triangle. *17* 1980. *18* Right. *19* Flemish. *20* Jacky Ickx.

1 When did high-mounted aerofoils start appearing in Formula One?
2 Lotus introduced a gas turbine-engined car to Formula One in which year?
3 Which team introduced a car with a high-mounted "tea tray" front wing?
4 Which team introduced a six-wheeled car in 1976?
5 Who designed this revolutionary car?
6 Which team followed suit in 1977?
7 Who designed this car?
8 How did the two teams' cars differ?
9 Who introduced ground-effect technology to Formula One?
10 In which year's world championship?
11 Which team introduced turbocharging to Formula One that same year?
12 What was the cubic capacity of all the engines in 1979?
13 What moving body part was outlawed at the end of 1980?
14 Renault was the first team to run a turbocharged engine. Which team followed suit in 1981?
15 Which team introduced a carbon-fibre monocoque in 1981?
16 A dual-chassis was introduced by which team in 1981 but never raced?
17 Which tyre manufacturer returned to Formula One midway through the 1981 season?
18 When Porsche became an engine supplier in 1983, what was the name of the company that financed it?
19 Which tyre supplier withdrew from Formula One at the end of 1984?
20 What was the name of the suspension that thought for itself in the late 1980s?

Answers FAN CULTURE (see Quiz 99)

1 John Frankenheimer. *2* John Young Stewart. *3* Jumper. *4* Because it was an anglicization of Jean-Pierre used by the March team. *5* Niki Lauda. *6* The Rat. *7* The Rabbit. *8* A scorpion. *9* A teddybear. *10* Vittorio Brambilla. *11* Because many felt that he drove with all the finesse of one. *12* Durex. *13* Jody Scheckter. *14* Ayrton Senna da Silva. *15* Mansellmania. *16* Naoki Hattori. *17* Bob Judd. *18* James Hunt. *19* Jonathan Palmer. *20* Jacques Villeneuve.

1 What was banned for 1985?

2 What was reduced for the same season?

3 The teams were told in 1987 that what type of engine was going to be outlawed for 1989?

4 What was the maximum capacity for normally aspirated engines?

5 What was moved back behind the line of the front axle in 1988?

6 Which tyre supplier returned to Formula One in 1989?

7 When did the scoring system last change?

8 What has a win been worth since then?

9 In 1992, when a circuit was blocked after an accident, the race was no longer stopped by a red flag. What was used instead?

10 What became mandatory for the 1994 season?

11 What is the name of the lever that keeps the fuel flowing during a pit stop?

12 Which team led the campaign for higher cockpit sides?

13 In which year did qualifying revert to just one session on the Saturday?

14 What sort of accident-recording devices were fitted to the cars from 1997?

15 How many red lights are lit and then go off to signal the start of a grand prix?

16 What sort of rubber was made mandatory for 1998?

17 Which team introduced "periscope" exhausts through the top of the sidepods in 1998?

18 After which 1998 grand prix were sidepod-mounted winglets banned?

19 How many tyres may a driver use in qualifying?

20 How long are stop-go penalties?

Answers *SCANDALS AND DISASTERS* (see Quiz 100)

1 Brabham. *2* Because it was thought to keep the car on the track by suction. *3* Cooling the engine. *4* Lotus. *5* Fred Bushell. *6* Spanish. *7* FOCA versus FISA. *8* David Thieme. *9* Osella. *10* Arrows. *11* Riccardo Patrese's. *12* It effectively had one chassis piggy-backing on top of the other and thus breached the rules. *13* The FOCA teams. *14* Didier Pironi. *15* Gilles Villeneuve. *16* It had flown out hordes of journalists to watch him win the world championship. *17* Ayrton Senna. *18* Frank Williams. *19* Elio de Angelis. *20* Marc Surer.

1   Name the director of the 1960s' film "Grand Prix".

2   What is the full version of Jackie Stewart's name?

3   What was the nickname the March team gave Jean-Pierre Jarier?

4   Why?

5   Which world champion left the sport and built up an airline before returning to Formula One acing?

6   What was the nickname coined for him at the 1977 Belgian Grand Prix by David Purley?

7   What did he call Purley for getting in his way?

8   What became the symbol of the Brabham team?

9   What was the emblem of the Hesketh team in the mid 1970's?

10 Which Italian driver was known as the Monza Gorilla?

11 Why?

12 Which Surtees team sponsor raised a few eyebrows in 1976?

13 Which world champion became World Superstars Champion on TV in 1981?

14 What was Ayrton Senna's full name?

15 Name the fever that gripped British fans in the late 1980s and early 1990s.

16 Which driver entered the 1991 Japanese Grand Prix thanks to hundreds of enthusiasts who paid to have their names on his Coloni's sidepods?

17 Name the American author who wrote a handful of novels based on Formula One.

18 Name the world champion who was foil to Murray Walker in BBC's commentary box.

19 Which British driver was the first to replace him?

20 Which former world champion had Dannii Minogue as his girlfriend in 1999??

Answers EQUIPMENT (see Quiz 97)

1 1968. *2* 1971. *3* March. *4* Tyrrell. *5* Derek Gardner. *6* March. *7* Robin Herd. *8* The Tyrrell had four wheels at the front, the March four at the back. *9* Lotus. *10* 1977. *11* Renault. *12* 3.5 litres. *13* Skirts. *14* Ferrari. *15* McLaren. *16* Lotus. *17* Goodyear. *18* TAG. *19* Michelin. *20* Active suspension.

1 Which team shocked the others when it entered what was described as a "fan car" in the 1978 Swedish Grand Prix?

2 Why was this thought to be illegal?

3 What did its designer say the fan was for?

4 The chairman of which team was arrested in 1979 on charges of trying to defraud the De Lorean Motor Company?

5 Who was this?

6 Which grand prix was pulled from the championship in 1980 after political division?

7 Which parties were at war?

8 Name the Lotus sponsor from Essex petroleum who was arrested in 1981 for financial malpractice.

9 Which team had a mechanic killed in the cramped Zolder pit lane in 1981?

10 Which team had a mechanic hit on the grid at the same race?

11 Whose car was he attending?

12 Why did the FIA refuse to allow Lotus to enter its 88B chassis for the 1981 British Grand Prix?

13 Which teams boycotted the 1982 San Marino Grand Prix?

14 Who broke an alleged pre-race agreement to win that race?

15 With whom did he fall out as a result of this?

16 Why was Renault embarrassed after Alain Prost lost out in the 1983 finale in South Africa?

17 Who refused to let Lotus sign Derek Warwick for 1986?

18 Which team boss was paralysed in a car crash before the start of the 1986 season?

19 Which Brabham driver died when testing at Paul Ricard in 1986?

20 Which Swiss driver ended his Formula One career after crashing in a rally, killing his co-driver?

Answers *RULES AND TACTICS* (see Quiz 98)

1 Chilled fuel. 2 Fuel capacity. 3 Turbo engines. 4 3.5 litres. 5 The drivers' feet. 6 Pirelli.
7 1991. 8 10 points. 9 A safety car. 10 Refuelling. 11 Deadman's handle. 12 Sauber. 13 1996.
14 Black boxes. 15 Five. 16 Grooved. 17 Ferrari. 18 San Marino. 19 16 (with up to 40 in a weekend). 20 10 seconds.

Hard Questions

Some among you will have reached this far relatively unscathed, still confident that you really know the subject. Well, maybe you do, but here is something to stretch you: 2,000 questions, some of which dig into the deep and long-forgotten recesses of their subject. I haven't asked which contemporary driver has twice been pulled over by the police for speeding on his way to the British Grand Prix, but I could have done. Equally, I haven't asked about the peculiar way in which Giulio Caibianca met his death at Modena in 1961 – his throttle stuck open and he shot through an open gate on to the street, crashing into a taxi and killing himself and the three passengers – but I could have done ...

This chapter is the one that will really test your knowledge about the places, drivers and teams that have been left behind as the sport hurtles into the twenty-first century in a form so far removed from the way it was that day at Silverstone in 1950 that it's hard to comprehend it really is the same sport. But despite all the changes and politics of racing, the heart still beats the same way for almost everyone involved.

One red light, two, three, four, five red lights. They're out! The race is go. Good luck!

1   Between which cities was the first-ever car race held?

2   In what year?

3   The first motor-racing fatality occurred in the Paris to Nice race in what year?

4   International racing began with a series named after which newspaper magnate?

5   What was unusual about mechanics at the turn of the century?

6   When was the first-ever grand prix held?

7   Which one was it?

8   Where was it held?

9   Who won it?

10 What make of car was he driving?

11 Why were there no grands prix between 1915 and 1920?

12 The first Italian Grand Prix was held where in 1921?

13 Who won it?

14 Who was the first British driver to win a grand prix?

15 At which grand prix did he achieve this feat?

16 Alfa Romeo hit the big time in 1924. Which driver scored its first win?

17 Which marque won the first world championship for manufacturers in 1925?

18 Which French marque scored its first win that same year?

19 Which other French marque made its breakthrough in the 1926 French Grand Prix?

20 Mercedes-Benz scored its first grand prix win in 1926 at Avus. Who was driving?

Answers WORLD CHAMPIONSHIPS 1955–59 *(see Quiz 3)*

1 Juan Manuel Fangio. **2** Mercedes. **3** Eugenio Castellotti. **4** Lancia. **5** Jean Behra and Peter Collins. **6** Maserati and Ferrari respectively. **7** Stirling Moss. **8** Ron Flockhart. **9** Juan Manuel Fangio. **10** A Maserati. **11** Mike Hawthorn and Peter Collins. **12** Eugenio Castellotti died testing for Ferrari and Alfonso de Portago died competing in Mille Miglia (a road race). **13** Maserati. **14** Juan Manuel Fangio. **15** The 1958 Dutch Grand Prix. **16** Stirling Moss. **17** Vanwall. **18** Avus. **19** Tony Brooks. **20** Jack Brabham.

1 The Indianapolis 500 was nominally part of the world championship. Who won it in 1950?

2 Which non-Alfa Romeo driver led the 1950 Belgian Grand Prix before his car developed engine trouble?

3 What was different about the Alfa Romeos used by Giuseppe Farina and Juan Manuel Fangio in the 1950 Italian Grand Prix?

4 Why did Juan Manuel Fangio retire from the 1950 Italian Grand Prix and lose the title to Giuseppe Farina?

5 Who finished the 1951 season as runner-up behind Juan Manuel Fangio?

6 For which team was he driving?

7 Name his team-mate who finished third overall.

8 Name either of the two grands prix this runner-up won in 1951.

9 Why did Alberto Ascari miss the first two grands prix of 1952?

10 Where did he finish in his first race of the 1952 season, the Belgian Grand Prix?

11 Who impressed the Silverstone crowd in 1952 by finishing third?

12 What make of car was he driving?

13 Formula One's first fatality occurred at which grand prix?

14 What happened?

15 Which driver was involved?

16 How did Alberto Ascari lose the lead on the last lap of the 1953 Italian Grand Prix?

17 Mercedes made its world championship bow in 1954. What colour were its cars?

18 Who was the Mercedes team manager?

19 With what make of car did Juan Manuel Fangio win the first two grands prix of 1954?

20 Which British driver led the 1954 Italian Grand Prix for Maserati?

Answers *WORLD CHAMPIONSHIPS 1960 & 1961* (see Quiz 4)

1 Ferrari. **2** Coventry Climax. **3** Jim Rathmann. **4** Cliff Allison. **5** John Surtees. **6** Lotus.
7 Jim Clark. **8** Lotus. **9** They considered Monza's banking unsafe. **10** Ferrari. **11** Phil Hill,
Wolfgang von Trips and Richie Ginther. **12** Jo Bonnier and Dan Gurney. **13** Rob Walker.
14 Olivier Gendebien. **15** Aintree. **16** Wolfgang von Trips. **17** Tony Brooks. **18** BRM.
19 Wolfgang von Trips. **20** Wolfgang von Trips.

1 Who won the 1955 world championship?
2 For which team?
3 Who was ranked third overall behind Stirling Moss?
4 For which team did he drive?
5 Juan Manuel Fangio won a three-way title fight at 1956's final grand prix, the Italian. Who were the two disappointed drivers that day?
6 What cars were they driving?
7 Who ended 1956 as runner-up?
8 Who gave Connaught its best-ever finish by coming third in the 1956 Italian Grand Prix?
9 Who won the 1957 German Grand Prix after a fight through the field?
10 What make of car was he driving?
11 Which two British drivers did he overhaul with a lap to go?
12 Name either of the two Ferrari drivers who died early in 1957, albeit not during grands prix.
13 Which works team was missing from the grids in 1958?
14 Which leading driver entered the first two grands prix of 1958 and then quit?
15 At which grand prix did drivers of British-built cars claim the first three places?
16 Who ended 1958 as runner-up?
17 In 1959, another works team quit. Which one was it this time?
18 Which circuit hosted the German Grand Prix for the one and only time in 1959?
19 Who won it for Ferrari?
20 Who was crowned 1959 world champion?

Answers THE ORIGINS OF FORMULA ONE (see Quiz 1)

1 Paris and Rouen. 2 1894. 3 1898. 4 Gordon Bennett. 5 They rode with the driver. 6 1896. 7 French. 8 Le Mans. 9 Ferenc Szisz. 10 A Renault. 11 Because of the First World War. 12 Brescia. 13 Jules Goux. 14 Henry Segrave. 15 The 1923 French Grand Prix. 16 Giuseppe Campari. 17 Alfa Romeo. 18 Delage. 19 Bugatti. 20 Rudolf Caracciola.

---

1 Which established team stuck with front-engined machines for 1960?

2 Which British engine was fitted to most of the rear-engined cars?

3 The Indianapolis 500 was a world championship round for the final time in 1960. Who won it?

4 Who was seriously injured in practice for the 1960 Monaco Grand Prix?

5 Which motorcycle racing champion made his world championship debut at Monaco in 1960?

6 For which team was he driving?

7 Which future British world champion scored his first points on his second outing?

8 For which team was he racing?

9 Why did the British teams boycott the 1960 Italian Grand Prix?

10 Which team was thus left to dominate that grand prix?

11 Name the three regular Ferrari drivers for 1961.

12 Who were the two regular Porsche drivers for 1961?

13 Who entered a Lotus for Stirling Moss?

14 Name the extra Ferrari driver who finished fourth in the 1961 Belgian Grand Prix.

15 Where was the 1961 British Grand Prix held?

16 Who won it?

17 Which British driver rounded off his career with third place at 1961's final race, the United States Grand Prix?

18 For which team was he driving?

19 Who ended the 1961 season as runner-up to champion Phil Hill?

20 Who led the most laps during the 1961 season?

Answers *WORLD CHAMPIONSHIPS 1950–54* (see Quiz 2)

1 Johnnie Parsons. *2* Raymond Sommer. *3* They used the all-new 159 model. *4* His gearbox seized. *5* Alberto Ascari. *6* Ferrari. *7* Jose Froilan Gonzalez. *8* German, Italian. *9* He was qualifying for and then competing in the Indianapolis 500. *10* He won it. *11* Mike Hawthorn. *12* A Cooper. *13* The 1953 Argentinian Grand Prix. *14* A boy ran across the track during the race and was hit. *15* Juan Manuel Fangio. *16* He spun. *17* Silver. *18* Alfred Neubauer. *19* A Maserati. *20* Stirling Moss.

1 Which famous driver was missing from the 1962 season?

2 Why was he missing?

3 Which American joined Graham Hill at BRM in 1962?

4 Who quit Cooper to race his own cars?

5 Name the Lotus driver who finished second in the 1962 season-opening Dutch Grand Prix.

6 Who was the Ferrari driver who chased third-placed team-mate Phil Hill home at Spa in 1962?

7 Who finished second to Jim Clark in the 1962 British Grand Prix?

8 For which team was he driving?

9 What chassis did this team enter for him?

10 Who ended 1962 as runner-up to Graham Hill?

11 Which team was missing from the grids in 1963?

12 Name the team formed by a breakaway of Ferrari employees.

13 Name the Ferrari drivers who went with them.

14 Who finished third for Cooper in the 1963 season-opening Monaco Grand Prix?

15 Who scored four wins in a row for Lotus in 1963 and went on to become world champion?

16 Name the works Cooper driver who finished second in the 1963 French Grand Prix.

17 Name the three British drivers on the podium at the 1963 British Grand Prix.

18 Who was the Dutch aristocrat who scored twice in 1963?

19 What make of car was he driving?

20 Which former world champion made it to the podium with a car of his own design for the first time in the 1963 Mexican Grand Prix?

Answers WORLD CHAMPIONSHIPS 1966 & 1967 *(see Quiz 7)*

1 Dan Gurney. 2 An Eagle. 3 Richie Ginther and Jochen Rindt. 4 John Surtees. 5 To rejoin Honda. 6 The 1966 Belgian Grand Prix. 7 The 1966 British Grand Prix. 8 Mike Parkes (Ludovico Scarfiotti was first). 9 Jo Siffert (Jochen Rindt and John Surtees were second and third). 10 Rob Walker. 11 Jackie Stewart. 12 Mike Spence. 13 Chris Amon. 14 Graham Hill. 15 Lotus. 16 Jim Clark (1967 Dutch Grand Prix). 17 Jack Brabham. 18 Jim Clark. 19 Jim Clark. 20 Jack Brabham.

1 Name the two principal Ferrari drivers for 1964.

2 Who were the BRM drivers for 1964?

3 Which Lotus driver chased the BRM duo home at Monaco that year?

4 Who prevented Brabham scoring a one-two in the 1964 French Grand Prix?

5 Which Brabham driver had to make do with third place that day?

6 Who won the 1964 German Grand Prix for Ferrari?

7 Which Swiss driver finished third in the 1964 United States Grand Prix?

8 Who entered the Brabham he was driving?

9 Name the three drivers who went to 1964's final round with a shot at the title.

10 Where was this final round held?

11 Which Japanese marque made its debut in 1964?

12 Who joined Jack Brabham and Dan Gurney at Brabham for 1965?

13 Name its two drivers.

14 Who chased Jim Clark home in the 1965 South African Grand Prix?

15 Who scored a point for sixth on his debut for BRM that day?

16 Who won the British Grand Prix for the fourth year in a row?

17 At which grand prix did Jim Clark wrap up his second world title?

18 Did he win that day?

19 Who rounded off the 1965 season at the Mexican Grand Prix by finishing third for Lotus?

20 Who finished the 1965 season as runner-up?

Answers **WORLD CHAMPIONSHIPS 1968 & 1969** *(see Quiz 8)*

1 Lotus. **2** Red, white and gold. **3** Ken Tyrrell. **4** Graham Hill. **5** Johnny Servoz-Gavin. **6** A Matra. **7** The 1968 Belgian Grand Prix. **8** Lotus. **9** Mario Andretti. **10** Lotus. **11** Jochen Rindt. **12** Jacky Ickx. **13** Cooper. **14** Chris Amon's. **15** They crashed after their high-mounted aerofoils broke. **16** Jo Siffert. **17** Jochen Rindt. **18** Piers Courage. **19** John Surtees (third – Jochen Rindt was first for Lotus). **20** Jacky Ickx.

1   Which driver quit the Brabham team for 1966?

2   What make of car did he race that year?

3   Name Cooper's two main drivers for 1966.

4   Who joined the team after starting the season with Ferrari?

5   Why did one of the original line-up leave mid-season?

6   At which grand prix was Jackie Stewart injured in a first-lap crash in the rain?

7   At which grand prix did the Brabham team score its first one-two?

8   Ferrari finished first and second at Monza in 1966. Which of their drivers was second?

9   Cooper drivers finished second, third and fourth in the 1966 United States Grand Prix. Which one was fourth?

10   Who entered his Cooper?

11   Who became the number one driver at BRM in 1967?

12   Who was his new number two?

13   Who became the number two at Ferrari that year?

14   Who finished second in the 1967 Monaco Grand Prix?

15   For which team?

16   Who gave the Ford Cosworth DFV its first win?

17   Who won the 1967 French Grand Prix for Brabham?

18   Who won the British Grand Prix for the fifth time in six years?

19   Who led coming into the final lap of the 1967 Italian Grand Prix then ran out of fuel?

20   Who did John Surtees pip to win the race?

Answers WORLD CHAMPIONSHIPS 1962 & 1963 (see Quiz 5)

1 Stirling Moss. 2 He'd been injured in a crash at Goodwood. 3 Richie Ginther. 4 Jack Brabham. 5 Trevor Taylor. 6 Ricardo Rodriguez. 7 John Surtees. 8 Bowmaker Racing Team. 9 A Lola. 10 Jim Clark. 11 Porsche. 12 ATS. 13 Giancarlo Baghetti and Phil Hill. 14 Bruce McLaren. 15 Jim Clark. 16 Tony Maggs. 17 Jim Clark, John Surtees and Graham Hill (in order). 18 Carel Godin de Beaufort. 19 A Porsche. 20 Jack Brabham.

1 Which team won the first race of the 1968 season in South Africa?

2 Sponsorship arrived in 1968 and the yellow and green Lotus livery was changed to what colours?

3 Which team boss snapped up Jackie Stewart's services for 1968?

4 The Spanish Grand Prix was back on the calendar in 1968. Who won this first race at Jarama?

5 Who led the opening laps of the 1968 Monaco Grand Prix then crashed?

6 What make of car was he driving?

7 At which grand prix did Bruce McLaren score the first win in a car bearing his name?

8 Both of which team's drivers retired from the lead of the 1968 British Grand Prix?

9 Which newcomer shocked the establishment by taking pole position for the 1968 United States Grand Prix?

10 For which team was he driving?

11 Who joined Graham Hill at Lotus for 1969?

12 Who filled the seat he'd vacated at Brabham?

13 In 1969, which former title-winning team had quit?

14 Whose Ferrari broke when he was leading the 1969 Spanish Grand Prix?

15 Why did both Lotus drivers retire from the 1969 Spanish Grand Prix?

16 Who finished second behind Jackie Stewart in the 1969 Dutch Grand Prix?

17 Who dropped out of the lead battle at the 1969 British Grand Prix with a loose wing?

18 Which Brabham-driving privateer finished second in the 1969 United States Grand Prix?

19 Which BRM driver made it to the podium in that race?

20 Who finished 1969 as runner-up to Jackie Stewart?

Answers *WORLD CHAMPIONSHIPS 1964 & 1965 (see Quiz 6)*

1 Lorenzo Bandini and John Surtees. *2* Richie Ginther and Graham Hill. *3* Peter Arundell.
4 Graham Hill. *5* Jack Brabham (Dan Gurney won). *6* John Surtees. *7* Jo Siffert (Graham Hill and John Surtees were first and second). *8* Rob Walker. *9* Jim Clark, Graham Hill and John Surtees (Surtees won it). *10* Mexico City. *11* Honda. *12* Denny Hulme. *13* Ronnie Bucknum and Richie Ginther. *14* John Surtees. *15* Jackie Stewart. *16* Jim Clark. *17* The 1965 German Grand Prix. *18* Yes. *19* Mike Spence. *20* Graham Hill.

1 How many teams entered the new March chassis in the first race of 1970, the South African Grand Prix?

2 Name two of the three works March drivers.

3 Who gave March its first win in the 1970 Spanish Grand Prix?

4 Which French driver finished third at Monaco in 1970 for his only podium visit?

5 For which team was he driving?

6 Who guided the classic Lotus 72 chassis to victory on its debut in 1970?

7 In which grand prix was this?

8 Who joined the Tyrrell team mid-season in 1970?

9 Which famous marque made its debut before the 1970 season was out?

10 Who finished 1970 as runner-up to Jochen Rindt?

11 Which triple world champion was missing from the grids in 1971?

12 Who lost victory in the 1971 season-opening South African Grand Prix when his rear radius arm came loose?

13 For which team was he driving?

14 Which team entered by a former world champion made its debut in 1971?

15 Which BRM driver died in a sportscar race mid-season in 1971?

16 Which driver led coming into the final lap of the 1971 Italian Grand Prix but failed to win?

17 Who finished 1971 as runner-up?

18 For which team had he been driving?

19 How many grands prix did he win in 1971?

20 In 1971, which team failed to win a grand prix for the first time since 1959?

Answers WORLD CHAMPIONSHIPS 1974 & 1975 (see Quiz 11)

1 Yardley. 2 Jacky Ickx. 3 Niki Lauda. 4 Patrick Depailler and Jody Scheckter. 5 Jody Scheckter. 6 Ferrari. 7 Carlos Reutemann. 8 Ronnie Peterson. 9 Niki Lauda. 10 Helmuth Koinigg. 11 Denny Hulme. 12 Jochen Mass. 13 Emerson Fittipaldi. 14 Niki Lauda. 15 Graham Hill. 16 Niki Lauda. 17 Brabham. 18 Carlos Reutemann. 19 He crashed on the slowing-down lap. 20 Tony Brise.

1 Who returned to Formula One in 1972 to become McLaren's number two?

2 Which team landed sponsorship from Marlboro for 1972?

3 Who won five grands prix to become 1972 world champion?

4 For which team was he driving?

5 What turned out to be notable about BRM's victory at Monaco in 1972?

6 Where was the 1972 Belgian Grand Prix held?

7 What was unusual about Chris Amon's Matra engine in the 1972 French Grand Prix?

8 Who led home a Ferrari one-two in the 1972 German Grand Prix?

9 Who followed him home in second place?

10 Who rounded off the 1972 season with two wins to finish as runner-up?

11 Who was the new number two driver at Lotus for 1973?

12 From which team had he transferred?

13 Who had replaced Clay Regazzoni as Jacky Ickx's number two at Ferrari?

14 Which Tyrrell driver finished second six times through the 1973 season?

15 In which grand prix did the track break up and cause many cars to skid off?

16 In 1973, which country hosted a grand prix for the first time?

17 Who triggered a massed pile-up at the end of the first lap of the 1973 British Grand Prix?

18 For which team was he driving?

19 Who won the 1973 Dutch Grand Prix?

20 Who impressed by finishing second in the 1973 United States Grand Prix in a March?

Answers WORLD CHAMPIONSHIPS 1976 & 1977 *(see Quiz 12)*

1 Niki Lauda. 2 Tom Pryce. 3 Parnelli (South African and United States West). 4 Lotus. 5 His car was adjudged to be too wide. 6 Tall air boxes. 7 Carlos Reutemann. 8 Rolf Stommelen then Larry Perkins. 9 Patrick Depailler. 10 Masahiro Hasemi. 11 Ensign. 12 John Watson. 13 Ground effects. 14 Niki Lauda. 15 In a flying accident. 16 Hans-Joachim Stuck. 17 Renault. 18 Jean-Pierre Jabouille. 19 James Hunt. 20 Niki Lauda.

1 In 1974, the number one and two McLaren drivers were sponsored by Marlboro and Texaco. Who backed Mike Hailwood's number three McLaren?

2 Who jumped ship from Ferrari to join Lotus for 1974?

3 Who replaced him at Ferrari?

4 Name Tyrrell's two new drivers for 1974.

5 Who won the 1974 British Grand Prix?

6 Which team won the 1974 German Grand Prix?

7 Who won the 1974 Austrian Grand Prix for Brabham?

8 Who won the 1974 Italian Grand Prix for Lotus after the Ferraris failed?

9 Who crashed out of the lead of the 1974 Canadian Grand Prix?

10 Which driver was killed during the 1974 United States Grand Prix?

11 Which former world champion was missing from the grids in 1975?

12 Who had taken his place at McLaren?

13 Who won the 1975 season-opening Argentinian Grand Prix?

14 Who won the 1975 Monaco Grand Prix for Ferrari?

15 Which former world champion retired in 1975 after failing to qualify at Monaco?

16 Whose victory at Paul Ricard in 1975 was his fourth of the year?

17 Which team won the 1975 German Grand Prix?

18 Who was its winning driver?

19 What did Vittorio Brambilla do after winning the 1975 Austrian Grand Prix?

20 Which novice driver died in a flying accident after the end of the 1975 season?

Answers WORLD CHAMPIONSHIPS 1970 & 1971 *(see Quiz 9)*

1 Two. March and Tyrrell entered March chassis for the South African GP. **2** Chris Amon, Mario Andretti, Jo Siffert. **3** Jackie Stewart. **4** Henri Pescarolo. **5** Matra. **6** Jochen Rindt. **7** Dutch. **8** François Cevert. **9** Tyrrell. **10** Jacky Ickx. **11** Jack Brabham. **12** Denny Hulme. **13** McLaren. **14** Surtees. **15** Pedro Rodriguez. **16** Ronnie Peterson. **17** Ronnie Peterson. **18** March. **19** None. **20** Lotus.

1   Who won the first two grands prix of 1976?

2   Who finished third for Shadow in the 1976 Brazilian Grand Prix?

3   For which team did Mario Andretti drive in the second and third grands prix of 1976?

4   For which team did he contest the other grands prix that year?

5   Why was James Hunt initially disqualified from the 1976 Spanish Grand Prix?

6   What had been banned for that race?

7   Who joined Ferrari after Niki Lauda was badly injured?

8   Who took his place at Brabham?

9   Who finished second behind Mario Andretti in the 1976 Japanese Grand Prix?

10   Who set the race's fastest lap?

11   To which team did Clay Regazzoni transfer in 1977 after being shown the door by Ferrari?

12   Which British driver joined Brabham in 1977?

13   What form of aerodynamic technology did Lotus introduce in 1977?

14   Who returned to winning ways for Ferrari in the 1977 South African Grand Prix?

15   How did Carlos Pace die?

16   Who replaced him at Brabham?

17   Which team made its championship debut at the 1977 British Grand Prix?

18   Who was its driver?

19   Who won the race?

20   The German Grand Prix moved to Hockenheim in 1977 as the Nürburgring was considered unsafe. Who won?

Answers *WORLD CHAMPIONSHIPS 1972 & 1973 (see Quiz 10)*
1 Peter Revson. 2 BRM. 3 Emerson Fittipaldi. 4 Lotus. 5 It was the marque's final grand prix win. 6 Nivelles. 7 It was a sportscar unit. 8 Jacky Ickx. 9 Clay Regazzoni.
10 Jackie Stewart. 11 Ronnie Peterson. 12 March. 13 Arturo Merzario. 14 François Cevert.
15 The 1973 Belgian Grand Prix. 16 Sweden. 17 Jody Scheckter. 18 McLaren. 19 Jackie Stewart. 20 James Hunt.

1   Who replaced Jochen Mass at McLaren in 1978?

2   To which team had Jochen Mass moved?

3   Who led the 1978 South African Grand Prix for Arrows until his engine blew?

4   Which Ferrari driver won at Long Beach in 1978?

5   Which team introduced the fan car in an attempt to keep up with Lotus?

6   Which grand prix did they win before the car was withdrawn?

7   Who won the 1978 Austrian Grand Prix for Lotus?

8   Which driver suffered head injuries in the pile-up at the start of the 1978 Italian Grand Prix?

9   Which driver was blamed by the others for causing the pile-up and banned by them from the next race?

10 Name the Lotus stand-in who led the 1978 Canadian Grand Prix.

11 Who joined Gilles Villeneuve at Ferrari for 1979?

12 Who ran a privately entered Lotus in 1979?

13 What nationality is he?

14 Which Ferrari driver led home a Ferrari one-two at Long Beach in 1979?

15 Who won the 1979 Spanish Grand Prix for Ligier?

16 Name the Tyrrell driver who finished third in the 1979 British Grand Prix.

17 Who inherited victory in the 1979 Dutch Grand Prix?

18 What kept Gilles Villeneuve behind Jody Scheckter in the 1979 Italian Grand Prix?

19 Who lost a wheel when leading the 1979 Canadian Grand Prix?

20 Who finished 1979 as runner-up?

Answers WORLD CHAMPIONSHIPS 1982 & 1983 *(see Quiz 15)*

1 Teo Fabi. 2 Long Beach. 3 Tyrrell. 4 Didier Pironi's. 5 Niki Lauda. 6 Derek Warwick. 7 He broke both of his legs at Hockenheim. 8 Patrick Tambay. 9 Mario Andretti. 10 Didier Pironi and John Watson. 11 Raul Boesel and Jean-Pierre Jarier. 12 Danny Sullivan. 13 Nelson Piquet. 14 Niki Lauda. 15 Alain Prost. 16 Andrea de Cesaris. 17 Brands Hatch. 18 Alain Prost. 19 Renault. 20 Andrea de Cesaris.

1 Name the two Alfa Romeo drivers for 1980.

2 Who were the two regular Lotus drivers for 1980?

3 What did Alan Jones do three times en route to victory in the 1980 Argentinian Grand Prix?

4 For which team was Clay Regazzoni driving when he was paralysed following a crash at Long Beach?

5 Who was second behind Nelson Piquet at Long Beach in 1980?

6 Where was the non-championship Formula FOCA race held at the height of the FISA v FOCA war?

7 Who won the 1980 British Grand Prix at Brands Hatch?

8 Who had made the early running for Ligier in the same race?

9 Who won three grands prix to finish 1980 as runner-up?

10 Name the two former world champions who quit Formula One after the 1980 season-closing Canadian Grand Prix.

11 Who took over the McLaren team for 1981?

12 Name the driver who joined Bruno Giacomelli at Alfa Romeo for 1981.

13 Why did Lotus withdraw from the 1981 San Marino Grand Prix?

14 Which team had one of its mechanics killed in the Zolder pit lane?

15 A mechanic had his legs broken on the grid for that same race. Which team was he from?

16 Why was the 1981 French Grand Prix split into two parts?

17 Who scored his only point by finishing sixth in the 1981 British Grand Prix for ATS?

18 Who won the 1981 Canadian Grand Prix to go to the final round in third place overall?

19 Who ended 1981 as runner-up?

20 Which new team's drivers qualified just twice all season?

Answers *WORLD CHAMPIONSHIPS 1984 & 1985* (see Quiz 16)
1 Michele Alboreto. 2 Andrea de Cesaris and François Hesnault. 3 Honda. 4 Because of heavy rain. 5 Alain Prost. 6 Ayrton Senna. 7 Nürburgring. 8 Alain Prost. 9 Estoril. 10 Elio de Angelis (Lotus). 11 Jacques Laffite. 12 Arrows. 13 Stefan Bellof and Martin Brundle. 14 Very wet. 15 Keke Rosberg. 16 Teo Fabi. 17 Zandvoort. 18 Niki Lauda. 19 Australia. 20 Michele Alboreto.

1 Who joined Derek Warwick at Toleman for 1982?

2 Where did Niki Lauda score the first win of his Formula One return?

3 Which was the only one of the FOCA teams to turn up for the 1982 San Marino Grand Prix?

4 Whose stationary car did Riccardo Paletti hit on the grid at Montreal?

5 Who won the 1982 British Grand Prix at Brands Hatch?

6 Who briefly ran second in that race?

7 How did Didier Pironi's career end?

8 Who won the 1982 German Grand Prix for Ferrari?

9 Who was called in to replace Pironi at Ferrari?

10 Which two drivers ended 1982 ranked equal second behind Keke Rosberg?

11 It was all-change at Ligier for 1983. Name the two new drivers.

12 Who was the American driving for Tyrrell in 1983?

13 Who won the first race of 1983 for Brabham?

14 Who finished second behind his team-mate at Long Beach in 1983?

15 Who won the 1983 Belgian Grand Prix?

16 Who finished second in the 1983 German Grand Prix for Alfa Romeo?

17 Which circuit hosted the 1983 Grand Prix of Europe?

18 Who lost out in the 1983 championship shoot-out at the final round?

19 For which team was he driving?

20 Who finished second behind race-winner Riccardo Patrese?

Answers WORLD CHAMPIONSHIP 1978 & 1979 (see Quiz 13)

1 Patrick Tambay. 2 ATS. 3 Riccardo Patrese. 4 Carlos Reutemann. 5 Brabham. 6 The 1978 Swedish Grand Prix. 7 Ronnie Peterson. 8 Vittorio Brambilla. 9 Riccardo Patrese. 10 Jean-Pierre Jarier. 11 Jody Scheckter. 12 Hector Rebaque. 13 Mexican. 14 Gilles Villeneuve. 15 Patrick Depailler. 16 Jean-Pierre Jarier. 17 Alan Jones. 18 Team orders. 19 Alan Jones. 20 Gilles Villeneuve.

1　Who joined René Arnoux at Ferrari in 1984?

2　Who were the new faces at Ligier that year?

3　What make of engine did Keke Rosberg use to finish second for Williams at Kyalami in 1984?

4　Why was the 1984 Monaco Grand Prix stopped early?

5　Who was in front when it was stopped?

6　Who was closing fast in second place?

7　Which circuit returned to the championship in 1984, albeit in hugely modified form?

8　Who won the race there?

9　Where did the championship shoot-out between the McLaren drivers take place that year?

10　Who ended up best-of-the-rest behind the McLaren drivers in 1984's final rankings?

11　Who rejoined Ligier for 1985?

12　Which team snapped up Gerhard Berger for his first full season?

13　Name the two regular Tyrrell drivers for 1985.

14　What were the weather conditions for the 1985 Portuguese Grand Prix?

15　Who averaged over 160mph around Silverstone to take pole position for the 1985 British Grand Prix?

16　Who caused a surprise by qualifying on pole position for Toleman for the 1985 German Grand Prix?

17　In 1985, which circuit hosted a grand prix for the final time?

18　Who won there?

19　Which country joined the world championship for the first time in 1985 and hosted the last race of the year?

20　Who finished 1985 as runner-up?

Answers *WORLD CHAMPIONSHIPS 1980 & 1981* (see Quiz 14)
1 Patrick Depailler and Bruno Giacomelli. **2** Mario Andretti and Elio de Angelis. **3** Spin.
4 Ensign. **5** Riccardo Patrese. **6** Jarama. **7** Alan Jones. **8** Didier Pironi. **9** Nelson Piquet.
10 Emerson Fittipaldi and Jody Scheckter. **11** Ron Dennis. **12** Mario Andretti. **13** Its Lotus 88B was banned. **14** Osella. **15** Arrows. **16** Because of heavy rain. **17** Slim Borgudd. **18** Jacques Laffite. **19** Carlos Reutemann. **20** Toleman.

1   Who had crossed over from Lotus to Brabham for 1986?

2   Toleman had metamorphosed into what team?

3   Name its drivers.

4   Who won the 1986 Monaco Grand Prix?

5   Who won four of the next five grands prix?

6   Who interrupted his run of wins by winning in Detroit?

7   Why was Marc Surer replaced at Arrows?

8   Which engine propelled Benetton to two late-season pole positions in 1986 but no wins?

9   Why did Keke Rosberg retire from the lead of the 1986 Australian Grand Prix?

10 What was Nigel Mansell's final ranking in 1986?

11 What was the final version of the Ford Cosworth DFV known as?

12 What engines were Lotus using in 1987, instead of Renault?

13 As a consequence, which driver filled the number two Lotus seat?

14 Which team caused the 1987 Belgian Grand Prix to be restarted when its cars collided?

15 Who picked up a surprise third place in the restart?

16 For which team was he driving?

17 Who made up for a late tyre stop to win the 1987 British Grand Prix?

18 Who did he overhaul in doing so?

19 Who won the 1987 Japanese and Australian Grands Prix?

20 For which team?

Answers WORLD CHAMPIONSHIP 1990 *(see Quiz 19)*

1 Gerhard Berger. **2** Martin Donnelly and Derek Warwick. **3** Nicola Larini. **4** Life. **5** Phoenix. **6** Alain Prost. **7** Alain Prost. **8** He had a puncture. **9** Thierry Boutsen. **10** Larrousse. **11** Ayrton Senna. **12** Alessandro Nannini. **13** Nigel Mansell. **14** Alain Prost ahead of Nigel Mansell. **15** His lower right arm was severed in a helicopter accident. **16** Roberto Moreno. **17** Johnny Herbert. **18** Gerhard Berger. **19** Ayrton Senna. **20** Nelson Piquet.

1 To which team did Nelson Piquet move for 1988?

2 Name the two Benetton drivers for 1988.

3 Who was disqualified from the 1988 Brazilian Grand Prix?

4 Why?

5 Who finished second behind his team-mate at Imola in 1988?

6 Which team's drivers finished third and fourth at Spa that year, and were then disqualified?

7 Which team broke McLaren's winning streak at Monza in 1988?

8 Which team's drivers finished third and fourth in that same race?

9 Nigel Mansell finished second twice in 1988. How many other races did he finish?

10 Where was the final race of the turbo era held?

11 Who moved from Williams to Ferrari for 1989?

12 Whose seat did he fill at Ferrari?

13 To which team did this individual move?

14 Who scored his best-ever result by finishing third on home ground in Brazil?

15 For which team was he driving?

16 Which team finished first and second in Canada in 1989?

17 Who finished third behind them for Dallara?

18 Who fought from 12th on the grid to win at the narrow Hungaroring?

19 Which team won the 1989 Japanese Grand Prix?

20 Who completed the 1989 season with victory in the Australian Grand Prix?

Answers WORLD CHAMPIONSHIP 1991 *(see Quiz 20)*

1 Jordan. *2* Nigel Mansell. *3* Mark Blundell and Martin Brundle. *4* Ayrton Senna. *5* Riccardo Patrese. *6* Williams. *7* Stefano Modena. *8* Mexico City. *9* Nigel Mansell. *10* Gerhard Berger. *11* Bertrand Gachot. *12* He had been jailed for attacking a taxi driver. *13* Monza. *14* Pierluigi Martini. *15* Fourth. *16* Jean Alesi. *17* Riccardo Patrese. *18* Alain Prost. *19* Gianni Morbidelli. *20* Sixth.

1 Who joined Ayrton Senna at McLaren for 1990?

2 Name the two new signings at Lotus?

3 Which Italian joined Ligier?

4 Which small Italian team never got past pre-qualifying?

5 Where was the first grand prix of the year held?

6 Who won the Brazilian Grand Prix for Ferrari?

7 Who qualified 13th for the Mexican Grand Prix yet came through to win?

8 What happened to Ayrton Senna?

9 Which Williams driver finished second behind Alain Prost in the British Grand Prix?

10 Both drivers for which midfield team scored points that day?

11 Who raced to victory in the German Grand Prix?

12 Which driver retired from the Hungarian Grand Prix after contact with Senna?

13 Who blocked his team-mate before going on to win the Portuguese Grand Prix?

14 In which order did the Ferrari drivers finish the Spanish Grand Prix?

15 What brought an end to Alessandro Nannini's Formula One career before the season was out?

16 Who replaced him at Benetton?

17 Who replaced the injured Martin Donnelly at Lotus?

18 Who led the opening lap of the Japanese Grand Prix then spun off?

19 Who wrapped up the title at the Japanese Grand Prix?

20 Who was ranked third overall after winning the final race?

Answers WORLD CHAMPIONSHIPS 1986 & 1987 *(see Quiz 17)*

1 Elio de Angelis. 2 Benetton. 3 Gerhard Berger and Teo Fabi. 4 Alain Prost. 5 Nigel Mansell.
6 Ayrton Senna. 7 He'd been injured when competing in a rally. 8 BMW. 9 Puncture.
10 Second. 11 The DFZ. 12 Honda. 13 Satoru Nakajima. 14 Tyrrell. 15 Andrea de Cesaris.
16 Brabham. 17 Nigel Mansell. 18 Nelson Piquet. 19 Gerhard Berger. 20 Ferrari.

---

1 Which team entered the world championship for the first time?

2 Who joined Riccardo Patrese at Williams?

3 Which two British drivers raced for Brabham?

4 Who started the season on a winning note in Phoenix?

5 Who was closing fast on Ayrton Senna in the closing laps at Interlagos?

6 For which team was he racing?

7 Who was elevated to second place in Canada when Nigel Mansell made a mistake on the final lap?

8 At which circuit did Ayrton Senna flip his McLaren in qualifying?

9 Who led every lap of the British Grand Prix at Silverstone?

10 Who grabbed second place when Senna stopped on the final lap that day?

11 Which Jordan driver missed the Belgian Grand Prix?

12 Why?

13 Where did the driver who replaced him for the Belgian Grand Prix score his first points?

14 Who gave Minardi its highest ever placing in the Portuguese Grand Prix?

15 In which position did he finish at Estoril?

16 Name the Ferrari driver who finished third that day.

17 Who was the Italian driver who won?

18 Who was fired by Ferrari before the final race of the year?

19 Who replaced him for the Australian Grand Prix?

20 In what position was he running when the race was stopped?

Answers *WORLD CHAMPIONSHIPS 1988 & 1989* *(see Quiz 18)*

1 Lotus. **2** Thierry Boutsen and Alessandro Nannini. **3** Ayrton Senna. **4** For changing cars after the parade lap. **5** Alain Prost. **6** Benetton. **7** Ferrari. **8** Arrows. **9** None. **10** Adelaide. **11** Nigel Mansell. **12** Michele Alboreto's. **13** Tyrrell. **14** Mauricio Gugelmin. **15** Leyton House. **16** Williams. **17** Andrea de Cesaris. **18** Nigel Mansell. **19** Benetton. **20** Thierry Boutsen.

1 Which Italian driver joined Ferrari?
2 Who was his team-mate?
3 Name the team with which Bertrand Gachot returned.
4 Which amateurish Italian team qualified just once.
5 Where?
6 Who was the lucky driver?
7 Where was the Spanish Grand Prix held?
8 Which British driver made his first attempt to qualify at that race?
9 For which team was he driving?
10 For which grand prix did he first qualify?
11 Which Lotus driver finished fourth in the French Grand Prix?
12 Which one finished sixth?
13 Who dropped out when running third in the closing laps of the British Grand Prix?
14 What interrupted Nigel Mansell's progress to the title in Hungary?
15 Which team won the Italian Grand Prix when the both Williamses failed?
16 Whose season peaked with second place in the Italian Grand Prix?
17 Where did Nigel Mansell score a record ninth win in one season?
18 Who scored his first point for Minardi in the Japanese Grand Prix?
19 Which team had both of its drivers on the Australian Grand Prix podium?
20 Who ranked third overall in his first full season?

Answers WORLD CHAMPIONSHIP 1994 *(see Quiz 23)*

1 JJ Lehto. 2 Jos Verstappen. 3 Rubens Barrichello and Eddie Irvine. 4 Jean Alesi and Gerhard Berger. 5 Pacific and Simtek. 6 Rubens Barrichello (third). 7 Nicola Larini. 8 Jean Alesi. 9 Alesi had injured his back in an accident in testing. 10 Michael Schumacher. 11 Andrea Montermini. 12 No. 13 Olivier Panis and Eric Bernard (second and third). 14 Michael Schumacher. 15 Philippe Adams. 16 Italian and Portuguese. 17 Jerez. 18 Michael Schumacher. 19 It was stopped due to heavy rain. 20 Gerhard Berger.

1   How had Alain Prost spent 1992?

2   Which Japanese driver had joined Tyrrell?

3   What make of engine was the team using?

4   Who was left on the sidelines when Ayrton Senna elected to stay on at McLaren?

5   Who equalled Minardi's best-ever finish when he was fourth at Kyalami?

6   Which new team scored points for fifth on its debut?

7   Who was their points-scoring driver?

8   At which circuit did Damon Hill climb on to the podium for the first time?

9   Who was slammed by the French press for his performance in the European Grand Prix?

10   In what position had he finished?

11   Who finished third for Ligier at Imola?

12   Who won the Monaco Grand Prix?

13   What cost Damon Hill victory in the British Grand Prix?

14   Who benefitted to win?

15   Which Ferrari driver scored his only top-three result of the year in the Hungarian Grand Prix?

16   At which corner did Alessandro Zanardi crash during qualifying for the Belgian Grand Prix?

17   Who did Christian Fittipaldi hit at the end of the Italian Grand Prix?

18   Who did Mika Hakkinen outqualify on his debut for McLaren at Estoril?

19   Who won the final two grands prix of the year?

20   Who ended the year as runner-up to Alain Prost?

Answers *WORLD CHAMPIONSHIP 1995 (see Quiz 24)*

Mark Blundell (Nigel Mansell had two races later in the season). **2** Mercedes. **3** Jordan.
Taki Inoue. **5** Ferrari (Jean Alesi and Gerhard Berger). **6** Benetton (Michael Schumacher and Johnny Herbert). **7** Damon Hill. **8** Michael Schumacher. **9** Jean Alesi (second).
10 David Coulthard. **11** Gerhard Berger (third). **12** Michael Schumacher. **13** First. **14** Damp.
15 He crashed out. **16** Nigel Mansell's. **17** Two. **18** Olivier Panis. **19** Gianni Morbidelli.
20 Footwork.

1. Which Benetton driver broke his neck before the start of the season?
2. Who was his stand-in?
3. Name the two Jordan drivers for 1994.
4. Who were the two regular Ferrari drivers?
5. Name the two teams making their world championship debut.
6. Which Jordan driver made it to the podium in the Pacific Grand Prix?
7. Which Ferrari stand-in driver finished second in the San Marino Grand Prix?
8. For whom was he covering?
9. Why?
10. Who made it four consecutive wins by topping the podium at Monaco?
11. Which Simtek replacement driver broke an ankle at the Spanish Grand Prix?
12. Did Michael Schumacher call into the pits when black-flagged in the British Grand Prix?
13. Name the Ligier drivers who finished on the podium at Hockenheim.
14. Who was first on the road in the Belgian Grand Prix?
15. Which Belgian driver had an outing for Lotus in that race?
16. Which grands prix did Michael Schumacher miss during his two-race ban?
17. Which circuit hosted the European Grand Prix?
18. Who won it?
19. Why was the Japanese Grand Prix run in two parts?
20. Who ran wide and let Nigel Mansell slip by to win the Australian Grand Prix?

Answers WORLD CHAMPIONSHIP 1992 *(see Quiz 21)*

1 Ivan Capelli. **2** Jean Alesi. **3** Venturi Larrousse. **4** Andrea Moda. **5** Monaco. **6** Roberto Moreno. **7** Circuit de Catalunya (Barcelona). **8** Damon Hill. **9** Brabham. **10** British. **11** Mika Hakkinen. **12** Johnny Herbert. **13** Ayrton Senna. **14** A puncture. **15** McLaren. **16** Martin Brundle's. **17** Estoril. **18** Christian Fittipaldi. **19** Benetton (Michael Schumacher and Martin Brundle, second and third). **20** Michael Schumacher.

1   Who started the season as the new number two at McLaren?

2   What engine was the team now using?

3   Which team now had the works Peugeot deal?

4   Which Japanese driver had joined Footwork?

5   Which team's drivers finished second and third behind Damon Hill at Imola?

6   Which team claimed a one-two in the Spanish Grand Prix?

7   Who started on pole position at Monaco but finished second?

8   Who used a superior pit-stop strategy to win the French Grand Prix?

9   Name the only non-British driver on the British Grand Prix podium.

10   Who finished second in the German Grand Prix?

11   Which Ferrari driver joined the Williams drivers on the podium at the Hungarian Grand Prix?

12   Who started in 16th place at the Belgian Grand Prix?

13   In what position did he finish the race?

14   What were the track conditions at the Nürburgring?

15   What happened to Damon Hill?

16   Whose record did Michael Schumacher equal when he took his ninth win of the year in Japan?

17   By how many laps did Damon Hill win the Australian Grand Prix?

18   Who finished second at Adelaide?

19   Who finished third?

20   For which team was he driving?

Answers *WORLD CHAMPIONSHIP 1993 (see Quiz 22)*

1 Taking a sabbatical. 2 Ukyo Katayama. 3 Yamaha. 4 Mika Hakkinen. 5 Christian Fittipaldi.
6 Sauber. 7 JJ Lehto. 8 Interlagos (second). 9 Alain Prost. 10 Third. 11 Martin Brundle.
12 Ayrton Senna. 13 Engine failure. 14 Alain Prost. 15 Gerhard Berger. 16 Eau Rouge.
17 Pierluigi Martini (his team-mate). 18 Ayrton Senna (his team-mate). 19 Ayrton Senna.
20 Ayrton Senna.

1   What championship had the new Williams number two driver just won?

2   Who filled Eddie Irvine's seat at Jordan?

3   Where had Johnny Herbert gone after his spell at Benetton?

4   Name the hapless Italian team that was back for a second season.

5   Which Ferrari driver followed the Williams duo home in the Australian Grand Prix?

6   Who was the only other driver on the same lap as Damon Hill in Brazil?

7   How many drivers were still on the track at the end of the Monaco Grand Prix?

8   Which team's drivers finished first and second in the Canadian Grand Prix?

9   Which team's drivers finished first and second in the French Grand Prix?

10 Why did Damon Hill retire from the British Grand Prix?

11 Why did Gerhard Berger retire from the lead of the German Grand Prix?

12 Which engine builder refused to provide engines to Forti at the German Grand Prix because of unpaid bills?

13 Name the Italian sportscar driver who bought himself a ride with Minardi mid-season.

14 Whose seat did he take?

15 Who won the Hungarian Grand Prix by a fraction from his team-mate?

16 Which McLaren driver made it to the podium in the Belgian Grand Prix?

17 Who finished third behind the Williams drivers at Estoril?

18 Second place in the Japanese Grand Prix left Michael Schumacher ranked where overall?

19 Whose accident at Suzuka cost Benetton second in the Constructors' Cup?

20 How many years had passed since Damon Hill's father Graham had last been world champion?

Answers WORLD CHAMPIONSHIP 1998 *(see Quiz 27)*

1 Giancarlo Fisichella and Alexander Wurz. 2 Pedro Diniz and Mika Salo. 3 Rubens Barrichello and Jan Magnussen. 4 Petronas. 5 Michael Schumacher. 6 Ferrari. Michael Schumacher was second, Eddie Irvine finished third. 7 McLaren. 8 Giancarlo Fisichella. 9 Mika Hakkinen. 10 Michael Schumacher. 11 Ferrari. 12 Mika Hakkinen. 13 Jordan. 14 Giancarlo Fisichella. 15 Mika Hakkinen. 16 Jacques Villeneuve. 17 Giancarlo Fisichella. 18 Jean Alesi. 19 Ferrari. 20 Damon Hill.

1 Who was the new number two driver at Williams?

2 Who was Damon Hill's new team-mate?

3 Name the two new drivers at Jordan.

4 Who had joined Mika Salo at Tyrrell?

5 To which team had Ukyo Katayama moved for his swansong year?

6 Which Benetton driver finished second at Interlagos?

7 Which French driver finished third there?

8 With whom did Damon Hill collide in the San Marino Grand Prix?

9 Who drove non-stop to fifth place at Monaco?

10 Who deputized for Gerhard Berger for three races mid-season?

11 Which Jordan driver had a spectacular accident at Montreal?

12 What did Gerhard Berger confirm at the German Grand Prix?

13 Which team just missed out on its first win in Hungary?

14 Who was driving the safety car that led the field at the Belgian Grand Prix?

15 Why was Mika Hakkinen disqualified from the Belgian Grand Prix?

16 Which team claimed pole position for the Italian Grand Prix?

17 Over whose car did Jean Alesi launch his Benetton at the A1-Ring?

18 Who collided with Michael Schumacher at the Luxembourg Grand Prix?

19 Why did Jacques Villeneuve have to contest the Japanese Grand Prix under appeal?

20 What was the official outcome of Michael Schumacher's collision with Jacques Villeneuve at Jerez?

Answers *WORLD CHAMPIONSHIP 1999* (see Quiz 28)

1 Jacques Villeneuve and Ricardo Zonta. **2** Supertec. **3** Luca Badoer and Marc Gene. **4** Heinz-Harald Frentzen. **5** Ricardo Zonta. **6** Ferrari. **7** McLaren. **8** Rubens Barrichello. **9** Eddie Irvine. **10** For overtaking Olivier Panis with all four wheels off the circuit. **11** Mika Salo because Eddie Irvine gave it to him. **12** McLaren and Jordan. **13** Williams. **14** Jacques Villeneuve. **15** Alessandro Zanardi. **16** Toranosuke Takagi. **17** Fourth. **18** Giancarlo Fisichella. **19** Alessandro Zanardi. **20** Michael Schumacher ahead of Eddie Irvine (second and third, respectively).

1 Name the two Benetton drivers.

2 Who were the two Arrows drivers?

3 Who started the season for Stewart?

4 What was the badge-name of the ex-Ferrari engines used by Sauber?

5 Who surprised the McLarens by taking pole position for the Argentinian Grand Prix?

6 Which team had both of its drivers finish on the podium at the San Marino Grand Prix?

7 Which team dominated the Spanish Grand Prix?

8 Who tangled with Eddie Irvine in this race?

9 Which McLaren driver won the Monaco Grand Prix?

10 Who hit Pedro Diniz's Arrows on the last lap at Monaco?

11 Which team's drivers finished first and second in the French Grand Prix?

12 Who had his lead slashed by the deployment of the safety car at the British Grand Prix?

13 Which team scored its first points of the year at Silverstone?

14 Who scooped a surprise pole position at the Austrian Grand Prix?

15 Who led the whole way to win?

16 Who scored his equal best result of the year by finishing third in the Hungarian Grand Prix?

17 Who brought out the safety car for the second time in the Belgian Grand Prix by slamming into Shinji Nakano?

18 Who finished third behind the Jordans in the Belgian Grand Prix?

19 Which team filled the front row for the Luxembourg Grand Prix?

20 Who grabbed fourth place from Heinz-Harald Frentzen at the final corner on the last lap of the Japanese Grand Prix?

Answers WORLD CHAMPIONSHIP 1996 *(see Quiz 25)*

1 Indycar (Jacques Villeneuve). 2 Martin Brundle. 3 Sauber. 4 Forti. 5 Eddie Irvine.
6 Jean Alesi. 7 Three (Olivier Panis, David Coulthard, Johnny Herbert). 8 Williams. 9 Williams.
10 He spun off because of a loose wheel. 11 Engine failure. 12 Cosworth. 13 Giovanni Lavaggi.
14 Giancarlo Fisichella's. 15 Jacques Villeneuve. 16 Mika Hakkinen (third). 17 Michael
Schumacher. 18 Third. 19 Jean Alesi's. 20 28.

1. Who drove for the new British American Racing team?
2. What engines were used by British American Racing?
3. Name the regular Minardi drivers.
4. Which Jordan driver finished second in the Australian Grand Prix?
5. Who was injured in practice for the Brazilian Grand Prix and missed three races?
6. Which team's drivers finished first and second in the Monaco Grand Prix?
7. The Spanish Grand Prix produced a one-two for which team?
8. Who qualified on pole position in the wet for the French Grand Prix?
9. Who raced to victory in the Austrian Grand Prix?
10. Why was David Coulthard given a stop-go penalty in the German Grand Prix?
11. Who took home the winner's trophy from the German Grand Prix?
12. Name the two teams that had both their drivers score points in the Hungarian Grand Prix.
13. Which team accused Ferrari's Mika Salo of obstruction at the Belgian Grand Prix?
14. Who recorded his first finish of the year at the Belgian Grand Prix?
15. Who had to slow down in the Italian Grand Prix because the floor of his car was loose?
16. Who rode over Luca Badoer's Minardi during the Italian Grand Prix?
17. What position did Luca Badoer reach in the European Grand Prix before retiring?
18. Which Benetton driver threw away victory in the European Grand Prix?
19. Which driver rounded out a poor season by retiring on the first lap of the Japanese GP?
20. In which order did the Ferrari drivers finish the race at Suzuka?

Answers *WORLD CHAMPIONSHIP 1997* (see Quiz 26)

1 Heinz-Harald Frentzen. 2 Pedro Diniz. 3 Giancarlo Fisichella and Ralf Schumacher.
4 Jos Verstappen. 5 Minardi. 6 Gerhard Berger. 7 Olivier Panis. 8 Shinji Nakano. 9 Mika
Salo. 10 Alexander Wurz. 11 Ralf Schumacher. 12 His retirement from Formula One.
13 Arrows. 14 Oliver Gavin. 15 His McLaren's fuel was deemed illegal. 16 Benetton.
17 Eddie Irvine's. 18 Ralf Schumacher. 19 Because he overtook under waved yellow flags in
practice. 20 He was removed from second place in the rankings.

1   Which was the first team to record the maximum score of eight points for a win in the Constructors' Cup?

2   Which was the second-best Italian marque in 1958?

3   British teams filled three of the top four places in the 1959 table. Which one was fourth?

4   Which team claimed the 1960 title?

5   Name its two drivers that year.

6   Which Italian marque made its debut in 1961?

7   Which British team was placed third overall in 1962?

8   Which future championship-winning team made its debut in 1962?

9   Where was this team ranked in 1963?

10 What team entered the Ferraris in the 1964 United States and Mexican Grands Prix?

11 What was the official name of the BRM team?

12 Apart from BRM, which two teams raced with BRM engines in 1965?

13 Which future championship-winning marque made its debut in 1966?

14 A future race-winning marque also made its debut that year. Which one?

15 Did Ferrari win a grand prix in 1967?

16 Who scored all of Honda's points that year?

17 Which famous marque scored its final points in 1968?

18 Who scored the bulk of champion Lotus's points that year?

19 Where was Lotus ranked in 1969?

20 What chassis did Rob Walker enter in 1969?

Answers THE CONSTRUCTORS' CUP 3 *(see Quiz 31)*

1 Brabham. 2 Shadow. 3 Matra. 4 Ensign. 5 Fourth. 6 Osella. 7 Spirit. 8 Theodore. 9 Alfa Romeo. 10 ATS. 11 Second. 12 Zakspeed. 13 Benetton. 14 Lotus. 15 McLaren. 16 Stefan Johansson and Alain Prost. 17 Benetton (Ferrari was second). 18 Rial. 19 Alain Prost and Ayrton Senna. 20 Onyx.

---

1 Which team won the 1970 Constructors' Cup?

2 Which future championship-winning team entered its own cars for the first time in 1970?

3 Which team was ranked equal third with March in 1971?

4 What was the name of the team entering the Brabhams in 1971?

5 Did Ferrari win a race in 1972, when the team finished fourth overall?

6 What make of car did Frank Williams enter in 1972?

7 Which American-financed team scored its first points in 1973?

8 Which Italian team scored the only point it ever scored that year?

9 Which team finished third in 1974?

10 Which famous British team scored its final points that year?

11 Which American team was ranked 10th in 1975?

12 Which team owned by a former world champion scored its only points in 1975?

13 Who scored McLaren's points in 1976?

14 Which Brazilian-owned team scored its first points in 1976?

15 Name the drivers who guided Ferrari to the 1977 title.

16 What engines did Brabham use in 1977?

17 Which French team scored its first points in 1978?

18 Name the British team that scored its final point in 1978.

19 Which short-lived team closed its doors at the end of 1979?

20 Which German team scored its first points in 1979?

Answers *THE CONSTRUCTORS' CUP 4 (see Quiz 32)*

1 Lamborghini. *2* Larrousse. *3* Jean Alesi and Alain Prost. *4* Jordan. *5* Brabham. *6* March.
7 Sauber. *8* Lotus. *9* Peugeot. *10* Pacific, Simtek. *11* Ferrari. *12* Forti. *13* Eddie Irvine and
Michael Schumacher. *14* Jordan. *15* Ligier (it became Prost). *16* Tyrrell. *17* Benetton.
18 Jordan. *19* British American Racing. *20* Arrows.

1 Which British team was ranked third overall in 1980?

2 Name the team that quit at the start of 1980.

3 What make of engine did the Ligiers use in 1981?

4 Which budget-conscious British team scored its final points in 1981?

5 Champions in 1981, where did Williams finish in 1982?

6 Which little-fancied Italian team scored its first points in 1982?

7 Which Honda-powered team made its debut in 1983?

8 Name the eastern-owned team that shut up shop at the end of 1983?

9 Which long-running Italian team scored its final points in 1984?

10 Which German team scored its final point in 1984?

11 Where did Ferrari finish in 1985?

12 Which German team entered the championship in 1985?

13 Which British team made its championship debut in 1986?

14 Which British team was ranked third overall behind Williams and McLaren in 1986?

15 Which team ended 1987 as runner-up?

16 Name its drivers.

17 1988 was McLaren's year, but which team ended up third?

18 Which German team scored its first points in 1988?

19 1989 was another McLaren year. Name its drivers.

20 Which British team scored the only points it ever scored in 1989?

1. Lotus finished eighth in 1990. What make of engine was it using?
2. Which other team used the same engine that year?
3. Ferrari finished third in 1991. Name its drivers.
4. Which new team scored its first points?
5. Which former championship-winning team bowed out at the end of 1992?
6. Which other once high-ranking team also shut its doors in 1992?
7. Which team scored its first points in 1993, finishing sixth?
8. Which famous team scored its final points in 1993?
9. What make of engine did McLaren use in 1994?
10. Name either of the British teams that were new in 1994?
11. Which team finished third in 1995?
12. Which Italian team joined the championship in 1995?
13. Ferrari was second in 1996. Name its drivers.
14. Which team used Peugeot engines in 1996?
15. Which French team ran under a new name in 1997?
16. Name the famous British team that scored its final points in 1997.
17. Which team dropped to fifth in 1998's final round?
18. Which team pipped it for fourth place?
19. Which team made its debut in 1999?
20. What engines did Arrows use in 1999?

Answers **THE CONSTRUCTORS' CUP 2** *(see Quiz 30)*

1 Lotus. **2** Tyrrell. **3** Ferrari. **4** Motor Racing Developments. **5** Yes, one (The German Grand Prix). **6** March. **7** Shadow. **8** Tecno. **9** Tyrrell. **10** BRM. **11** Parnelli. **12** Hill. **13** James Hunt and Jochen Mass. **14** Fittipaldi. **15** Niki Lauda and Carlos Reutemann. **16** Alfa Romeo. **17** Renault. **18** Surtees. **19** Wolf. **20** ATS.

1 On which marque of sportscar was the AFM based?

2 Name the team's principal?

3 Which two drivers scored points for AGS?

4 Who was the team's first designer?

5 In what years did Alfa Romeo drivers win the world championship?

6 A company owned by Carlo Chiti ran Alfa Romeo's cars on its return to Formula One. What was it called?

7 Which company that took over from them in 1983?

8 Which South African driver entered the Alfa Special?

9 Who was the brains behind the Alta marque?

10 Name the two main marques that later fitted Alta engines.

11 In which year did Chris Amon enter his own chassis in Formula One?

12 Which was its only grand prix start?

13 Who was the principal of the Andrea Moda team?

14 Name the team's two drivers in 1992.

15 Who was the first Arrows designer?

16 Which British driver spent four years with Arrows?

17 In which year did the Arzani Volpini attempt to qualify for a grand prix?

18 Who built the engines used by the Aston chassis in 1952?

19 Name either of the drivers.

20 Why were the Aston Martins outdated in 1959?

Answers THE TEAMS 3 *(see Quiz 35)*

1 Green. *2* Bruce McLaren. *3* Cosworth. *4* BMS Scuderia Italia. *5* Roberto Lippi.
6 Len Terry. *7* Bruce McLaren. *8* Luigi Colani. *9* Paul Emery. *10* ENB and later Scirocco.
11 East Germany. *12* Edgar Barth. *13* Ecurie Nationale Belge. *14* Maserati. *15* Dave Baldwin.
16 Boro. *17* Because of a disagreement with the team sponsor. *18* Leslie Johnson. *19* Walter Brun. *20* Oscar Larrauri and Stefano Modena.

1 Which German driver raced for ATS between 1982 and 1984?

2 Did either of the ATS drivers score a point in 1963?

3 When the chassis appeared again in 1964, it had been reworked and renamed as what?

4 Who drove it?

5 Who designed the first BAR chassis?

6 Name the two principal drivers who raced for Beatrice.

7 Who raced the Bellasi chassis in 1971?

8 Which designer has had two spells with Benetton?

9 Who was Benetton team boss in 1999?

10 Who designed the Brabham chassis from 1973 to 1986?

11 What nationality is he?

12 Who scored BRM's first win in 1959?

13 Who scored BRM's last win in 1972?

14 Who was the number one BRP driver?

15 Which famous French marque entered only one grand prix?

16 Who drove the car in that 1956 French Grand Prix?t

17 Who failed to qualify the lone Cistalia in the 1952 Italian Grand Prix?

18 Who designed all the Connaught Formula One cars?

19 In which year did Connew arrive in Formula One?

20 Which French driver raced the car?

Answers *THE TEAMS 4 (see Quiz 536*

1 It was the last front-engined Formula One car. *2* Jack Fairman, Stirling Moss. *3* Mike Hawthorn. *4* Michele Alboreto. *5* Richard Divila. *6* Chico Serra. *7* Damon Hill. *8* Alan Jenkins. *9* Shannon. *10* Mike Parkes. *11* Stuart Lewis-Evans. *12* Len Terry. *13* Keith Greene. *14* Amedee. *15* Renault. *16* Easton Neston. *17* Frank Dernie. *18* Paul Ricard. *19* Amsterdam. *20* White.

1   What colour were the works Coopers?

2   Who raced for Cooper from 1959 to 1965?

3   Which engine builder built a four-wheel drive Formula One car in 1969 that never raced?

4   Which team commissioned Dallara to build a Formula One car for 1988?

5   Who drove a De Tomaso at the Italian Grand Prix from 1961 to 1963?

6   Who was Eagle's designer?

7   Which driver supported Dan Gurney in 1967?

8   Who designed the Eifelland March's bodywork?

9   Name the founder of the Emeryson marque.

10   Which two marques ran its chassis?

11   In which country was EMW based?

12   Who drove an EMW in the 1953 German Grand Prix, its one outing?

13   What does the acronym ENB stand for?

14   What engine did ENB use in its one-off chassis in 1961?

15   Who designed the Ensigns between 1975 and 1979?

16   What was the Ensign entered as in 1976?

17   Why the change of name?

18   Who bought the ERA marque from its Bourne birthplace?

19   Which Swiss sportscar racer founded the EuroBrun marque?

20   Who were his drivers in 1988?

Answers THE TEAMS 1 *(see Quiz 33)*

1 BMW. *2* Alex von Falkenhausen. *3* Roberto Moreno and Gabriele Tarquini. *4* Christian Vanderpleyn. *5* 1950 and 1951. *6* Autodelta. *7* Euroracing. *8* Peter de Klerk. *9* Geoffrey Taylor. *10* Connaught and HWM. *11* 1974. *12* Spanish. *13* Andrea Sassetti. *14* Perry McCarthy and Roberto Moreno. *15* Tony Southgate. *16* Derek Warwick. *17* 1955. *18* Butterworth. *19* Bill Aston, Robin Montgomerie-Charrington. *20* They were front-engined.

1   What turned out to be notable about the Ferguson P99 in 1961?

2   Name either of the drivers who shared it on its one outing.

3   Who was the first British driver to race for Ferrari?

4   Which Italian driver led the team from 1984 to 1988?

5   Who was the Fittipaldi designer from 1975 to 1977?

6   Who was Fittipaldi's driver in 1982, its final year?

7   Which future world champion raced a Footwork in Formula 3000?

8   Who was the Footwork designer from 1991 to 1993?

9   Which mysterious company sponsored Forti in 1996 then failed to pay up?

10   Who attempted to qualify the unusual-looking Fry for the 1959 British Grand Prix?

11   For whom had the chassis been intended, before his death?

12   Which designer better known for sportscars was responsible for the 1961 Gilby?

13   Who raced it in 1961 and 1962?

14   What was the first name of the Gordini founder?

15   With which French automotive manufacturer did Gordini later become connected?

16   Name the stately home that was Hesketh's base.

17   Who designed the final Hesketh, the 1977–78 308E?

18   From where were the Hill personnel returning when their light aircraft crashed?

19   Where was Honda's first European racing base from 1964?

20   What colour were all Honda's Formula One cars?

Answers *THE TEAMS 2* (see Quiz 34)

1 Manfred Winkelhock. **2** No. **3** Derrington-Francis. **4** Mario Araujo de Cabral. **5** Malcolm Oastler. **6** Alan Jones and Patrick Tambay. **7** Silvio Moser. **8** Rory Byrne. **9** Rocco Benetton. **10** Gordon Murray. **11** South African. **12** Jo Bonnier. **13** Jean-Pierre Beltoise. **14** Innes Ireland. **15** Bugatti. **16** Maurice Trintignant. **17** Piero Dusio. **18** Rodney Clarke. **19** 1972. **20** François Migault.

1   Name the two main HWM drivers in 1952 and 1953.

2   In which two years would you have found Iso Marlboros on the grid?

3   Who finished fourth in one in the second year?

4   Which racing driver founded JBW?

5   What make of engine powered the JBW in 1959 and 1960?

6   Who gave Jordan its second win, in 1999?

7   Who is Jordan's race director?

8   Who was charged with attempting to qualify the Kauhsen in 1979?

9   Which ex-Ferrari driver merged the Kauhsen with his own?

10 Who was charged with driving the Klenk on its one-off outing in the 1954 German Grand Prix?

11 What did Kojima achieve on its Formula One debut in the 1976 Japanese Grand Prix?

12 Name one of the drivers who raced a Kojima in the 1977 Japanese Grand Prix.

13 Who drove the Kurtis Kraft on its one Formula One outing in the 1959 United States Grand Prix?

14 For what sort of racing had this chassis been developed?

15 Who designed the Lamborghini 291?

16 What was the name of the team that entered it?

17 Name either of the Lancia drivers in 1954?

18 Which Japanese driver raced for Larrousse in 1992?

19 What nationality was the LDS marque?

20 From whose initials was the name derived?

Answers THE TEAMS 7 (see Quiz 39)

1 Jean-Luc Lagardere. 2 Jean-Pierre Beltoise. 3 Williams (FW04). 4 Orange. 5 Robin Herd. 6 Gordon Coppuck. 7 Alfred Neubauer. 8 Karl Kling. 9 1978. 10 He did. 11 Cesare Fiorio. 12 Aldo Costa. 13 Gregor Foitek and JJ Lehto. 14 Alan Jenkins. 15 Jean-Pierre van Rossem. 16 Elie Bayol, Louis Chiron, Franco Rol. 17 Tony Southgate. 18 Alfa Romeo. 19 Rory Byrne. 20 Reynard.

1   Which British racer founded the Lec marque?
2   Who designed the Lec CRP1 in 1977?
3   Who was the Leyton House boss?
4   Which future star designer was responsible for their cars from 1988 to 1990?
5   What format of engine was fitted to the Life chassis through most of 1990?
6   Name either of the drivers who failed to qualify it.
7   Why were Ligier chassis given the prefix JS?
8   The boss of which other team took over Ligier in 1994?
9   Who drove the Lola on its comeback in 1985?
10   Who scored Lotus's first ever grand prix win?
11   Who scored Lotus's last grand prix win?
12   Which driver commissioned the Lyncar Formula One car?
13   Who was the founder of the marque?
14   In what year did the Japanese Maki marque arrive in Formula One?
15   Name any of the drivers who attempted to qualify it.
16   The head of which racing-car constructors designed the March Formula One chassis in 1982?
17   Name either of the drivers in March's final line-up in 1992.
18   What engines powered the March chassis that year?
19   Who designed Maserati's classic 250F?
20   Who scored Maserati's final Formula One win, in 1957?

Answers *THE TEAMS 8 (see Quiz 40)*

1 Velco Miletich. **2** Maurice Philippe. **3** Geoff Ferris. **4** ATS. **5** Williams. **6** Henri Pescarolo. **7** Silver. **8** Dan Gurney. **9** John Barnard. **10** Jarno Trulli. **11** Frank Costin. **12** It was wooden. **13** Philippe Alliot and Manfred Winkelhock. **14** A Lotus (79). **15** Bernard Dudot. **16** Because it was the work of former Ferrari designer Gustav Brunner. **17** Andrea de Cesaris, Christian Danner. **18** Leo Ress. **19** Lance Reventlow. **20** 1962.

1 Name the man behind the Matra Sports arm of Matra?

2 Who was a constant in Matra chassis from 1967 to 1971?

3 From what chassis was the 1977 McGuire BM1 derived?

4 What colour was the McLaren livery from 1968 to 1971?

5 Who designed the chassis in those years?

6 Who designed the classic McLaren M23?

7 Name Mercedes-Benz's charismatic team manager.

8 Who was Fangio's Mercedes-Benz team-mate in both 1954 and 1955?

9 In which year did Arturo Merzario enter his first Merzario chassis in Formula One?

10 Who drove it?

11 Which former Ferrari team boss managed Minardi in 1999?

12 Name Minardi's designer from 1989 to 1997.

13 Which two drivers raced the Monteverdi in 1990?

14 Who designed the Onyx chassis of both 1989 and 1990?

15 Who took over the team at the end of 1989?

16 Name a driver who raced an OSCA.

17 Which British designer was responsible for the Osella FA1E in 1983?

18 What make of engine did Osella use from 1983 to 1988?

19 Who was responsible for the design of the first Pacific in 1994?

20 Which marque had commissioned the design before handing it over?

Answers THE TEAMS 5 *(see Quiz 37)*

1 Peter Collins and Lance Macklin. 2 1973 and 1974. 3 Arturo Merzario. 4 Brian Naylor. 5 Maserati. 6 Heinz-Harald Frentzen. 7 Trevor Foster. 8 Gianfranco Brancatelli. 9 Arturo Merzario. 10 Theo Helfrich. 11 Fastest lap. 12 Kazuyoshi Hoshino, Noritake Takahara. 13 Rodger Ward. 14 Oval racing. 15 Mauro Forghieri. 16 Modena Team. 17 Alberto Ascari or Luigi Villoresi. 18 Ukyo Katayama. 19 South African. 20 (Louis) Douglas Serrurier.

1 Who was a founding partner at Parnelli who wasn't represented in the team name?

2 Who designed the Parnelli chassis?

3 Who was the sole Penske designer?

4 Which team took over the Penske chassis for 1977?

5 The Politoys was the name given to the first car from which future title-winning marque?

6 Who drove it?

7 What colour were the works Porsche entries?

8 Who achieved the marque's only pole position, in 1962?

9 Which British designer worked with Prost in 1999?

10 Which Prost driver finished second in the 1999 European Grand Prix?

11 Who designed the Protos in 1967?

12 What was unusual about its monocoque?

13 Name the drivers for RAM's final attempt at Formula One in 1985?

14 On what contemporary chassis was the Rebaque HR100 based?

15 Who was in charge of Renault's engines, even when they later were supplied to other teams?

16 Why was the 1988 Rial (the ARC1) known as the Blue Ferrari?

17 Name either of the drivers who scored points for Rial.

18 Who has been the Sauber designer since the team arrived in Formula One?

19 Which American racing driver financed the Scarab marque?

20 In which year did Scarab enter the world championship?

Answers *THE TEAMS 6* (see Quiz 38)

1 David Purley. *2* Mike Pilbeam. *3* Akira Akagi. *4* Adrian Newey. *5* W12. *6* Gary Brabham, Bruno Giacomelli. *7* In memory of Guy Ligier's friend Jo Schlesser. *8* Benetton (Flavio Briatore). *9* Alan Jones. *10* Stirling Moss. *11* Ayrton Senna. *12* John Nicholson. *13* Martin Slater. *14* 1974. *15* Howden Ganley, Hiroshi Fushida, Tony Trimmer. *16* Adrian Reynard. *17* Paul Belmondo or Karl Wendlinger. *18* Ilmor. *19* Gioacchino Colombo. *20* Juan Manuel Fangio.

1   Which marque did Hugh Powell buy-out to form Scirocco in 1962?

2   Who was the team's main driver in 1963?

3   Who designed every Shadow bar the final model?

4   Name either of the founders of the Shannon marque?

5   Who drove the Shannon on its one grand prix outing, the 1966 British Grand Prix?

6   In which year did Simtek fold?

7   Which Italian driver was racing for the team at the time?

8   Which manufacturer did Spirit reintroduce to Formula One in 1983, this time as an engine supplier?

9   From which country did the Stebro marque originate?

10 Name the driver charged with driving it in the 1963 Canadian Grand Prix?

11 Who gave Stewart its first victory, in 1999?

12 Who took over the detailed work on Stewart's SF-3?

13 In which year did Surtees break into Formula One?

14 Which Brazilian set two fastest laps in a Surtees in 1973?

15 Which Italian-born entrant took over the Sunbeam-Talbot-Darracq concern in 1935 and lent it his name?

16 Which Talbot works driver appeared on the podium twice in 1950?

17 On which make of car was the Tec Mec based?

18 Which sportscar team entered it on its one outing, the 1959 United States Grand Prix?

19 Which Italian brothers formed the Tecno marque?

20 Which New Zealander gave Tecno its only point in 1973?

Answers *THE DRIVERS 1 (see Quiz 43)*

1 HWM. 2 Northern Ireland. 3 RAM. 4 Lotus. 5 Formula Two. 6 A Brabham. 7 Minardi.
8 BMS Scuderia Italia. 9 San Marino. 10 Benetton. 11 Gerhard Berger. 12 Touring cars or sportscars. 13 No. 14 Brabham. 15 19. 16 Ferrari. 17 March. 18 Swedish. 19 BRM.
20 March.

1 Who designed the first Theodore?

2 Name either of the Token team's patrons when it entered Formula One in 1974.

3 From what business did the Toleman Group make the money to go racing?

4 Which domestic appliances company sponsored Toleman from 1981 to 1983?

5 In which year did Trojan have a crack at Formula One?

6 Who was the designer?

7 In which English county was Tyrrell based?

8 Which fuel company backed Tyrrell through the 1970s?

9 Which bank backed Tyrrell in 1977 and 1978?

10 Who designed the bodywork of the late 1950s' Vanwalls?

11 Which designer from a rival marque designed their chassis and suspension?

12 What nationality was the Veritas marque?

13 Who designed the Veritas chassis?

14 Who has been the Williams designer since 1978?

15 In which English county is Williams based?

16 How many drivers have Williams helped to the world title?

17 In which country did Wolf score its maiden win?

18 How many years did Wolf spend in Formula One?

19 What colour was the livery of the Wolf Williams chassis?

20 What fictitious cigarette brandname did Zakspeed carry on its flanks to get around tobacco advertising bans?

Answers *THE DRIVERS 2 (see Quiz 44)*

1 Williams. *2* Indycar. *3* Jordan. *4* It marked the shortest ever career in Formula One – he reached only the first corner. *5* French. *6* One. *7* Formula Junior. *8* Maserati. *9* Antonio. *10* Token. *11* Hesketh. *12* Mosport Park. *13* A Lotus. *14* An Aston. *15* Lotus. *16* Lotus. *17* European. *18* 1992. *19* One. *20* Lotus.

1 George Abecassis founded and raced for which marque?

2 From which country does Kenneth Acheson hail?

3 Which team gave him his Formula One break?

4 Philippe Adams had two outings for which team in 1994?

5 Which British single-seater championship did Adams win in 1993?

6 Kurt Ahrens Jr was driving what Formula Two car when he finished seventh in the 1969 German Grand Prix?

7 In 1981, Michele Alboreto raced in Formula Two for a marque that in 1985 graduated to Formula One. Which one?

8 For which team did Alboreto drive a Lola in 1993?

9 In which 1994 grand prix did Alboreto shed a wheel in the pit lane?

10 Jean Alesi transferred to which team in 1996?

11 Who was his team-mate there?

12 Name either of the racing categories Philippe Alliot turned to after Formula One?

13 Has Alliot ever won the Le Mans 24 Hours with Peugeot?

14 For which team did Giovanna Amati attempt to qualify in 1992?

15 How old was Chris Amon when he made his world championship debut?

16 For which team did he drive from 1967 to 1969?

17 For which team did he finish second twice in 1970?

18 What nationality is Conny Andersson?

19 In 1977, four outings led to four non-qualifications for Andersson with which team?

20 What car did Mario Andretti race in 1970?

Answers *THE TEAMS 9* (see Quiz 41)

1 Emeryson. 2 Tony Settember. 3 Tony Southgate. 4 Hugh Aiden-Jones, Paul Emery.
5 Trevor Taylor. 6 1995 (they ran from 1994 to midway through 1995). 7 "Mimmo"
Schiattarella. 8 Honda. 9 Canada. 10 Peter Broeker. 11 Johnny Herbert at the European GP.
12 Gary Anderson. 13 1970. 14 Carlos Pace. 15 Antonio Lago. 16 Louis Rosier. 17 Maserati
(250F). 18 Camoradi. 19 The Pederzani brothers. 20 Chris Amon.

Answers – see page 257

1 Mario Andretti had a one-off outing for which team in the 1982 United States West Grand Prix?

2 To what category of racing did Michael Andretti return in 1994?

3 For which team did Marco Apicella have a one-off outing in the 1993 Italian Grand Prix?

4 What was notable about his race?

5 In which 1982 grand prix did René Arnoux disobey Renault team orders?

6 How many grands prix did Arnoux drive in 1985 before Ferrari dropped him?

7 In what category was Peter Arundell a champion before graduating to Formula One?

8 With which works team did Alberto Ascari start the 1954 season?

9 Ascari's father was also a racing driver. What was his name?

10 With which team did Ian Ashley enter Formula One, in 1974?

11 For which team did he race in 1977?

12 Where did his Formula One career come to an end because of an accident in qualifying?

13 What car did Gerry Ashmore drive in his brief Formula One career?

14 What car did Bill Aston drive?

15 What privately entered chassis did Richard Attwood race in 1965?

16 For which works team did he finish fourth at Monaco in 1969?

17 In which 1999 grand prix was Luca Badoer set for fourth place before his gearbox failed?

18 In which year was Badoer Formula 3000 Champion?

19 How many seasons did Giancarlo Baghetti spend as a works Ferrari driver?

20 Baghetti drove for which British team in the 1967 Italian Grand Prix?

Answers *THE TEAMS 10* (see Quiz 42)

1 Ron Tauranac. 2 Tony Vlassopoulo, Ken Grob. 3 Car transporting. 4 Candy. 5 1974. 6 Ron Tauranac. 7 Surrey. 8 Elf. 9 First National City Bank. 10 Frank Costin. 11 Colin Chapman. 12 German. 13 Ernst Loof. 14 Patrick Head. 15 Oxfordshire. 16 Seven – Alan Jones, Keke Rosberg, Nelson Piquet, Nigel Mansell, Alain Prost, Damon Hill and Jacques Villeneuve. 17 Argentina. 18 Three (1977, 1978, 1979). 19 Dark blue. 20 East (as opposed to West).

1. Where did Julian Bailey score the Formula 3000 win that helped him land a Formula One ride for 1988?

2. When Bailey was dropped by Lotus in 1991, who took his place?

3. At which circuit did Mauro Baldi score his best Formula One result, fifth, in 1983?

4. Has Baldi ever won the Le Mans 24 Hours?

5. Lorenzo Bandini drove what car for Scuderia Centro Sud in the first half of 1963?

6. Did Bandini ever win the Le Mans 24 Hours?

7. How many times did Bandini finish in the top three at Monaco?

8. What was Fabrizio Barbazza's highest Formula One finishing position?

9. Who entered Skip Barber in Formula One?

10. What American single-seater formula did Skip Barber create?

11. Who replaced Paolo Barilla at Minardi at the end of 1990?

12. Which championship did Rubens Barrichello win in his first year in Europe?

13. For which 1999 grand prix did Barrichello qualify in pole position?

14. Which German failed to qualify a Lotus on four occasions in 1991?

15. What car did Edgar Barth campaign in three of his five grand prix outings?

16. What was the first name of Signor Bassi who made a one-off appearance in the 1965 Italian Grand Prix?

17. With what car did Elie Bayol make his Formula One debut?

18. Don Beauman drove what make of car for Sir Jeremy Boles in the 1954 British Grand Prix?

19. What was Karl-Gunther Bechem's pseudonym?

20. Jean Behra finished second twice in which grand prix?

Answers THE DRIVERS 5 *(see Quiz 47)*

1 Sebring (1959). **2** ATS. **3** Cooper (in both 1963 and 1964). **4** Kyalami (third). **5** Mika Hakkinen. **6** Jochen Mass. **7** All American Racers (Eagle). **8** Giuseppe Farina. **9** Cooper. **10** A Brabham. **11** A Cooper. **12** Silverstone. **13** South African. **14** Three. **15** Hungaroring,1990 (the other two were the 1989 Canadian and Australian Grands Prix). **16** Yes (tenth in the 1994 Spanish Grand Prix). **17** Panoz. **18** 1966. **19** Goodwood. **20** Canadian.

1 With which team did Derek Bell have a one-off outing in 1969?

2 Where did Stefan Bellof achieve his best 1985 result – fourth?

3 What profession helped Paul Belmondo's father earn the family fortune?

4 With which team did he start his Formula One career in 1992?

5 For which British entrant did Tom Belso enjoy four outings in 1974?

6 Who was Jean-Pierre Beltoise's team-mate at Matra International in 1969?

7 Which French oil company backed Jean-Pierre Beltoise's final year with BRM in 1974?

8 In which country did Allen Berg spend his post-Formula One career chasing single-seater titles?

9 What nationality was occasional Gordini racer Georges Berger?

10 Which future Ferrari driver beat Gerhard Berger to the European Formula Three title in 1984?

11 Who was Gerhard Berger's team-mate at Benetton in 1986?

12 With which team did Eric Bernard have a one-off outing, his last in Formula One, in 1994?

13 Name the Italian who tried to qualify a Coloni in 1989.

14 Mike Beuttler's best finish was seventh in which 1973 grand prix?

15 Did Lucien Bianchi ever win the Le Mans 24 Hours?

16 Which team ran Bianchi in its Lotus in 1961?

17 What nationality is 1950s Maserati racer Gino Bianco?

18 With which team did Hans Binder make his Formula One debut, in 1976?

19 In what year did Clemente Biondetti give Jaguar its only Formula One outing by fitting one of its engines in his Ferrari?

20 What nationality was Gordini racer Pablo Birger?

Answers THE DRIVERS 6 (see Quiz 48)

1 Alfa Romeo. *2* Toni. *3* Kauhsen. *4* Alan Brown. *5* A Cooper. *6* Moroccan. *7* Formula Atlantic. *8* Yeoman Credit Racing. *9* Stebro. *10* Three (Belgian, German, Italian). *11* Yeoman Credit Racing. *12* Formula Three. *13* Australian. *14* Wolf Williams. *15* Veritas. *16* Stefan Bellof. *17* Monaco. *18* Gordini. *19* Mexico City. *20* British Racing Partnership.

1 Harry Blanchard finished seventh in the inaugural United States Grand Prix at which circuit?

2 With which team did Michael Bleekemolen have four outings in 1977?

3 Trevor Blokdyk entered the South African Grand Prix twice with what make of car?

4 Mark Blundell's first visit to a Formula One podium came where in 1993?

5 Who was Blundell's team-mate in 1995?

6 Who was Raul Boesel's team-mate at March in 1982?

7 Which American team gave Bob Bondurant two outings in 1966?

8 Who guided Felice Bonetto to a shared third place in the 1951 Italian Grand Prix by taking over his car?

9 Which British chassis did Joakim Bonnier drive in 1963?

10 Which car did Bonnier race in 1964 and 1965?

11 Which car did Roberto Bonomi race in the 1960 Argentinian Grand Prix?

12 Where did Slim Borgudd score his only point?

13 What nationality is Luki Botha?

14 How many grands prix did Thierry Boutsen win?

15 Where was the last of these?

16 Has David Brabham ever finished in the first 10 in a Formula One grand prix?

17 With which sportscar marque has he been associated in the late 1990s?

18 In which year did Jack Brabham score five grand prix wins in a row?

19 At which British circuit was Jack Brabham injured in 1999?

20 What nationality is Bill Brack?

Answers THE DRIVERS 3 *(see Quiz 45)*

1 Brands Hatch. 2 Johnny Herbert. 3 Zandvoort. 4 Yes (1994). 5 A BRM. 6 Yes (1963).
7 Three – 1962 (third), 1965 (second), 1966 (second). 8 Sixth. 9 Gene Mason Racing.
10 Barber-Dodge Pro Series. 11 Gianni Morbidelli. 12 GM Lotus Euroseries. 13 French.
14 Michael Bartels. 15 Porsche. 16 Giorgio. 17 OSCA. 18 A Connaught. 19 Bernhard Nacke.
20 Argentinian (1956, 1957).

1 With which team did Vittorio Brambilla make his Formula One comeback in 1979?

2 By what first name was Antoine Branca better known?

3 For which team did Gianfranco Brancatelli make two attempts to qualify in 1979?

4 Eric Brandon formed Ecurie Richmond with which British contemporary?

5 What car did they run?

6 Tommy Bridger had only one grand prix outing. At which 1958 grand prix was that?

7 In which British series did Tony Brise shine in 1974?

8 Which team ran Chris Bristow in 1960?

9 What car did Canadian Peter Broeker drive in the 1963 Canadian Grand Prix?

10 How many grands prix did Tony Brooks win in 1958?

11 For which team did Tony Brooks race a Cooper in 1960?

12 In what formula did Alan Brown star before arriving in Formula One in 1952?

13 What nationality is Warwick Brown?

14 With which team did Warwick Brown have his only outing, in 1976?

15 With what make of car did Adolf Brudes enter the 1952 German Grand Prix?

16 Who was Martin Brundle's first team-mate at Tyrrell?

17 At which 1994 grand prix did Brundle finish second?

18 For which team did Clemar Bucci race in 1954?

19 At which circuit did Ronnie Bucknum score his only points?

20 Which team ran Ivor Bueb in a Cooper in 1959?

Answers THE DRIVERS 4 *(see Quiz 46)*

1 McLaren. *2* Detroit. *3* Acting. *4* March. *5* Frank Williams. *6* Jackie Stewart. *7* Motul.
8 Mexico. *9* Belgian. *10* Ivan Capelli. *11* Teo Fabi. *12* Lotus. *13* Enrico Bertaggia.
14 Spanish. *15* No. *16* UDT Laystall Racing. *17* Brazilian. *18* Ensign. *19* 1950. *20* Argentinian.

1 Which British team fielded Luiz Pereira Bueno in the 1973 Brazilian Grand Prix?
2 Ian Burgess raced a Lotus for which American team in 1961?
3 In what make of car did Roberto Bussinello make his Formula One debut in 1961?
4 What nationality is Tommy Byrne?
5 Which team gave Byrne his Formula One break?
6 Which Swedish driver entered Giulio Cabianca in the 1958 Italian Grand Prix?
7 Which Formula One rival beat Alex Caffi to the 1986 Italian Formula Three title?
8 Which team gave John Campbell-Jones his Formula One break in 1962?
9 Did Adrian Campos ever finish in the first 10 of a grand prix?
10 Which team ran John Cannon in the 1971 United States Grand Prix?
11 Eitel Cantoni raced a Maserati for which team in 1952?
12 Which European title did Ivan Capelli win in 1984?
13 Whose death gave Capelli his Formula One break with Tyrrell?
14 Which top Italian team entered Piero Carini in the 1953 Italian Grand Prix?
15 At which 1956 grand prix did Eugenio Castellotti finish second?
16 What nationality is Johnny Cecotto?
17 For which manufacturer has Cecotto shone in touring cars through the 1980s and 1990s?
18 In which year did François Cevert score his only grand prix win?
19 With which driver did Eugene Chaboud share his only points-scoring drive?
20 With what make of car did Jay Chamberlain enter three 1962 grands prix?

Answers THE DRIVERS 9 (see Quiz 51)

1 Frank Williams. 2 Watkins Glen (previously second at Monaco). 3 Ecurie Evergreen. 4 Lotus.
5 Bristol. 6 Alta. 7 American. 8 Scarab. 9 Legionnaires' disease. 10 BMW. 11 1982.
12 Tyrrell (1980 Argentinian and British Grands Prix). 13 Martin Brundle. 14 Argentina.
15 Scuderia Centro Sud. 16 Ferrari. 17 A Brabham. 18 Jan Lammers. 19 Paul Ricard.
20 Brabham.

1 Lotus founder Colin Chapman practised for which team at the 1958 French Grand Prix?

2 Dave Charlton ran his Lotus under which team banner in the early 1970s?

3 Who did Ferrari sign in place of Eddie Cheever in 1978?

4 Which Italian marque ran Cheever's 1979 Formula Two campaign?

5 In what country was Ettore Chimeri killed practising for a sportscar race?

6 Which Italian car did Louis Chiron campaign in 1953?

7 What car did Johnny Claes race in 1950 and 1951?

8 Who entered the car in those two world championships?

9 In which year did Jim Clark become world champion for the first time?

10 Who was Clark's team-mate in 1967?

11 Where did Peter Collins score his first grand prix win?

12 Did Peter Collins ever win the British Grand Prix?

13 With which car did Bernard Collomb make his grand prix debut, in 1961?

14 Who pipped Erik Comas to the 1989 Formula 3000 crown?

15 Who was Erik Comas's team-mate at Larrousse in 1993?

16 What nationality is George Constantine?

17 Privateer John Cordts raced what car in the 1969 Canadian Grand Prix?

18 David Coulthard drove for which former world champion in Formula Three?

19 In which year did Coulthard win the British Grand Prix?

20 In which 1999 grand prix did Coulthard crash out of the lead?

Answers *THE DRIVERS 10* (see Quiz 52)

1 Nürburgring. 2 Portuguese. 3 Belgian. 4 Spa-Francorchamps. 5 She became the first woman to start a Formula One grand prix (Belgian). 6 A Maserati. 7 A Maserati. 8 South African. 9 Spanish. 10 Japan. 11 Pacific (in 1995; the first was Larrousse in 1994). 12 1972. 13 Swiss GP. 14 Peter Collins. 15 Swiss. 16 OSCA. 17 Ecurie Francorchamps. 18 A Brabham. 19 March. 20 Forti.

1 Piers Courage's 1966 Formula Three team-mate later helped shape his Formula One career. Who was he?

2 In 1969, Piers Courage came second for the second time that season. At which circuit?

3 Which team entered a Brabham for Chris Craft in two 1971 grands prix?

4 Jim Crawford raced for which works team in 1975?

5 What sportscar marque is owned by occasional 1950s Formula One racer Anthony Crook?

6 Geoffrey Crossley raced what make of car at two 1950 grands prix?

7 What nationality is Chuck Daigh?

8 Which chassis did Daigh campaign in 1960?

9 What illness slowed down Yannick Dalmas in 1988?

10 With which manufacturer did Dalmas win the Le Mans 24 Hours in 1999?

11 In which year did Derek Daly race a Theodore?

12 With which team did Daly score his best results – two fourths?

13 Who was Christian Danner's team-mate at Zakspeed in 1987?

14 From which country did Jorge Daponte hail?

15 Which team ran a Cooper for Colin Davis in two 1959 grands prix?

16 Which Italian team gave Andrea de Adamich his Formula One break in 1968?

17 De Adamich ran what car for himself in 1973?

18 Who was Elio de Angelis's team-mate on his first year in Formula One?

19 Where was de Angelis killed during testing in 1986?

20 For which team was he driving at the time?

Answers THE DRIVERS 7 *(see Quiz 49)*

1 Surtees. 2 Camoradi International. 3 A De Tomaso. 4 Irish. 5 Theodore. 6 Joakim Bonnier. 7 Nicola Larini. 8 Emeryson. 9 No. 10 BRM. 11 Escuderia Bandeirantes. 12 Formul Three. 13 Stefan Bellof's. 14 Ferrari. 15 French. 16 Venezuelan. 17 BMW. 18 1971 (United States Grand Prix). 19 Philippe Etancelin. 20 Lotus (he entered the British, German and Italian GPs, but qualified for only the British).

1   Where did Carel Godin de Beaufort suffer fatal injuries in 1964?
2   What nationality is Mario Araujo de Cabral?
3   Which 1983 grand prix did Andrea de Cesaris lead?
4   Where did de Cesaris's engine fail in 1991, when he was lying second?
5   What record did Maria-Teresa de Filippis set in 1958?
6   What car did she drive that year?
7   What car did Emmanuel de Graffenried race for most of his Formula One career?
8   Which grand prix did Peter de Klerk enter on four occasions?
9   What nationality is Pedro de la Rosa?
10 In what country did he race before making it to Formula One?
11 Which was the second team with which Jean-Denis Deletraz had a go at Formula One?
12 In which year did Patrick Depailler win the Monaco Formula Three race?
13 In which non-championship Formula One race did Depailler finish second in 1975?
14 Who shared second place in the 1956 British Grand Prix with Alfonso de Portago?
15 What nationality was Max de Terra?
16 For which Italian works team did Alessandro de Tomaso race in 1959?
17 What was the name of Charles de Tornaco's team that ran his Ferrari?
18 With which car did Emilio de Villota take his first crack at Formula One in 1976?
19 De Villota's final attempt came in 1982 with which chassis?
20 With which new team did Pedro Diniz break in to Formula One?

Answers THE DRIVERS 8 (see Quiz 50)

1 Vanwall. *2* Scuderia Scribante. *3* Gilles Villeneuve. *4* Osella. *5* Cuba. *6* OSCA. *7* Lago-Talbot. *8* Ecurie Belge. *9* 1963. *10* Graham Hill. *11* Spa-Francorchamps. *12* Yes (1958). *13* A Cooper. *14* Jean Alesi. *15* Philippe Alliot. *16* American. *17* A Brabham. *18* Jackie Stewart. *19* 1999. *20* European.

1   In which year did Pedro Diniz break into Formula One?

2   At which 1996 grand prix was Diniz engulfed by flames?

3   Who was Jose Dolhem's half-brother?

4   What car did Dolhem campaign in 1974?

5   Who was Martin Donnelly's team-mate in 1990?

6   Which North American racing series did Mark Donohue win in 1973?

7   What car did Donohue change to two races before his death?

8   What nationality is 1959 Maserati racer Fritz d'Orey?

9   Ken Downing qualified what car fifth for the 1952 British Grand Prix?

10 Bob Drake gave which classic Italian car its final outing in the 1960 United States Grand Prix?

11 Which British car did Paddy Driver race in the 1974 South African Grand Prix?

12 For what business is Piero Drogo better known than driving racing cars?

13 What is Johnny Dumfries's title?

14 How did George Eaton's family make their money?

15 With which once-famous team did Guy Edwards have his last stab at the world championship in 1977?

16 Vic Elford had a one-off outing in 1971 for which team?

17 Did Elford ever win the Le Mans 24 Hours?

18 Which racing-car marque was founded by Paul Emery?

19 From which country did Paul England hail?

20 Which major British race did Harald Ertl win in 1973?

Answers THE DRIVERS 13 *(see Quiz 55)*

1 Alessandro Zanardi. 2 South African. 3 Reine Wisell. 4 Skol. 5 1989. 6 German. 7 Lotus. 8 Johnny Herbert. 9 Brabham. 10 Italian. 11 Osella. 12 Michael Schumacher and Karl Wendlinger. 13 Japan. 14 Monza. 15 Belgium. 16 Surtees. 17 Osella. 18 Rial (he moved from Onyx for the Japanese and Australian GP but failed to qualify for either). 19 Coloni. 20 Derek Daly.

---

1 What was the last Grand Prix team to give Harald Ertl a shot at Formula One?

2 Which of his compatriots brought Nasif Estefano from Argentina to race his car?

3 With what make of car did Philippe Etancelin build his reputation in the 1920s?

4 Which declining team ran Bob Evans in two 1976 grands prix?

5 Corrado Fabi's best result, seventh, came at which 1984 grand prix?

6 Did Teo Fabi ever finish in the top three in a grand prix?

7 To which team did Fabi return in 1985?

8 Who replaced Pascal Fabre before the end of his only season of Formula One?

9 What made Luigi Fagioli quit Formula One?

10 Which four-wheel drive car did Jack Fairman race in the 1961 British Grand Prix?

11 In which year did Juan Manuel Fangio become world champion with Ferrari?

12 Which team guided Fangio to his fifth world title in 1957?

13 In which year did Fangio retire from racing?

14 Who finished second behind Giuseppe Farina in the 1950 British Grand Prix?

15 What did Farina, who had been badly burned, need to keep him going in the 1955 Argentinian Grand Prix?

16 Which team ran Rudi Fischer throughout his Formula One career?

17 What car did Mike Fisher drive in the 1967 Canadian Grand Prix?

18 At which 1996 grand prix did Giancarlo Fisichella crash with his team-mate at the start?

19 In which 1999 grand prix did Fisichella spin out of the lead?

20 Who entered John Fitch in a Maserati in the 1955 Italian Grand Prix?

Answers *THE DRIVERS 14* *(see Quiz 56)*

1 Frank Williams. **2** Argentinian. **3** Camoradi International. **4** Peter Gethin. **5** Australian. **6** Le Mans. **7** HWM. **8** Lotus. **9** 1961. **10** The British. **11** Twice (1950, 1957). **12** Chico andi. **13** Embassy Racing. **14** Dallas. **15** Osella. **16** Life. **17** Graham Hill. **18** Monaco (1961, 963, 1964). **19** HWM. **20** Alfa Romeo.

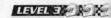
1. Which future Formula One rival did Christian Fittipaldi beat to the 1991 Formula 3000 title?
2. At which 1993 grand prix did Christian Fittipaldi score his first fourth place?
3. Who was Emerson Fittipaldi's team-mate in 1971?
4. What company's name was displayed on Emerson Fittipaldi's car in 1980?
5. In which year did Emerson Fittipaldi win the Indianapolis 500 for the first time?
6. Wilson Fittipaldi's best result was fifth in which 1973 grand prix?
7. For which works team did Ron Flockhart finish sixth in the 1960 French Grand Prix?
8. With which British driver did Gregor Foitek collide in a Formula 3000 race at Brands Hatch?
9. Gregor Foitek started 1990 with which grand prix team?
10. Swiss driver Franco Forini won which Formula Three title in 1985?
11. Forini was entered for three 1987 grands prix by which team?
12. Which future Formula One rivals raced Heinz-Harald Frentzen in their Formula Three days?
13. In which country did Frentzen race before getting his Formula One break?
14. Where did Frentzen score his second 1999 win?
15. From which country does Paul Frere hail?
16. With which team did Beppe Gabbiani have his first crack at Formula One in 1978?
17. With which team did Beppe Gabbiani have his second attempt at Formula One?
18. To which team did Bertrand Gachot transfer at the end of his first season, 1989?
19. With which team did Bertrand fail to qualify in 1990?
20. Who did Patrick Gaillard replace when he got his Formula One break?

Answers THE DRIVERS 11 *(see Quiz 53)*

1 1995. **2** Argentinian. **3** Didier Pironi. **4** A Surtees. **5** Derek Warwick. **6** CanAm. **7** A March. **8** Brazilian. **9** A Connaught. **10** Maserati 250F. **11** Lotus. **12** Designing sportscar bodywork. **13** The Marquis of Bute. **14** They own Canada's leading department stores. **15** BRM. **16** BRM. **17** No. **18** Emeryson. **19** Australia. **20** Tourist Trophy.

1 Which British entrant fielded a car for Nanni Galli in 1973?

2 In which 1953 grand prix did Oscar Galvez score his only points?

3 Fred Gamble raced a Behra Porsche for which American team in 1960?

4 Which 1971 team-mate beat Howden Ganley to the 1970 British Formula 5000 title?

5 What nationality is Frank Gardner?

6 Where did Jo Gartner die in 1986?

7 Tony Gaze turned out at four 1952 grands prix in what make of car?

8 "Geki" raced for which British team in the 1965 and 1966 Italian Grands Prix?

9 In which year did Olivier Gendebien finish fourth in a Ferrari 1-2-3-4 in the Belgian Grand Prix?

10 In which national Formula Three championship did Marc Gene learn his racecraft?

11 How many times did Bob Gerard finish sixth in the British Grand Prix?

12 With whom did Gerino Gerini share his fourth-place drive in the 1956 Argentinian Grand Prix?

13 Which team gave Peter Gethin his final grand prix outing in 1974?

14 At which American street circuit did Piercarlo Ghinzani score his only points in 1984?

15 For which team was Ghinzani driving that day?

16 With which Italian team did Bruno Giacomelli waste 1990 failing to pre-qualify?

17 Who was Richie Ginther's team-mate throughout his entire spell at BRM?

18 In which grand prix did Ginther finish second three times but never win?

19 Yves Giraud-Cabantous swapped to which car for 1952?

20 For which manufacturer did Ignazio Giunti race in sportscars in the late 1960s?

Answers THE DRIVERS 12 (see Quiz 54)

1 ATS. **2** Alessandro de Tomaso. **3** Bugatti. **4** Lotus. **5** United States (Dallas). **6** Yes, twice the 1984 United States Detroit and the 1987 Austrian Grands Prix, third both times). **7** Toleman. **8** Roberto Moreno. **9** Team orders. **10** A Ferguson. **11** 1956. **12** Maserati. **13** 1958. **14** Luigi Fagioli. **15** Morphine. **16** Ecurie Espadon. **17** A Lotus. **18** Monaco. **19** European. **20** Stirling Moss.

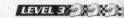
1   What nationality was Francesco Godia?

2   Jose Froilan Gonzalez raced a Maserati in 1950 for which Italian racer?

3   Gonzalez made a comeback at Silverstone in 1956 for which British team?

4   With which fellow Uruguayan did Oscar Gonzalez share sixth in the 1956 Argentinian Grand Prix?

5   What relation was Aldo Gordini to the founder of the Gordini marque?

6   Did Jean-Marc Gounon ever finish in the first 10 of a grand prix?

7   Which team entered Keith Greene for all but one of his grand prix outings?

8   In which 1959 grand prix did Masten Gregory finish third?

9   Which privately entered British team ran a Lotus for Gregory in 1962?

10 Olivier Grouillard scored his only point at which 1989 grand prix?

11 Where did Miguel Angel Guerra break his ankle on his grand prix debut?

12 In 1987, at which American circuit did Roberto Guerrero suffer injuries that left him in a coma?

13 For how many teams did Mauricio Gugelmin race in his Formula One career?

14 In what category of racing is Gugelmin now competing?

15 What was Dan Gurney's team known as when it ran in Formula One from 1966 to 1968?

16 With which legendary American racer did Gurney win the 1967 Le Mans 24 Hours?

17 Hubert Hahne threatened legal action against which marque when he failed to qualify for the 1970 German Grand Prix?

18 In which year did Mike Hailwood finish second in the Italian Grand Prix?

19 Where did Hailwood break his leg, an accident which ended his racing career?

20 What was Mike Hailwood's nickname?

Answers THE DRIVERS 17 *(see Quiz 59)*

1 Dutch. 2 Penske. 3 RAM Racing. 4 An AFM. 5 Veritas. 6 Formula Three. 7 1977.
8 Tyrrell. 9 Monza (1995; first win – 1995 British Grand Prix). 10 Richard Attwood. 11 Renault.
12 He hadn't qualified and started illegally. 13 ATS. 14 Middlebridge. 15 Adelaide. 16 Retire.
17 1973. 18 1975. 19 Belgian. 20 Cooper.

1   Who was Mika Hakkinen's closest rival in British Formula Three?

2   What are the colours on Mika Hakkinen's helmet?

3   In which year did Hakkinen score his first grand prix win?

4   In 1998, where did Hakkinen make an extra call to the pits?

5   In which 1999 grand prix did Hakkinen lose a wheel?

6   Which former Formula One champion manages Hakkinen's career?

7   What car did Bruce Halford race in 1960?

8   What racing-car construction company was founded by Jim Hall?

9   In what North American championship did its cars shine?

10   What car did Duncan Hamilton race to seventh in the 1952 Dutch Grand Prix?

11   In which year did Hamilton race to victory in the Le Mans 24 Hours?

12   What car did he share with Tony Rolt in that race?

13   What nationality was Walt Hansgen?

14   What venerable car did Cuth Harrison race to seventh in the 1950 British Grand Prix?

15   Brian Hart drove what radical Formula Two car in the 1967 German Grand Prix?

16   What is Hart's current involvement with motor racing?

17   At which British circuit was Paul Hawkins killed in 1969?

18   What item of fashion apparel was Mike Hawthorn seldom seen without?

19   With what car did Mike Hawthorn start his 1955 season?

20   Did Hawthorn ever win the Le Mans 24 Hours?

Answers THE DRIVERS 18 *(see Quiz 60)*

1 Switzerland. **2** Bernard White. **3** Fittipaldi. **4** Heros Racing. **5** Bruce McLaren. **6** Emerson Fittipaldi. **7** Japanese. **8** TV commentator. **9** A heart attack. **10** 1966. **11** Ensign. **12** Ligier. **13** Argentinian. **14** Monaco. **15** Reg Parnell. **16** British Racing Drivers' Club. **17** JJ Lehto. **18** A1-Ring (he scored his first win at Melbourne). **19** Jaguar Racing. **20** Brabham.

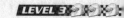
1 What nationality is Boy Hayje?

2 What car did Boy Hayje race once in 1976?

3 Which team ran Hayje's March in 1977?

4 Which German car did Willi Heeks qualify ninth for the 1952 German Grand Prix?

5 With which German car did Theo Helfrich race in the 1952 and 1953 German Grands Prix?

6 Which British championship did Brian Henton win in 1974?

7 In which year did Henton race the Boro chassis?

8 For which team did Johnny Herbert race after he was dropped by Benetton in 1989?

9 Where did Herbert score his second win?

10 With whom did Hans Herrmann share victory in the Le Mans 24 Hours in 1970?

11 With which team did François Hesnault have a one-off run that marked the end of his career?

12 What was unusual about Hans Heyer's only Formula One start, in the 1977 German Grand Prix?

13 For which team was he driving?

14 For which team did Damon Hill lead a number of Formula 3000 races in 1990?

15 At which circuit did Damon Hill's 1994 title hopes come to a crashing halt?

16 What did Damon Hill spend 1999 threatening to do?

17 In which year did Graham Hill form his own team?

18 When did his 18 year Formula One career come to an end?

19 At which 1961 grand prix did Phil Hill lead a Ferrari clean sweep?

20 Phil Hill scored his final point in 1964 for which British team?

Answers THE DRIVERS 15 *(see Quiz 57)*

1 Spanish. 2 Achille Varzi. 3 Vanwall. 4 Alfredo Uria. 5 Son. 6 Yes (ninth in 1994 French Grand Prix). 7 Gilby Engineering. 8 Dutch. 9 UDT Laystall Racing. 10 French. 11 Imola. 12 Indianapolis. 13 Two (Leyton House and Jordan). 14 Indycars. 15 All American Racers. 16 A.J. Foyt. 17 March. 18 1972. 19 Nürburgring. 20 "Mike the Bike".

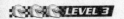
1   From which country did Peter Hirt hail?

2   David Hobbs raced a BRM twice in 1967 for which privateer entrant?

3   Ingo Hoffmann had an abortive Formula One career with which team?

4   Which team ran Kazuyoshi Hoshino in the 1976 and 1977 Japanese Grands Prix?

5   Who was Denny Hulme's team-mate in 1968?

6   Who was Hulme's team-mate in 1974, his final season?

7   In which 1977 grand prix did James Hunt score his final win?

8   What was Hunt's profession after retiring from the cockpit?

9   What caused Hunt's death in 1993?

10 In which year did Jacky Ickx make his grand prix debut?

11 Which British team ran Ickx between 1976 and 1978?

12 With which team did Ickx spend 1979, his final year in Formula One?

13 What nationality is 1950s racer Jesus Iglesias?

14 Where was Taki Inoue tipped on to his head by a safety car?

15 Which privateer entrant ran Innes Ireland in a Lotus in 1965?

16 Of what sporting club did Innes Ireland become president in the early 1990s?

17 Who was Eddie Irvine's Formula 3000 team-mate at Pacific in 1989?

18 Where did Irvine score his second 1999 victory?

19 For which team will Irvine race in 2000?

20 Chris Irwin came seventh on his debut in the 1967 British Grand Prix for which team?

1   Which British entant gave Jean-Pierre Jabouille his Formula One break in 1974?

2   With which French engine was Jean-Pierre Jarier's Shadow fitted in 1975?

3   Jarier rounded off his Formula One career with which French team?

4   Which French team ran Stefan Johansson in 1988?

5   Which major race did Johansson win in 1997?

6   Leslie Johnson bought a racing marque and drove one of its cars in the 1950 British Grand Prix. What make of car was this?

7   In which 1962 grand prix did Bruce Johnstone race for BRM?

8   What car did Alan Jones drive on his Formula One debut in 1975?

9   Jones changed mid-season to which other team?

10 With which team did Ukyo Katayama spend his last Formula One season?

11 Rupert Keegan spent 1982, his final season of driving Formula One, with which team?

12 Which British chassis did Eddie Keizan race in the 1973 and 1974 South African Grands Prix?

13 Joe Kelly drove what make of car in the 1950 and 1951 British Grands Prix?

14 Which team entered Loris Kessel in a Brabham in 1976?

15 What car did the AAW Racing Team enter for Leo Kinnunen in 1974?

16 Which road race did Hans Klenk win for Mercedes in 1952?

17 Karl Kling was third in the 1955 British Grand Prix. Name his team-mates who were first and second.

18 For which team was Helmuth Koinigg driving when he died at Watkins Glen in 1974?

19 What nationality was Robert la Caze?

20 Which championship did Jacques Laffite win in 1975?

Answers THE DRIVERS 21 *(see Quiz 63)*

1 Sauber. *2* Ensign. *3* Racewear. *4* Mercedes. *5* Ecurie Galloise. *6* Third place (twice – 1958 Belgian and Portuguese Grands Prix). *7* 1976. *8* RAM Racing. *9* Veritas. *10* Lago-Talbot. *11* 1972. *12* Volkswagen dealer. *13* Team manager. *14* BS Fabrications. *15* Hill-climbing. *16* American. *17* Stirling Moss. *18* Frank Williams. *19* Ken Tyrrell. *20* Maserati.

1   To which British team did Jacques Laffite move in 1983?

2   Has Jacques Laffite ever won the Le Mans 24 Hours?

3   Which team gave Franck Lagorce two grand prix outings in 1994?

4   Did Jan Lammers ever finish in the first 10 of a grand prix?

5   At which 1995 grand prix did Pedro Lamy score points for Minardi?

6   What nationality was Francisco Landi?

7   Which small Italian team arrived in Formula One with Nicola Larini in 1987?

8   What is Oscar Larrauri's nickname?

9   In which year were Gerard Larrousse and Hans Herrmann pipped for victory by Jackie Ickx and Jackie Oliver in the Le Mans 24 Hours?

10   In which year did Niki Lauda clinch his second world title?

11   At which 1979 grand prix did Lauda quit, for the first time?

12   Roger Laurent raced to sixth in the 1952 Belgian Grand Prix for which local team?

13   Has Giovanni Lavaggi ever finished in the first 10 of a grand prix?

14   Chris Lawrence ran what Italian engine in his Cooper in 1966?

15   Which British entrant gave Michel Leclere his Formula One break in 1975?

16   What make of car was Neville Lederle driving when he came sixth in the 1962 South African Grand Prix?

17   In which year did Geoff Lees win the Formula Two title?

18   With which works team did Lees make his final Formula One outing in 1982?

19   In which country has Lees based his racing since then?

20   Which British championship did JJ Lehto win in 1988?

Answers *THE DRIVERS 22* (see Quiz 64)

1 Champ Cars. *2* Montlhery. *3* Fuel. *4* He didn't fit in the cockpit. *5* 1993. *6* Donington Park. *7* An accident that led to the amputation of one of his legs. *8* Belgian. *9* His car lost a wheel. *10* Scuderia Milano. *11* 1971. *12* Formula 3000. *13* Minardi. *14* Penske. *15* Connaught. *16* Hillclimbing. *17* Lotus. *18* Talbot. *19* Bremgarten. *20* 1983.

1   For which team did JJ Lehto score points on its first outing?

2   Which British team ran Lamberto Leoni in 1978?

3   In what racing-related business did Les Leston become a leading figure?

4   For which works team was Pierre Levegh driving when he died at Le Mans in 1955?

5   Which team ran Welshman Jack Lewis in 1962?

6   What was the highest position that Stuart Lewis-Evans achieved in Formula One?

7   In what year did Guy Ligier arrive in Formula One with his own team?

8   Which team ran Lella Lombardi in a Brabham in 1976?

9   Ernst Loof was best known for designing which German racing cars?

10   Which French car did Henri Louveau drive on his two world championship outings?

11   John Love contested the South African Grand Prix from 1962 through until when?

12   What was American Pete Lovely's job that financed his racing?

13   What was Jean Lucas's role at Gordini before he raced for them?

14   Which privateer team ran Brett Lunger in 1978, his final grand prix year?

15   In which branch of motorsport is one-time Formula One racer Mike MacDowel famous?

16   What nationality was Herbert Mackay-Fraser?

17   In 1956, Lance Macklin raced a Maserati entered by which contemporary driver's team?

18   Which British entrant gave Damien Magee his one grand prix start in 1975?

19   Which British entrant ran Tony Maggs in Formula Junior in 1961?

20   To which team did Umberto Maglioli move in 1956?

Answers THE DRIVERS 19 *(see Quiz 61)*

1 Frank Williams. 2 Matra. 3 Ligier. 4 Ligier. 5 Le Mans 24 Hours. 6 An ERA. 7 South African. 8 Hesketh. 9 Embassy Racing. 10 Minardi. 11 March. 12 Tyrrell. 13 Alta. 14 RAM Racing. 15 Surtees. 16 Carrera Panamericana. 17 Stirling Moss and Juan Manuel Fangio. 18 Surtees. 19 Moroccan. 20 Formula Two.

1   In what category is Jan Magnussen rebuilding his career?

2   At which circuit was Guy Mairesse killed in 1954?

3   What was Nigel Mansell soaked in at his first grand prix, Champagne or fuel?

4   Why did Mansell struggle with his McLaren in 1995?

5   In which year did Mansell win the Indycar championship?

6   At which British circuit was Mansell injured in a touring car race?

7   What brought an end to Sergio Mantovani's career in 1955?

8   In which 1952 grand prix did Robert Manzon finish third?

9   What cost Manzon second place in the 1953 Argentinian Grand Prix?

10 Which team gave Onofre Marimon his Formula One break in 1951?

11 In which year did Helmut Marko win the Le Mans 24 Hours?

12 In what category has Marko run a successful team in the 1990s?

13 For which team did Tarso Marques make his Formula One debut in 1996?

14 Which top Indycar team gave Marques an outing in 1999?

15 What car did Leslie Marr campaign in the 1954 and 1955 British Grands Prix?

16 Tony Marsh is a multiple champion in what branch of motorsport?

17 Marsh raced which Formula Two chassis to eighth in the 1958 German Grand Prix?

18 For which works team did Eugene Martini race in 1950?

19 At which circuit did he crash heavily, effectively ending his career?

20 In which year was Pierluigi Martini European Formula Three champion?

Answers *THE DRIVERS 20* (see Quiz 62)

1 Williams. 2 No. 3 Ligier. 4 Yes, three times (all in 1979 – 10th in the Belgian and German, ninth in the Canadian Grands Prix). 5 Australian. 6 Brazilian. 7 Coloni. 8 Poppy. 9 1969. 10 1977 (Lauda won his first world title in 1975). 11 Canadian. 12 Ecurie Francorchamps. 13 Yes (10th in the 1996 Hungarian Grand Prix). 14 Ferrari. 15 Tyrrell. 16 Lotus. 17 1981. 18 Lotus. 19 Japan. 20 Formula Three.

1   What was Pierluigi Martini's highest-ranked grand prix finish?
2   At which 1991 grand prix did he achieve this?
3   Which major European championship did Jochen Mass win in 1972?
4   Has Jochen Mass ever won the Le Mans 24 Hours?
5   With which team did Mass round off his Formula One career in 1982?
6   Which British entrant gave Jean Max his only grand prix run in 1971?
7   What nationality is Michael May?
8   What was May's main role in racing (more than driving)?
9   Which works team gave Tim Mayer his only grand prix start in 1962?
10   At which Australian circuit was Mayer killed in 1964?
11   For what is Mayer's brother Teddy best known?
12   François Mazet raced a March belonging to whom in the 1971 French Grand Prix?
13   Did Ken McAlpine ever finish in the first 10 of a grand prix?
14   In what year did Bruce McLaren make his world championship debut?
15   What record does Bruce McLaren still hold?
16   Who was Bruce McLaren's partner when he won the Le Mans 24 Hours in 1966?
17   With which team did Perry McCarthy seldom even get out on to the track to attempt to prequalify?
18   In which year was this?
19   In which year did Brian McGuire attempt to qualify his own chassis for the British Grand Prix?
20   What make of car did Graham McRae race in the 1973 British Grand Prix?

Answers THE DRIVERS 25 *(see Quiz 67)*

1 Jordan (Schumacher moved to Benetton). 2 Champ Cars. 3 James Hunt. 4 Surtees. 5 Charles Vogele. 6 Monza. 7 Cooper and Lotus. 8 Lotus. 9 No. 10 A Cooper. 11 Scuderia Ambrosiana. 12 Ecurie Ecosse. 13 Spanish. 14 Second. 15 Formula Two. 16 Fourth (twice – 1987 British and 1989 Australian Grands Prix). 17 Twice (sixth in the Canadian and Hungarian Grands Prix). 18 Minardi. 19 Lancia. 20 Thierry Boutsen.

1. In what other sport did Carlos Menditeguy excel?
2. What was the highest placing that Arturo Merzario ever scored?
3. Merzario had a one-off for which team in 1975?
4. What was the highest placing that Roberto Mieres ever achieved?
5. To what sport did Mieres turn when he retired?
6. Did François Migault ever finish in the first 10 of a grand prix?
7. Name Migault's BRM team-mates from 1974.
8. John Miles recorded his best finish, fifth, in which 1970 grand prix?
9. For which injured compatriot did Andre Milhoux stand-in for his only grand prix start?
10. At which circuit did Gerhard Mitter die in 1969?
11. What make of Formula Two car was Mitter driving when this happened?
12. Who was Stefano Modena's team-mate at Brabham in 1989?
13. In what category of racing has Modena shone since quitting Formula One?
14. Andrea Montermini finished second in the 1992 Formula 3000 series behind which compatriot?
15. Montermini's third crack at Formula One was with which team in 1996?
16. What unusual car did Robin Montgomerie-Charrington drive in the 1952 Belgian Grand Prix?
17. In which year did Gianni Morbidelli become Italian Formula Three champion?
18. What was unusual about the race in which Morbidelli scored his first world championship points?
19. Who did Morbidelli replace at Sauber midway through 1997?
20. Which major championship was won by Roberto Moreno in 1988?

1 To which team did Roberto Moreno move in a driver swap with Michael Schumacher towards the end of 1991?

2 In what championship has Moreno become known as "super-sub"?

3 Dave Morgan's greatest claim to fame was being punched by which future world champion at Crystal Palace in 1970?

4 Morgan's only grand prix outing was with which team in 1975?

5 Which privateer entrant ran Silvio Moser in 1968?

6 Moser died from injuries incurred at which circuit in 1974?

7 Which two British marques did Stirling Moss give their first Formula One wins?

8 What car did Stirling Moss drive in his final season of Formula One?

9 Did Moss ever win the Le Mans 24 Hours?

10 What car did Gino Munaron race through most of 1960?

11 David Murray raced a Maserati for which team in 1950 and 1951?

12 What famous Scottish sportscar team did Murray found in 1952?

13 In which 1954 grand prix did Luigi Musso finish second?

14 In what position did Musso finish the 1957 British Grand Prix at Aintree?

15 Which Japanese title did Satoru Nakajima win five times before graduating to Formula One?

16 What was Nakajima's best finishing position?

17 How many times did Shinji Nakano finish in the points in 1997?

18 With which works team did Alessandro Nannini race in Formula Two?

19 Unable to break into Formula One, for which works sportscar team did Nannini shine?

20 Who was Nannini's team-mate at Benetton in 1988?

Answers THE DRIVERS 23 *(see Quiz 65)*

1 Fourth. 2 San Marino. 3 Touring Car. 4 Yes (in 1989, driving with Stanley Dickens and Manuel Reuter). 5 March. 6 Frank Williams. 7 Swiss 8 Fuel injection engineer. 9 Cooper. 10 Longford. 11 Being McLaren team manager. 12 Jo Siffert. 13 No. 14 1958. 15 Youngest driver to win a grand prix (he won the 1959 United States Grand Prix aged 22). 16 Chris Amon. 17 Andrea Moda. 18 1992. 19 1977. 20 Iso Williams.

1 Name Emanuele Naspetti's two leading rivals in Formula 3000 in 1992.

2 In what category of racing has Naspetti shone in the late 1990s?

3 Massimo Natili raced what make of car for Scuderia Centro Sud in 1961?

4 What was the name of the car that Brian Naylor built and raced in 1959?

5 Did Naylor ever race it to a top 10 finish?

6 What is the Tiff of Tiff Needell short for?

7 Why was Needell's grand prix debut delayed from 1979 to 1980?

8 With which team did Patrick Neve make his grand prix debut in 1976?

9 Neve's best result was seventh in which 1977 grand prix?

10 Which British championship did John Nicholson win in 1973 and 1974?

11 With what car did Nicholson enter the British Grand Prix in 1974 and 1975?

12 What has been Nicholson's line of business since retiring from the cockpit?

13 What nationality was Helmut Niedermayr?

14 In which grand prix did Brausch Niemann appear twice in the early 1960s?

15 Gunnar Nilsson won the last five rounds of which championship in 1975?

16 How many times did Nilsson appear on a grand prix podium in 1976?

17 In which championship did Hideki Noda head home Rubens Barrichello and David Coulthard in one race?

18 Rodney Nuckey drove what car when he made his only grand prix start in 1953?

19 From which country does one-off 1950s racer Robert O'Brien hail?

20 What car did Jackie Oliver drive to victory at Le Mans in 1969?

Answers *THE DRIVERS 24 (see Quiz 66)*

1 Polo. **2** Fourth (three times – the 1973 Brazilian and South African, and the 1974 Italian Grands Prix). **3** Fittipaldi. **4** Fourth (three times – the 1954 Swiss and Spanish, and the 1955 Dutch Grands Prix). **5** Yacht racing. **6** No. **7** Jean-Pierre Beltoise and Henri Pescarolo. **8** South African. **9** André Pilette. **10** Nürburgring. **11** BMW. **12** Martin Brundle. **13** Touring cars. **14** Luca Badoer. **15** Forti. **16** The Aston-Butterworth. **17** 1989. **18** It was stopped early and half points awarded (1991 Australian Grand Prix). **19** Nicola Larini. **20** Formula 3000.

1 With which British-based team did Jackie Oliver enter three grands prix in 1971?

2 Oliver's penultimate grand prix was in 1973 and his final one in 1977. True or false?

3 Which team entered Danny Ongais in a Penske in 1977?

4 The same team entered Ongais unsuccessfully in what chassis in 1978?

5 Arthur Owen drove what car in the 1960 Italian Grand Prix?

6 With which compatriot did Carlos Pace head to Europe in 1970?

7 In which 1973 grand prix did Pace visit the podium for the first time?

8 Pace started 1977 with second place behind whom in the Argentinian Grand Prix?

9 Nello Pagani went on to manage which famous motorcycle racing team in the late 1950s?

10 In which grand prix was Ricardo Paletti killed in 1982?

11 Which company sponsored Torsten Palm's 1975 outings in a Hesketh?

12 Palm managed the career of which Swedish hope?

13 In which year did Jonathan Palmer win the Formula Two title?

14 What is the name of the single-seater formula that Palmer founded in 1998?

15 For which top Formula 3000 team did Olivier Panis win the title in 1993?

16 Which make of tyres did Panis use to good effect in 1997?

17 Panis is now managed by which former world champion?

18 Massimiliano Papis has been shining in which other category in the late 1990s?

19 By what name is Papis better known?

20 With which little team did Mike Parkes make his first attempt to qualify for a grand prix in 1959?

Answers THE DRIVERS 29 *(see Quiz 71)*

1 Formula Three. *2* Politoys. *3* A Surtees. *4* Tyrrell. *5* Gulf Oil. *6* 1969. *7* Paul Ricard.
8 Austrian. *9* Moroccan. *10* A Lotus. *11* Auto Union. *12* Alfa Romeo. *13* 1951. *14* Scirocco.
15 Son. *16* BRM. *17* Maserati. *18* OSCA. *19* A Lotus. *20* He lost the lower half of one leg in 1970 yet still raced.

---

1 What was Mike Parkes's principal role with Ferrari?

2 Which non-championship Formula One race did Parkes win in 1967?

3 Reg Parnell's final grand prix outing was in the 1954 British Grand Prix when he raced a Ferrari for which Italian team?

4 Which team did he manage in 1959 after he quit driving?

5 What relation to Reg Parnell is Tim Parnell?

6 Tim Parnell first raced a Cooper then what make of chassis in the early 1960s?

7 Which European title did Riccardo Patrese win in 1976?

8 After which 1978 grand prix was Patrese ostracized by other drivers?

9 Patrese scored two wins for which team in 1991?

10 What record does Patrese hold?

11 What car did Canadian Al Pease enter in his home grand prix from 1967 to 1969?

12 With what car did Roger Penske make his Formula One debut in 1961?

13 Around which driver did Penske build his early management career?

14 For which team did Cesare Perdisa race in 1957?

15 What made Perdisa quit racing later that year?

16 With which unusual car did Larry Perkins attempt to make his Formula One debut in 1974?

17 For which two teams did Perkins race in 1977?

18 What is Perkins's nickname?

19 In which 1969 grand prix did Xavier Perrot drive a Formula Two Brabham?

20 From which country does Xavier Perrot hail?

Answers *THE DRIVERS 30 (see Quiz 72)*

1 1978. **2** Nigel Mansell. **3** Japan and Australia. **4** Indianapolis 500. **5** Pescara Racing Club. **6** 1977. **7** Patrick Depailler. **8** Jean-Pierre Jaussaud. **9** Brands Hatch. **10** Ivan Capelli. **11** Scuderia Italia. **12** Gordini. **13** Dutch. **14** Hillclimbing. **15** Connaught. **16** Surtees. **17** French. **18** Louis Rosier. **19** Ferrari. **20** Brabham.

1 Henri Pescarolo won which European championship in 1967?
2 What unusual chassis did Pescarolo race (once) for Frank Williams in 1972?
3 Pescarolo's final season in Formula One, 1976, was spent driving which car for the BS Fabrications team?
4 What make of car did Alessandro Pesenti-Rossi drive in several 1976 grands prix?
5 The colours of which oil company, better known for its sportscar programme, were seen on Pesenti-Rossi's car?
6 In which year did Ronnie Peterson win the Monaco Formula Three race?
7 At which circuit did Peterson score his first grand prix win in 1973?
8 Which was the last grand prix that Peterson won before he died in 1978?
9 François Picard contested only one grand prix in 1958. Which one?
10 What car did Ernest Pieterse enter in South African Grands Prix in the early 1960s?
11 Of which pre-war works team was Paul Pietsch a minor member?
12 Pietsch was given a run by which Italian works team in the 1951 German Grand Prix?
13 André Pilette finished sixth on his debut in the Belgian Grand Prix in what year?
14 With which little-fancied car did Pilette tackle two grands prix for Equipe Belge in 1964?
15 What relation to André is Teddy Pilette?
16 With which declining British team did Teddy Pilette struggle in 1977?
17 What car did Luigi Piotti campaign in 1956 and 1957?
18 Piotti's final crack at Formula One came with which make of car in 1958?
19 What car did David Piper enter in the 1960 British Grand Prix?
20 What is unusual about Piper?

Answers THE DRIVERS 27 (see Quiz 69)

1 McLaren. 2 True. 3 Interscope Racing. 4 Shadow. 5 A Cooper. 6 Wilson Fittipaldi.
7 Austrian Grand Prix (third). 8 Jody Scheckter. 9 MV Agusta. 10 Canadian GP. 11 Polar
Caravans. 12 Eje Elgh. 13 1983. 14 Formula Palmer Audi. 15 DAMS. 16 Bridgestone.
17 Keke Rosberg. 18 Champ Cars. 19 Max. 20 Fry.

1 When did Nelson Piquet win one of the two British Formula Three series?

2 Who was Piquet's team-mate when he won his third world title in 1987?

3 In which countries did Piquet score a brace of wins to round off the 1990 season?

4 Piquet suffered major leg injuries when practising for which race in 1992?

5 Which small Italian team entered Renato Pirocchi in a Cooper for the 1961 Italian Grand Prix?

6 In which year did Didier Pironi win the Monaco Formula Three race?

7 Who was Pironi's team-mate in his first year with Tyrrell?

8 With whom did Pironi share the Le Mans-winning Renault-Alpine in 1978?

9 In 1980, at which circuit was Pironi denied victory by a puncture, after a drive through the field?

10 Emanuele Pirro finished second to whom in the 1986 Formula 3000 series?

11 To which team did Pirro move in 1990?

12 For which French team did Jacques Pollet race in the mid 1950s?

13 What nationality is Ben Pon?

14 Which British championship did Dennis Poore win in 1950?

15 Poore finished fourth in the 1952 British Grand Prix for which marque?

16 American Sam Posey had two cracks at Formula One with what make of car?

17 Charles Pozzi finished sixth in which 1950 grand prix?

18 With whom did Pozzi share his car?

19 Pozzi later became the French importer for which sportscar marque?

20 What make of chassis did Jackie Pretorius field for himself in the 1968 and 1971 South African Grands Prix?

Answers *THE DRIVERS 28* (see Quiz 70)

1 Development engineer. *2* International Trophy. *3* Scuderia Ambrosiana. *4* Aston Martin. *5* Son. *6* A Lotus. *7* European Formula Three. *8* Italian. *9* Williams. *10* The most grand prix starts (256). *11* An Eagle. *12* A Cooper. *13* Mark Donohue. *14* Ferrari. *15* Family pressure. *16* An Amon. *17* BRM and Surtees. *18* Cowangie Kid. *19* German. *20* Switzerland.

1 Which regular entrant entered a car for Jackie Pretorius in the 1973 South African Grand Prix?

2 What car did David Prophet field for himself in the 1963 and 1965 South African Grands Prix?

3 How did Prophet die at Silverstone in 1981?

4 In what sport did Alain Prost nearly turn professional before car racing?

5 Where did Prost score his first grand prix win, in 1981?

6 When did Prost first fail to win the world championship at the final round?

7 How many of his four world titles did Prost achieve with McLaren?

8 Who was Tom Pryce's team-mate at Shadow for three years?

9 How many times did Pryce make it to a grand prix podium?

10 Which British championship did David Purley win in 1976?

11 With what medal was Purley rewarded for his attempts to extricate Roger Williamson from his burning car?

12 Which works team ran Dieter Quester in the 1974 Austrian Grand Prix?

13 Which second division British chassis did Ian Raby race in 1963?

14 Who overshadowed Bobby Rahal in their days in North American Formula Atlantic?

15 Rahal raced in Formula Three for which team before trying Formula One?

16 Nano da Silva Ramos held dual nationality. Name his parent countries.

17 Pierre-Henri Raphanel endured a torrid maiden season of Formula One in 1989 with which team?

18 Raphanel moved mid-season to which team with little change in fortune?

19 What nationality was Roland Ratzenberger?

20 In which country did Ratzenberger focus his racing before he made it to Formula One?

Answers THE DRIVERS 33 (see Quiz 75)

1 Yes, twice (eighth in the 1977 German and Canadian Grands Prix). 2 He drives the medical chase car. 3 A Veritas. 4 Le Mans 24 Hours. 5 Formula Two. 6 Watkins Glen. 7 Masten Gregory. 8 A Connaught. 9 Brabham. 10 Rikky von Opel. 11 Lotus. 12 Lotus. 13 1968. 14 Norisring. 15 Second (1961 Italian). 16 Targa Florio. 17 A Lotus. 18 Maserati. 19 A Connaught. 20 Duncan Hamilton.

1   Who did Hector Rebaque replace when he joined Brabham midway through 1980?

2   In what championship did Rebaque race after quitting Formula One?

3   Brian Redman raced sporadically for many teams. Which was his last one?

4   Has Redman ever won the Le Mans 24 Hours?

5   Name the Formula Two team that entered Alan Rees for two grands prix.

6   Of which two teams was Rees a founder member?

7   Which championship did Clay Regazzoni win in 1970?

8   Who was Regazzoni's team-mate at Ferrari in 1971?

9   For which team was Regazzoni driving when he had his paralysing accident?

10 What is Regazzoni's current occupation?

11 Name the South American Formula Two series in which Carlos Reutemann honed his skills?

12 With which team did Reutemann fail to win a race in 1979?

13 In which 1981 grand prix did Reutemann ignore team orders?

14 Who did he refuse to let through for victory?

15 What nationality was Lance Reventlow?

16 What is the name of the car that Reventlow designed and built for himself and raced in 1960?

17 Which team re-introduced Peter Revson to Formula One in the 1971 United States Grand Prix?

18 Revson joined which team for 1974?

19 At which circuit did Revson die in testing that year?

20 John Rhodes drove in just one Formula One grand prix, the 1965 British. He is best known for racing what?

Answers *THE DRIVERS 34 (see Quiz 76)*

1 Shadow. *2* Fred Opert. *3* Fittipaldi. *4* Dallas. *5* International (and German) Touring Cars. *6* His son, Jean-Louis. *7* German. *8* Super Nova. *9* Vincenzo Sospiri. *10* Dutch. *11* Yes, five times (seventh in the 1985 Australian, eighth in the 1984 Italian and 1986 Austrian, ninth in the 1984 German and 1985 Austrian Grands Prix). *12* A Lotus. *13* Indianapolis 500. *14* A Maserati. *15* United States. *16* Boris. *17* A Connaught. *18* Stefano Modena. *19* Silverstone (sixth in 1989). *20* (Aurora) British Formula One.

1 Did Alex Ribeiro ever finish a grand prix in the first 10?

2 What is Ribeiro's current role at grands prix?

3 Fritz Riess drove what German car to seventh place in the 1952 German Grand Prix?

4 What major race did Riess win for Mercedes in 1952?

5 In what formula was Jochen Rindt the main man in the late 1960s?

6 Where did Rindt score his first grand prix win for Lotus in 1969?

7 With whom did Rindt drive a Ferrari to victory in the 1965 Le Mans 24 Hours?

8 What car did John Riseley-Pritchard drive in the 1954 British Grand Prix?

9 Richard Robarts had three outings for which team in 1974?

10 Who took over Robarts's seat?

11 Which British works team ran Alberto Rodriguez Larreta in the 1960 Argentinian Grand Prix?

12 Which British team gave Pedro Rodriguez a second chance in 1966?

13 In which year did Pedro Rodriguez win the Le Mans 24 Hours in a Ford GT40?

14 Where did Pedro Rodriguez die in a sportscar race in 1971?

15 Ricardo Rodriguez qualified in what position for his first grand prix?

16 Ricardo Rodriguez won which Italian road race for Ferrari in 1962?

17 What car was Ricardo Rodriguez driving when he crashed to his death in the 1962 Mexican Grand Prix?

18 Which works team gave Franco Rol three grand prix outings in 1950?

19 What car did Rob Walker enter for Tony Rolt in the 1953 and 1955 British Grands Prix?

20 With whom did Tony Rolt share the Le Mans 24 Hours-winning Jaguar in 1953?

Answers THE DRIVERS 31 (see Quiz 73)

1 Frank Williams. 2 Brabham. 3 In a helicopter crash. 4 Football. 5 Dijon-Prenois. 6 1983. 7 Three (1985, 1986, 1989). 8 Jean-Pierre Jarier. 9 Twice (third in the 1975 Austrian and 1976 Brazilian Grands Prix). 10 Shellsport British Formula One & Formula 5000 series. 11 George Medal. 12 Surtees. 13 Gilby. 14 Gilles Villeneuve. 15 Walter Wolf Racing. 16 Brazil and France. 17 Coloni. 18 Rial. 19 Austrian. 20 Japan.

1   Which team gave Bertil Roos a one-off outing in the 1974 Swedish Grand Prix?

2   Which team entrant ran Keke Rosberg in Formula Atlantic and Formula Two?

3   Rosberg raced for which team in 1980?

4   In 1984, at which street circuit did Rosberg win while others crashed into the surrounding walls?

5   In which championship did Rosberg run a team in the mid 1990s?

6   With whom did Louis Rosier win the 1950 Le Mans 24 Hours?

7   In which 1956 grand prix did Louis Rosier score his final points, for fifth?

8   With which top team did Ricardo Rosset win races in Formula 3000?

9   Who was Rosset's team-mate in both Formula 3000 and Formula One?

10 What nationality is Huub Rothengatter?

11 Did Rothengatter ever finish in the first 10 of a grand prix?

12 In what car did Lloyd Ruby make his only grand prix appearance (the 1961 United States Grand Prix)?

13 American Troy Ruttman won which big race in 1952?

14 Ruttman drove which car for Scuderia Centro Sud at two 1958 grands prix?

15 Canadian Peter Ryan raced just once in Formula One. In which 1961 grand prix was this?

16 What was Bob Said's real first name?

17 What car did Said race in the 1959 United States Grand Prix?

18 Who beat Luis Perez Sala to the 1987 Formula 3000 title?

19 Where did Sala score his only point?

20 In which British series did Eliseo Salazar make his name in 1980?

1 Eliseo Salazar's best result, fifth, came in which 1982 grand prix?
2 Which team did Mika Salo join in 1998?
3 Who was Salo's team-mate there that year?
4 For whom was Salo a stand-in at Ferrari in 1999?
5 Which British team entered Roy Salvadori in a Maserati from 1954 to 1956?
6 Who was Salvadori's partner when he won the Le Mans 24 Hours in 1959?
7 What was Consalvo Sanesi's original role with Alfa Romeo?
8 For which team did Stephane Sarrazin have a one-off outing in the 1999 Brazilian Grand Prix?
9 For which injured driver was Sarrazin standing in?
10 For which team was Sarrazin the test driver that year?
11 With which works team did Ludovico Scarfiotti twice finish fourth in 1968?
12 Scarfiotti won the Le Mans 24 Hours for Ferrari in 1963 sharing with whom?
13 With which works team did Giorgio Scarlatti enjoy his most successful season in 1957?
14 Did Ian Scheckter ever finish in the first 10 of a grand prix?
15 Who was Ian Scheckter's team-mate in 1977?
16 Which Formula One team ran Jody Scheckter in Formula Two in 1972?
17 At which circuit did Jody Scheckter make his grand prix debut at the end of that year?
18 Who was Jody Scheckter's team-mate throughout his spell with Tyrrell?
19 How many years did Jody Scheckter spend with Wolf?
20 Who was Jody Scheckter's team-mate at Wolf in 1977?

Answers *THE DRIVERS 37* (see Quiz 79)

1 Adelaide. 2 Nine (in 1995). 3 Norberto Fontana. 4 Italian GP (he was third). 5 A puncture (he was leading with 17 laps to go). 6 BRM. 7 Team management. 8 Argentinian. 9 Lister. 10 International Trophy. 11 A Connaught. 12 Emeryson. 13 Martin Brundle. 14 Ayrton Senna da Silva. 15 1986. 16 Suzuka. 17 Damon Hill. 18 Alberto Ascari. 19 1979. 20 Thierry Boutsen.

1 Name the team that Harry Schell's father ran pre-war. It was taken over by his mother and Harry drove for it in 1950.

2 For which French works team did Harry Schell race in 1953?

3 Who was Tim Schenken's Brabham team-mate in 1971?

4 With which works sportscar team did Schenken shine in 1972?

5 Which team gave Albert Scherrer his only Formula One outing in 1953?

6 What brought Domenico Schiattarella's Formula One career to a close?

7 What make of car did Heinz Schiller race for Ecurie Filipinetti in 1962?

8 Who was Schiller's team-mate?

9 Which team gave Jean-Louis Schlesser his Formula One break in 1983?

10 Schlesser famously had a one-off drive in the 1988 Italian Grand Prix for which team?

11 With which top driver did Schlesser collide?

12 Of which future Formula One team owner was Jo Schlesser a good friend?

13 What relation to Jo Schlesser was Jean-Louis?

14 Which national Formula Three title did Bernd Schneider win in 1987?

15 Has Schneider ever won the Le Mans 24 Hours?

16 What nationality was Rudolf Schoeller?

17 Which American sportscar team entrant ran Bob Schroeder in the 1962 United States Grand Prix?

18 In which year did Michael Schumacher win the German Formula Three title?

19 Which works sportscar team ran Michael Schumacher that same year?

20 Who was Michael Schumacher's Ferrari team-mate from 1996 to 1999?

Answers THE DRIVERS 38 (see Quiz 80)

1 LDS. 2 Italian. 3 He failed to qualify. 4 Emeryson. 5 Scirocco Powell. 6 Jim Hall.
7 Mexican. 8 ERA. 9 Heart trouble. 10 AC Cobra. 11 New Zealand. 12 Brabham.
13 Cooper. 14 March. 15 1952. 16 Mexican. 17 Lotus. 18 BRM. 19 Touring cars.
20 McLaren.

1 At which circuit did Michael Schumacher claim the 1994 world title despite failing to finish the race?

2 What is the most grands prix that Michael has won in a year?

3 Which future Sauber driver was Ralf Schumacher's main rival for the 1995 German Formula Three title?

4 In which grand prix besides the Belgian did Ralf Schumacher visit the podium in 1998?

5 What cost Ralf Schumacher victory in the 1999 European Grand Prix?

6 With which team did Vern Schuppan make his Formula One debut in 1972?

7 In what capacity is Schuppan still involved in motor racing?

8 What nationality is 1950s racer Adolfo Schwelm-Cruz?

9 With which marque was Archie Scott-Brown connected for most of his sportscar career?

10 In which non-championship race did Archie Scott-Brown finish second in 1956?

11 Piero Scotti drove what car on his one-off outing in the 1956 Belgian Grand Prix?

12 What car did Ecurie Maarsbergen enter for Wolfgang Seidel in the 1962 Dutch Grand Prix?

13 Who was Ayrton Senna's chief rival in Formula Three?

14 What was Senna's full name?

15 In which of his years with Lotus did Senna open his campaign with three straight pole positions?

16 At which circuit did Senna collide with Alain Prost in 1989 and 1990?

17 Who was Senna's team-mate at Williams in 1994?

18 With whom did Dorino Serafini share his car in the 1950 Italian Grand Prix?

19 In which year was Chico Serra British Formula Three champion?

20 Who took over from Serra at Arrows during the 1983 season?

Answers THE DRIVERS 35 *(see Quiz 77)*

1 San Marino. 2 Arrows. 3 Pedro Diniz. 4 Michael Schumacher. 5 Gilby Engineering.
6 Carroll Shelby. 7 Test driver. 8 Minardi. 9 Luca Badoer. 10 Prost. 11 Cooper. 12 Lorenzo
Bandini. 13 Maserati. 14 Yes (tenth in the 1977 Dutch Grand Prix). 15 Alex Ribeiro.
16 McLaren. 17 Watkins Glen. 18 Patrick Depailler. 19 Two. 20 Nobody – it was a one-car
team.

1 Doug Serrurier raced his own car in three South African Grands Prix in the 1960s. What was it?

2 Johnny Servoz-Gavin finished second in which 1968 grand prix?

3 What happened in the 1970 Monaco Grand Prix that triggered Servoz-Gavin to quit racing?

4 Tony Settember raced what make of car in 1962?

5 Name the team that Settember formed with Hugh Powell for 1963.

6 With which sportscar racer was Hap Sharp associated in the 1960s?

7 In which 1963 grand prix did Sharp just miss out on a point in a Reg Parnell Lotus?

8 In what make of car did Brian Shawe-Taylor finish eighth in the 1951 British Grand Prix?

9 What forced Carroll Shelby to quit racing at the end of 1960?

10 Shelby combined with AC to create what legendary car in the 1960s?

11 From which country does 1960s racer Tony Shelly hail?

12 What car did Jo Siffert race from 1964 to 1966?

13 Siffert swapped to which other British-built car in 1966?

14 After a strong year with a privately entered Lotus in 1969, which works team ran Siffert in 1970?

15 In which year was André Simon a works Ferrari driver?

16 What nationality was Moises Solana?

17 Which works team ran Solana in his home grand prix four times in the 1960s?

18 Alex Soler-Roig's final year in Formula One, 1972, was spent with which team?

19 In what category did Soler-Roig achieve rather more success?

20 Which team gave Stephen South a one-off outing at Long Beach in 1980?

Answers THE DRIVERS 36 *(see Quiz 78)*

1 Ecurie Bleue. 2 Gordini. 3 Graham Hill. 4 Ferrari. 5 HWM. 6 The folding of Simtek midway through 1995. 7 Lotus. 8 Jo Siffert. 9 RAM Racing. 10 Williams. 11 Ayrton Senna. 12 Guy Ligier. 13 Nephew. 14 German. 15 No. 16 Swiss. 17 John Mecom. 18 1990. 19 Mercedes. 20 Eddie Irvine.

1   Which French team gave Mike Sparken a run in the 1955 British Grand Prix?

2   Mike Spence had a full season with Lotus in 1964 because which driver was injured?

3   Who was Spence's team-mate at Lotus in 1964?

4   Who was Alan Stacey's team-mate at Lotus in 1960?

5   What car did Gaetano Starrabba enter for himself in the 1961 Italian Grand Prix?

6   Which team ran Ian Stewart in the 1953 British Grand Prix in a Connaught?

7   At which sport did Jackie Stewart excel before motor racing?

8   Who was Stewart's first Formula One team-mate, in 1965?

9   A crash at which circuit in 1966 convinced Stewart that circuits ought to be made safer?

10   To which motor manufacturer did Jackie Stewart sell Stewart Grand Prix in 1999?

11   Which team entered Jimmy Stewart in the 1953 British Grand Prix in a Cooper?

12   Which team-mate outshone Siegfried Stohr at Arrows in 1981?

13   For which works sportscar team did Rolf Stommelen race in the late 1960s?

14   Which March-based car did Stommelen drive in 1972?

15   In which 1976 grand prix did Stommelen score his final point?

16   What historic result did Philippe Streiff record for AGS at Brands Hatch in 1984?

17   Which team gave Streiff his Formula One debut at the end of that year?

18   Hans Stuck drove for which works team in the 1930s?

19   What car did Hans Stuck drive in 1953?

20   In what category did Hans-Joachim Stuck shine when still a teenager?

1 In which year did Hans-Joachim Stuck twice appear on the podium for Brabham?

2 Has Hans-Joachim Stuck ever won the Le Mans 24 Hours?

3 Why did Otto Stuppacher fail to start the 1976 Italian Grand Prix?

4 What privately entered car was Stuppacher driving?

5 In which non-championship race did Danny Sullivan finish second in 1983?

6 What championship did Marc Surer win in 1979?

7 Did Surer ever make it to a grand prix podium?

8 With which team did Surer have his Formula One swansong in 1986?

9 With which motorcycle manufacturer was John Surtees a multiple world champion?

10 At which circuit did John Surtees score his first Formula One grand prix win, in 1963?

11 Surtees injured his back in a CanAm race at which North American circuit in 1965?

12 Surtees raced for which British works team in 1969?

13 Aguri Suzuki raced for which Japanese team in European Formula 3000?

14 Aguri Suzuki had a one-off drive for which team in the 1994 Pacific Grand Prix?

15 Toshio Suzuki replaced Philippe Alliot in which team at the end of 1993?

16 With what car did Jacques Swaters make his Formula One debut in 1951?

17 Which British team ran Noritake Takahara in the 1976 Japanese Grand Prix?

18 What car did Kunimitsu Takahashi race for the Meiritsu Racing Team in the 1977 Japanese Grand Prix?

19 What were the two colours on Patrick Tambay's helmet?

20 At which circuit did Tambay score his second and last Formula One win?

Answers *THE DRIVERS 42 (see Quiz 84)*

Olivier Panis. **2** European. **3** A Lotus. **4** Veritas. **5** BRM. **6** Uruguay (Eitel Cantoni and Oscar Gonzalez are the other two). **7** Targa Florio. **8** Fondmetal. **9** Ensign. **10** A McLaren. **11** Tyrrell. **12** Jan Magnussen. **13** Formula Atlantic. **14** Carlos Reutemann. **15** Jochen Mass. **16** Craig Pollock. **17** Ricardo Zonta. **18** Uncle. **19** Arrows. **20** Maserati.

1 In which 1989 grand prix did Gabriele Tarquini score his only point?

2 Who was Tarquini's team-mate at AGS in 1990?

3 In which year did Piero Taruffi score his only grand prix win?

4 Which British team gave Taruffi his final Formula One outing in 1956?

5 Henry Taylor finished a surprise fourth in which 1960 grand prix?

6 For which team was Henry Taylor driving a Cooper that day?

7 In which year did John Taylor finish sixth in the French Grand Prix?

8 John Taylor died later that year from burns suffered at which circuit?

9 Where was Mike Taylor badly injured when he crashed in practice in 1960?

10 Trevor Taylor was the champion two years running in which junior formula?

11 Which team ran Trevor Taylor in 1964?

12 Who commandeered the Tyrrell team's spare car so that Mike Thackwell couldn't race in the re-start of the 1980 Canadian Grand Prix?

13 Alfonse Thiele was entered in a Cooper in the 1960 Italian Grand Prix by which team?

14 Eric Thompson was a works driver for which sportscar team?

15 Ecurie Ecosse entered Leslie Thorne in the 1954 British Grand Prix in what car?

16 What locally built car did Sam Tingle race in South African Grands Prix in the 1960s?

17 Which British works team gave Desmond Titterington øhis lone grand prix outing in 1956?

18 Which team entered Tony Trimmer in the 1977 and 1978 British Grands Prix?

19 With which fellow Formula One ace did Maurice Trintignant share the Le Mans winning Ferrari in 1954?

20 Which French marque did Trintignant give its only grand prix outing, in 1956?

Answers THE DRIVERS 39 *(see Quiz 81)*

1 Gordini. *2* Peter Arundell. *3* Jim Clark. *4* Innes Ireland. *5* A Lotus. *6* Ecurie Ecosse.
7 Clay-pigeon shooting. *8* Graham Hill. *9* Spa-Francorchamps. *10* Ford. *11* Ecurie Ecosse.
12 Riccardo Patrese. *13* Porsche. *14* Eifelland. *15* German. *16* He won the final Formula Two race. *17* Renault. *18* Auto Union. *19* An AFM. *20* Touring cars.

1 Who has been Jarno Trulli's team-mate through 1998 and 1999?

2 Trulli finished second in which 1999 grand prix?

3 What car did Guy Tunmer drive in the 1975 South African Grand Prix?

4 Toni Ulmen was the top driver for which German marque in the early 1950s?

5 Which British works team ran Bobby Unser in two 1968 grands prix?

6 Alfredo Uria is one of only three Formula One drivers to come from which South American country?

7 Little known for his Formula One exploits, Nino Vaccarella was famed for winning which Italian race three times?

8 Eric van de Poele's last three Formula One outings in 1992 came with which Italian team?

9 Which team ran Gijs van Lennep in 1975?

10 What car did Basil van Rooyen race in the 1969 South African Grand Prix?

11 For which team did Jos Verstappen race in 1997?

12 Who did Verstappen replace at Stewart midway through 1998?

13 In which formula did Gilles Villeneuve star in the mid 1970s?

14 Who was Gilles Villeneuve's team-mate at Ferrari in 1978?

15 Who was driving the March that Villeneuve hit when he crashed fatally in 1982?

16 Who is Jacques Villeneuve's former ski teacher turned manager?

17 Who was Jacques Villeneuve's main team-mate at BAR in 1999?

18 What relation is Jacques Villeneuve Sr to the current Jacques?

19 Which team gave Jacques Villeneuve Sr his first crack at Formula One in 1981?

20 With which Italian car did Luigi Villoresi contest his final year of Formula One in 1956?

Answers *THE DRIVERS 40 (see Quiz 82)*

1 1977 (third in the German and Austrian Grands Prix). 2 Yes (in 1986 and 1987). 3 He left the circuit because he'd failed to qualify, not knowing that three drivers had been disqualified and he was in. 4 A Tyrrell. 5 The Race of Champions. 6 Formula Two. 7 No (fourth place in the 1981 Brazilian Grand Prix was his best finish). 8 Arrows. 9 MV Agusta. 10 Nürburgring. 11 Mosport Park. 12 BRM. 13 Footwork. 14 Jordan. 15 Larrousse. 16 Lago-Talbot. 17 Surtees. 18 Tyrrell. 19 Blue and white. 20 Imola (1983).

1 Which British team owner ran Jo Vonlanthen in the 1975 Austrian Grand Prix?

2 Wolfgang von Trips raced for which German marque in 1959?

3 Name Wolfgang von Trips's team-mate who took the 1961 title after von Trips's death.

4 American Fred Wacker Jr raced for which French team in 1953 and 1954?

5 Dave Walker was given his Formula One debut in a turbine-powered car entered by which team?

6 With which British car was Peter Walker associated both before and after the Second World War?

7 What car did Heini Walter race for Ecurie Filipinetti in the 1952 German Grand Prix?

8 Which British team entered Rodger Ward in a Lotus for the 1963 United States Grand Prix?

9 In which championship did Derek Warwick race against Nelson Piquet and Chico Serra in 1978?

10 Who was Warwick's team-mate at Renault in 1984?

11 With which manufacturer did Warwick win the 1992 Le Mans 24 Hours?

12 With which team did Warwick round off his Formula One career in 1993?

13 Which small team ran John Watson in 1974?

14 What did Watson do when he scored his first grand prix win?

15 Who was Watson's team-mate at both Brabham and McLaren?

16 Where did Watson run out of fuel on the last lap in 1977 and lose victory?

17 When did Watson win the British Grand Prix?

18 With which works sportscar team did Karl Wendlinger become a winner in 1990?

19 Name Wendlinger's 1993 team-mate.

20 What was Wendlinger's highest-ever grand prix finish?

Answers *THE DRIVERS 45* *(see Quiz 87)*

1 Eliseo Salazar. *2* BMW. *3* Ronnie Peterson. *4* John Miles. *5* March. *6* Dutch. *7* Ensign.
8 Norberto Fontana, Ralf Schumacher, Jarno Trulli. *9* International Touring Cars. *10* Monaco.
11 Johnny Herbert. *12* 1997 and 1998. *13* Chip Ganassi Racing. *14* Super Nova.
15 Mercedes. *16* French. *17* Frank Williams. *18* Interlagos. *19* Hector Rebaque. *20* Tyrrell.

 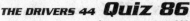

1 Which works team fielded a car for Peter Westbury in the 1970 United States Grand Prix?

2 Under what team banner did Ken Wharton race in 1952?

3 Wharton raced for which British works team in 1955?

4 In which non-championship race did Wharton suffer burns?

5 What relation was Graham Whitehead to Peter Whitehead?

6 Peter Whitehead won the 1951 Le Mans 24 Hours for which marque?

7 What special version of a Ferrari did Peter Whitehead race in the 1951 British Grand Prix?

8 Peter Whitehead drove what car in the 1953 and 1954 British Grands Prix?

9 Bill Whitehouse raced only in the 1954 British Grand Prix. What car did he drive?

10 In what sport did Robin Widdows compete at the Olympics for Britain?

11 Which works team ran Widdows in the 1968 British Grand Prix?

12 From which works team did Eppie Wietzes rent a car for the 1967 Canadian Grand Prix?

13 Wietzes had another crack at the same race with what car in 1974?

14 Which team ran Mike Wilds at four grands prix in 1974?

15 Wilds was back with which team, briefly, in 1975?

16 Which top team gave Jonathan Williams his only grand prix outing (the 1967 Mexican Grand Prix)?

17 What prestigious Formula Two race did Roger Williamson win in 1973?

18 Why did Williamson fail to start the 1973 British Grand Prix?

19 In which boycotted 1960 race did Vic Wilson make his grand prix debut?

20 Which team gave Manfred Winkelhock his first shot at Formula One in 1980?

Answers THE GREAT RACES 1 *(see Quiz 88)*

Reims. **2** Alberto Ascari. **3** Jose Froilan Gonzalez. **4** Juan Manuel Fangio. **5** A Maserati.
Mike Hawthorn. **7** A Ferrari. **8** The last one. **9** Thillois straight. **10** Juan Manuel Fangio.
Mike Hawthorn. **12** Nürburgring. **13** A Ferrari. **14** Peter Collins. **15** Juan Manuel Fangio.
16 Maserati. **17** His planned pit stop was very slow. **18** Penultimate. **19** Luigi Musso.
20 Stirling Moss.

1 Who was Manfred Winkelhock's team-mate at ATS in 1982?
2 What engine powered Winkelhock's progress in 1983 and 1984?
3 Who was Reine Wisell's arch-rival in Formula Three?
4 Who did Wisell replace at Lotus at the end of 1970?
5 Wisell rounded off his career with a one-off drive for which works team in the 1974 Swedish Grand Prix?
6 What nationality is Roelof Wunderink?
7 Wunderink drove for which team for half of 1975?
8 Name any of the future grand prix rivals Alexander Wurz raced against in German Formula Three in 1995.
9 In which international category did Wurz race in 1996?
10 At which 1998 grand prix did Wurz refuse to be intimidated by Michael Schumacher?
11 Who was Alessandro Zanardi's team-mate at Lotus in 1993?
12 In which years did Zanardi win the Indycar title?
13 For which team was Zanardi driving in those years?
14 Ricardo Zonta won the Formula 3000 crown for which team in 1997?
15 For which manufacturer did Zonta become International GT champion in 1998?
16 At which 1999 grand prix did Zonta record his first finish for BAR?
17 Which team owner gave Renzo Zorzi his grand prix debut in 1974?
18 At which circuit did Zorzi score his only point?
19 Who squeezed Ricardo Zunino out of Brabham during 1980?
20 Which team gave Zunino his final Formula One outing in 1981?

Answers THE DRIVERS 43 *(see Quiz 85)*

1 Frank Williams. 2 Porsche. 3 Phil Hill. 4 Gordini. 5 Lotus. 6 ERA. 7 A Porsche. 8 Reg Parnell. 9 British Formula Three. 10 Patrick Tambay. 11 Peugeot. 12 Footwork. 13 Goldie Hexagon Racing. 14 Shaved off his beard. 15 Niki Lauda. 16 Paul Ricard. 17 1981. 18 Mercedes. 19 JJ Lehto. 20 Fourth (three times – 1992 Canadian, 1993 Italian and 1994 San Marino Grands Prix).

1 At which circuit was the 1953 French Grand Prix held?

2 Name the reigning world champion who qualified on pole for Ferrari.

3 Who led the early laps for Maserati?

4 Another Argentinian took the lead. Who was that?

5 What make of car was he driving?

6 He was then joined at the front in a slipstreaming duel with which British driver?

7 What make of car he driving?

8 At which corner did this British driver take the lead for good on the final lap?

9 This corner was at the end of which straight?

10 Who finished second?

11 Which British driver led the opening laps of the 1957 German Grand Prix?

12 At which circuit was it held?

13 What make of car was he driving?

14 Name his team-mate who was up there with him.

15 Who started from pole position?

16 For which team was he driving?

17 Why did his race plan go wrong?

18 When did the race-winner take the lead, on the final or the penultimate lap?

19 Name the third Ferrari driver who finished fourth?

20 And who was the best-placed Vanwall driver, in fifth?

Answers THE DRIVERS 44 (see Quiz 86)

1 BRM. **2** Scuderia Franera. **3** Vanwall. **4** International Trophy. **5** Half brother. **6** Jaguar. **7** Thinwall Special. **8** A Cooper. **9** A Connaught. **10** Bobsleigh. **11** Cooper. **12** Lotus. **13** Brabham. **14** Ensign. **15** BRM. **16** Ferrari. **17** Monza Lotteria. **18** His car was eliminated in a first lap pile-up and the restart was treated as a new race. **19** Italian. **20** Arrows.

1   Who qualified his Ferrari in pole position for the 1961 French Grand Prix?

2   What was that year's Ferrari 156 better known as?

3   Name the driver in pole position's team-mate, who stayed with him then led before retiring?

4   Who was the second American in the third Ferrari who also led?

5   Who took the lead when the third Ferrari became the third Ferrari to retire, and went on to win?

6   What make of car was he driving?

7   Who entered his car for the race?

8   What was notable about his victory?

9   Dan Gurney and Jo Bonnier pushed him hard for which team?

10   Which Lotus driver finished third?

11   How many drivers arrived at the 1964 Mexican Grand Prix, the season's finale, with a chance of the title?

12   For which teams were they driving?

13   Which of them led away?

14   Which of them dropped out of the reckoning?

15   Which driver had his car damaged by his team-mate?

16   Why did the race leader lose the lead and with it the title?

17   Who came through to win the race?

18   Who won the title?

19   What make of car was the race-winner driving?

20   Which team entered the Ferraris for both this race and the previous one?

Answers THE CIRCUITS 1 *(see Quiz 91)*

1 Clockwise. 2 Horses. 3 Casablanca. 4 Aintree. 5 It's a runway. 6 Hans Herrmann.
7 Bricks. 8 Nicola Foulston. 9 Druids. 10 Achille Varzi. 11 Switzerland banned motor racing
from within its boundaries after the 1955 Le Mans disaster. 12 Parque Almirante Brown.
13 Chris Amon. 14 Nigel Mansell and Ayrton Senna. 15 Elf. 16 An extinct volcano. 17 Louis
Rosier. 18 The track went through a tunnel. 19 Ayrton Senna. 20 Swiss.

1 Chris Amon started the 1971 Italian Grand Prix from pole position in what make of car?

2 Who led the early laps in a Ferrari?

3 Which former motorcycle ace came from 17th to lead?

4 For which team was he driving?

5 How did Chris Amon blow his chance of victory?

6 Ronnie Peterson led into the final lap for which team?

7 Which Tyrrell driver was right on his tail?

8 Who won for BRM?

9 Who finished second?

10 Which driver rounded out the top three?

11 Why was Peter Revson's win in the 1973 British GP all the sweeter?

12 Where was the race held that year?

13 Who qualified on pole for Lotus?

14 Who triggered the accident that took out half of the field and forced a restart?

15 For which team was he driving?

16 Which young BRM driver ran second in the early part of the race?

17 Which two-time World Champion spun out at Stowe?

18 Which reigning World Champion ran second behind his teammate before his transmission broke?

19 Who finished third for McLaren?

20 Which young British driver finished fourth in a privately-entered March?

1 Do cars generally run in a clockwise or anti-clockwise direction around most circuits?

2 What was raced in Adelaide's Victoria Park before Formula One?

3 On the outskirts of which Moroccan city was the Ain-Diab circuit?

4 On which now defunct British circuit would you have found Tatts Corner?

5 What is the other use of the back straight at Anderstorp?

6 Who was thrown from his car at Avus's Sudkurve in 1959 and survived?

7 What was the Nordkurve banking made out of?

8 Who owned Brands Hatch until being bought out in 1999?

9 What's the name of the hairpin at Brands?

10 Which Italian racing great died at Bremgarten in 1948?

11 Why did Bremgarten host no more grands prix after 1954?

12 Name the park in which the Buenos Aires circuit is located.

13 Who won the non-championship Formula One race there in 1971, yet never won a grand prix?

14 Which two drivers ran wheel-to-wheel at Catalunya in 1991?

15 What is the name of the tight right at the end of the main straight at Catalunya?

16 The Clermont-Ferrand circuit is built on what?

17 It was originally named after which French driver?

18 What was unusual about the Detroit grand prix circuit?

19 Who won there three years running?

20 When Dijon-Prenois hosted a grand prix in 1982, which one was it?

Answers THE GREAT RACES 2 *(see Quiz 89)*

1 Phil Hill. *2* The Sharknose. *3* Wolfgang von Trips. *4* Richie Ginther. *5* Giancarlo Baghetti.
6 A Ferrari. *7* FISA (Federazione Italiane Scuderie Automobilistiche – not the sporting body
Federation Internationale de Sport Automobiles). *8* It was his maiden world championship outing. *9*
Porsche. *10* Jim Clark. *11* Three (Jim Clark, Graham Hill & John Surtees). *12* Lotus, BRM & Ferrari
respectively. *13* Jim Clark. *14* Graham Hill. *15* John Surtees's team-mate, Lorenzo Bandini. *16*
Engine failure. *17* Dan Gurney. *18* John Surtees. *19* Brabham. *20* North American Racing team.

1   Who won the 1975 grand prix held at Dijon-Prenois?

2   What is the first corner of each lap at Donington Park called?

3   What is the name of the corner at the lowest point of the Donington circuit?

4   What was the name of the original 1930s circuit on which the East London circuit was built in 1959?

5   Why was viewing so good on the 1959 circuit?

6   In which decade was the Estoril circuit built?

7   Why was Hockenheim truncated in 1966?

8   Which was the last of the three chicanes to be added to Hockenheim's country loop?

9   At which corner did Eddie Irvine spin at the Hungaroring during the 1999 Hungarian Grand Prix?

10   Name the corner at the highest point of the Imola circuit.

11   Name the double-apex right-hander at Imola that brings the track back to the level of the pits?

12   Who owns the Indianapolis Motor Speedway?

13   Which is the only corner of the regular Indianapolis circuit that the Formula One cars will use in 2000?

14   In which direction do the cars run around Interlagos?

15   What natural feature did the original Interlagos cross twice?

16   In which Brazilian city is Jacarepagua located?

17   Who won five of the 10 grands prix held there?

18   Which famous circuit designer is responsible for Jarama's layout?

19   Name either of the motorcycle racing heroes after whom two corners at Jerez are named.

20   Complete the name of this corner on the original Kyalami layout: xxxxxx Sweep?

Answers *THE GREAT RACES 3* (see Quiz 90)

1 A Matra. **2** Clay Regazzoni. **3** Mike Hailwood. **4** Surtees. **5** Instead of removing a tear-off strip, he pulled off his entire visor. **6** March. **7** François Cevert. **8** Peter Gethin. **9** Ronnie Peterson **10** François Cevert. **11** He had wagered £100 on his success. **12** Silverstone. **13** Ronnie Peterson. **14** Jody Scheckter. **15** McLaren. **16** Niki Lauda. **17** Jackie Stewart. **18** Emerson Fittipaldi. **19** Denny Hulme. **20** James Hunt.

1 When was a grand prix last held at Kyalami?
2 Between which two corners on the main Le Mans circuit does the Bugatti circuit peel off to the infield?
3 Who won the only grand prix to be held on the Bugatti circuit?
4 What category of cars gave the Long Beach circuit a race-test the year before Formula One arrived?
5 A downhill ess at Magny-Cours is named after which German circuit?
6 An uphill ess at Magny-Cours is named after which Italian circuit?
7 In which direction do the cars race around the Melbourne circuit?
8 At which circuit in the Americas did drivers use the crowd as their turn-in point?
9 Through which square does the Monaco circuit pass?
10 Name the famous bar in Monaco at which post-race celebrations are traditionally held?
11 In which country would you have found the Monsanto circuit?
12 Its main straight was actually part of the main roads into which city?
13 Name the circuit found outside the Canadian town of St Jovite.
14 This circuit hosted the Canadian Grand Prix just twice; 1968 was the first time, when was the second?
15 Which was the last year in which Montjuich Park hosted the Spanish Grand Prix?
16 Who won that race?
17 Name the island on which the Montreal circuit is built.
18 Around what sporting facility is the Montreal circuit built?
19 At which of Monza's corners did Mika Hakkinen spin out of the lead in 1999?
20 On the entry to which corner at Monza did Jochen Rindt have a fatal accident in 1970?

Answers THE BUSINESS OF FORMULA ONE 1 *(see Quiz 95)*

1 Thinwall. 2 Yeoman Credit. 3 United Dominions Trust. 4 Gold Leaf. 5 Elf. 6 STP.
7 Brooke Bond Oxo. 8 John Player. 9 Yardley. 10 Marlboro. 11 Politoys. 12 Rolf Stommelen (Eifelland Caravans). 13 UOP. 14 Motul. 15 Viceroy. 16 Penske. 17 Tyrrell. 18 March.
19 Martini. 20 Tecno.

1 Which Formula One driver was killed in a sportscar race at Mosport Park in 1985?

2 Which German circuit is overlooked by a castle?

3 What is the name of the uphill, final chicane at this circuit?

4 What was remarkable about the track surface at Oporto?

5 Name the fast corner at the end of Paul Ricard's back straight.

6 On the outskirts of which Spanish city was the Pedralbes circuit located?

7 After whom was the main straight named?

8 Which Italian circuit had the longest lap ever used in Formula One?

9 This circuit hosted just one world championship grand prix. It was won by Stirling Moss in which year?

10 Which American circuit had its start/finish straight in Jefferson Street?

11 Which Californian circuit hosted the second-ever United States Grand Prix?

12 At which French circuit would you have found the Nouveau Monde hairpin?

13 At which corner at Silverstone did Michael Schumacher break his leg in 1999?

14 At which corner did Mika Hakkinen lose a wheel in the same race?

15 What was the name of the tricky kink on the original Spa-Francorchamps layout?

16 Approaching which corner at Spa-Francorchamps did Michael Schumacher hit David Coulthard in 1998?

17 Which Japanese circuit hosted the Pacific Grand Prix in 1994 and 1995?

18 The circuit is also known by the name of the closest town. What is it?

19 Name the fast corner that leads on to Zandvoort's main straight.

20 Which circuit hosted the first Austrian Grand Prix?

1 Which trade name appeared on the side of a privately run Ferrari in 1951?

2 Which financial institution gave a team its name in 1960?

3 It spawned a second team in 1961 known as UDT-Laystall Racing. For what was UDT an acronym?

4 When Lotus cars changed from British racing green to red, gold and white in 1968, who was the sponsor?

5 The Tyrrell team landed backing from which French oil company in 1970?

6 Which oil additive company sponsored March from 1970 to 1973?

7 Surtees was backed by which general grocery company from 1971 to 1973?

8 Lotus livery changed again to black and gold in 1972. Who was the sponsor?

9 Which cosmetics company swapped its sponsorship from BRM to McLaren for 1972?

10 Which tobacco company took over the sponsorship of BRM in 1972?

11 Which model car company backed Frank Williams's 1972 campaign?

12 If you wanted a caravan, to which driver would you have turned in 1972?

13 Who was the Shadow team's sponsor when it arrived in Formula One?

14 Which French oil company backed the three BRMs in 1974?

15 The American Parnelli team arrived in 1974 with sponsorship from which tobacco brand?

16 Which team was sponsored by First National City Bank from 1974 to 1976?

17 Which team did the bank move on to?

18 Beta Tools sponsored which team from 1974 to 1976?

19 Which drinks company sponsored Brabham in the mid 1970s?

20 From which smaller team had this company defected?

Answers THE CIRCUITS 3 *(see Quiz 93)*

1 1993. 2 Dunlop Curve and Esses. 3 Jack Brabham (in 1967). 4 Formula 5000.
5 Nürburgring. 6 Imola. 7 Clockwise. 8 Mexico City. 9 Casino Square. 10 Tip-Top.
11 Portugal. 12 Lisbon. 13 Mont Tremblant. 14 1970. 15 1975. 16 Jochen Mass. 17 Ile de Nôtre Dame. 18 An Olympic-quality rowing lake. 19 The first chicane (Variante). 20 Parabolica.

1 A model car manufacturer backed which British team in 1975?

2 Name the Brazilian company that backed the Fittipaldi team in the late 1970s.

3 Ligier arrived in Formula One in 1976 with backing from which tobacco company?

4 Which adult glamour magazine backed Hesketh in 1976 and 1977?

5 If you wanted a refrigerator in the mid 1970s, to which British driver would you have turned?

6 If you smoked cigars in 1977, which team would you have followed?

7 Brabham turned to which dairy products company for sponsorship in 1978?

8 Name the Italian fuel company that became synonymous with Ferrari?

9 German brewer Warsteiner backed which team from 1978 to 1980?

10 Which camera manufacturer backed Hesketh in 1978?

11 To which team did this company move on in 1979?

12 If you wanted to buy a washing machine in 1979, which team would have come to mind?

13 Which oil company named after an English county backed Lotus from 1979 to 1981?

14 Which truck builder sponsored Williams in 1980 and 1981?

15 Denim after-shave was the sponsor of which team from 1980 to 1982?

16 Which Italian washing machine manufacturer sponsored Toleman in 1981?

17 Guinness sponsored which team in 1981?

18 Which pop group backed Slim Borgudd's ATS in 1981?

19 If you wanted an outboard motor, which team would you have thought of in 1982?

20 Café de what backed Roberto Guerrero's Ensign in 1982?

Answers *THE CIRCUITS 4* (see Quiz 94)

1 Manfred Winkelhock. 2 Nürburgring. 3 Veedol-S. 4 It included tramlines and cobbles.
5 Signes. 6 Barcelona. 7 General Franco. 8 Pescara. 9 1957. 10 Phoenix. 11 Riverside.
12 Rouen. 13 Stowe. 14 Woodcote. 15 Masta. 16 Pouhon. 17 TI Circuit. 18 Aida. 19 Bosuit.
20 Zeltweg (1964).

1   How many cylinders did the engines in the dominant Alfa Romeos have in 1950?

2   What boosted their power output?

3   Ferrari arrived with a different engine format to which it stayed true for years. What was it?

4   Which team attempted to run a V16 engine in the 1950s?

5   Which was the first Formula One car to carry side fuel tanks?

6   In what year did it make its debut?

7   What format of engine did it introduce to Formula One?

8   In which year did the driver of a rear-engined car win the world title for the first time?

9   What make of car was this?

10 Porsche made its first works attack on Formula One in 1961 with what engine format?

11 Who made the first four-wheel drive car to race in Formula One?

12 In what year was this?

13 Name either of the two drivers who shared it in that year's British Grand Prix.

14 Which other marques dabbled with four-wheel drive?

15 Which team introduced monocoque chassis to Formula One?

16 This idea had been hatched by whom?

17 What form of chassis did it supersede?

18 In which year was the Ford Cosworth DFV introduced to Formula One?

19 What was its layout format?

20 Which team gave the engine its debut?

Answers FAN CULTURE *(see Quiz 99)*

1 Yellow. 2 Blue. 3 White. 4 (British Racing) Green. 5 Orange. 6 Red. 7 White with blue stripes. 8 Felice Bonetto. 9 Le Petoulet. 10 Rat droppings. Some were found in his fuel tank. 11 Denis Jenkinson. 12 Mercedes. 13 Les Leston. 14 The tifosi. 15 A prancing horse. 16 The North American Racing Team. 17 Blue and white. 18 Black Jack. 19 He was well known for his scowl and bad moods. 20 The Bear.

1　How many points did a win count for in 1950?

2　What capacity were the engines in the first world championship?

3　What year did the world championship adopt Formula Two regulations?

4　In which year did the rules change so that 2.5 litre engines were adopted?

5　Points were extended down to which finishing position in 1960?

6　When did 1.5 litre engines become mandatory?

7　In what year did a win become worth 9 points?

8　The engine rules changed again in 1966, to what fixed capacity?

9　In which year were high-mounted aerofoil wings banned?

10　In 1973, the maximum length of a grand prix was reduced to how many miles?

11　A maximum time span was introduced as well. How long was it?

12　Formula One ran with tall engine air boxes until several races into which year?

13　When turbocharged engines arrived in 1977, what was their maximum capacity?

14　Teams used to run their cars below legal weight in 1982 by dumping water from a brake cooling system. How did they make their cars legal?

15　What sort of bottom for the cars were made mandatory for 1983?

16　What sort of aerodynamics were banned?

17　What form of injection was made legal for 1984?

18　Which team had its points taken away for a technical infringement in 1984?

19　What was this infringement?

20　Which drivers were penalised for this infringement?

Answers *SCANDALS AND DISASTERS* (see Quiz 100)

1 Mike Hawthorn. *2* Bump-starting his stalled car facing traffic. *3* Stirling Moss. *4* Wolfgang von Trips. *5* Ferrari. *6* Sebring. *7* Spa-Francorchamps. *8* Alan Stacey. *9* Italian. *10* Wolfgang von Trips. *11* Jim Clark. *12* Piers Courage. *13* Roger Williamson. *14* It could not go along the grass verge facing traffic. *15* David Purley. *16* Officials blocked the pit-lane exit. *17* He took a short-cut to the pits. *18* A marshal crossing the track beyond a blind brow struck his face with a fire extinguisher. *19* To put out team-mate Renzo Zorzi's blazing parked car. *20* Riccardo Patrese.

1   What are the national racing colours of Belgium?

2   What are the national racing colours of France?

3   What are the national racing colours of Germany?

4   What are the national racing colours of Great Britain?

5   What are the national racing colours of Holland?

6   What are the national racing colours of Italy?

7   What are the national racing colours of the United States?

8   Which 1950s Italian driver was known as "Il Pirata"?

9   What was 1950s driver Maurice Trintignant's nickname?

10   What did it mean?

11   Name the British journalist who won the 1955 Mille Miglia as co-driver to Stirling Moss in 1955.

12   For which manufacturer were they competing?

13   Which occasional 1950s Formula One driver went on to launch his own racewear empire?

14   What are fans of Ferrari known as?

15   What is the symbol of the Ferrari team?

16   Scuderia Ferrari didn't enter the works Ferraris in the 1964 US and Mexican Grands Prix. Who did?

17   The cars weren't entered in their normal red livery. What was their colour scheme?

18   What was Jack Brabham's nickname?

19   Why?

20   What Brabham's long-time team-mate Denny Hulme's nickname?

Answers EQUIPMENT (see Quiz 97)

1 Eight. 2 A supercharger. 3 V12. 4 BRM. 5 Lancia D50. 6 1954. 7 V8. 8 1959 (Jack Brabham). 9 A Cooper. 10 Flat 4. 11 Ferguson. 12 1961. 13 Jack Fairman, Stirling Moss. 14 Lotus, Matra and McLaren. 15 Lotus. 16 Colin Chapman. 17 Tubeframe. 18 1967. 19 V8. 20 Lotus.

1   Which driver nearly lost the 1958 title race on a technicality at the end of the Portuguese Grand Prix?

2   What was his supposed offence?

3   Which rival gave evidence that would clear him?

4   Tony Brooks was challenging for the 1959 title when he was hit by one of his team-mates during the last race. Who was this?

5   For which team was he driving at the time?

6   At which circuit was this?

7   British drivers Chris Bristow and Alan Stacey were both killed at which track in 1960?

8   Which of them crashed after being hit in the face by a bird?

9   At which 1961 grand prix were 14 spectators killed when a car flew into the crowd?

10   Which driver died in the accident?

11   Which British driver had he clashed with?

12   Which British driver burned to death when he crashed in the 1970 Dutch Grand Prix?

13   Which British driver burned to death when he crashed in the 1973 Dutch Grand Prix?

14   Why didn't the closest fire tender come to his assistance?

15   Who pulled over and tried to rescue the trapped driver?

16   Why was Niki Lauda unable to rejoin the British Grand Prix in 1974?

17   What offence – after the race had been stopped – caused James Hunt to have his victory in the 1976 British Grand Prix taken away from him?

18   How was Tom Pryce killed in the 1977 South African Grand Prix?

19   Why were the marshals crossing the track?

20   Which driver was eventually found not guilty of the manslaughter of Ronnie Peterson in the 1978 Italian Grand Prix?

Answers *RULES AND TACTICS (see Quiz 98)*

1 8. 2 1.5 litres. 3 1952. 4 1954. 5 Sixth. 6 1961. 7 1961. 8 3 litres. 9 1969. 10 200 miles. 11 Two hours. 12 1976. 13 1.5 litres. 14 They were allowed to top them up again after the race. 15 Flat bottoms. 16 Ground effects. 17 Water injection. 18 Tyrrell. 19 Having lead balls in the water tanks. 20 Stefan Bellof and Martin Brundle.

NOTES

NOTES

NOTES